ACOUSTIC NOISE MEASUREMENTS

by
J. R. Hassall, M. Sc.
and
K. Zaveri, M. Phil.

January 1979

4th edition   1st print

ISBN 87 87355 30 2

CONTENTS

1. INTRODUCTION

Introduction

Within the last few years, concern about the protection of the environment has grown rapidly as it has become generally recognised that the steady rise in pollution of all kinds cannot be allowed to continue indefinitely. The acoustic environment has likewise suffered from the increase in the use and power of machines in the workplace, increasing road traffic, larger aircraft, etc. To combat this, many countries and communities have recently introduced legislation making it a legal requirement to measure community noise levels, to reduce noise from vehicles at source, and to maintain acceptable noise levels in factories to prevent hearing loss.

This activity has led to a greater appreciation of the benefits of a quiet environment and a preference for quieter domestic products, if these are available. The quieter item therefore often has a sales advantage over its more noisy competitor which may be reflected in the command of a higher price. Economic advantages are also apparent in property values which are lower in noisy areas than in quiet areas.

The cost of insulating against the noise must also be considered. The control of noise is therefore of importance not only in the prevention of hearing damage and in providing an acceptable acoustic environment, but also from the economic point of view.

The aim of acoustic noise measurement is to provide objective physical measurements of noise which can be compared with predetermined criteria in order to judge its acceptability. In order to ensure the quality and uniformity of the measurement results as far as possible, the equipment specifications and the measurement procedures are subject to national and international standards of various severities depending on the application. Standards for survey methods are least strict, and laboratory methods for testing to noise specifications and for research and development purposes are usually the most exhaustive.

As in many other spheres of work, the quality of the result is governed to a large extent by the care and effort expended in obtaining it and the quality of the instrumentation used. There is no short cut. Instrumentation should be of high quality, and chosen carefully for the job to be done. It must be accurately calibrated, have the correct characteristics, dynamic range, frequency range, and accuracy, and the measurements should be carried out in a manner which minimises the influence of wind, reflections, ground absorption, etc. on the results. Only in this way can the noise engineer, acoustician, or health officer have faith in his data.

The purpose of this book then is to lead the reader into the principles of noise measurement, the noise units, criteria currently employed, and Brüel & Kjær instrumentation for its measurement and analysis, via the basic physics of sound and examples of typical measurements made under practical conditions.

The book has in general been compiled by J. R. Hassall while K. Zaveri has contributed section 5.1, on sound power measurement and given ideas and suggestions during its preparation. The general layout adopted by Professor Jens Trampe Broch, the author of the previous editions of this book, has been broadly retained. However, chapters 2 and 3 have been extended a little. The second now includes, among other things, a more detailed explanation of the attenuation of sound from different types of source, the effects on propagation of wind and temperature gradients, and the interaction of sound fields from more than one source. The third chapter includes sections on hearing loss and noise units.

Chapter 2 briefly describes the physical properties of sound and vibration as they apply to acoustic noise measurements. The production of a sound wave from a mechanically vibrating source and its propagation in an elastic medium is described with reference to the types of noise source, the effect of the atmosphere and the influence of absorption, reflection and diffraction. The importance of these factors and the type of sound field (i.e. free-field or diffuse) on the choice of suitable instrumentation and measuring techniques is explained.

The use of decibel rather than absolute quantities to describe parameters in acoustics comes about because of the enormous dynamic range of common noises and the fact that the hearing mechanism responds in a logarithmic way to a stimulus. The basic characteristics of noise signals and the purpose of frequency analysis are then discussed.

Chapter 3 deals with psychoacoustic matters, beginning with the mechanism of hearing, and going on to masking, loudness, the perception of impulsive noise and the development of hearing loss, both as a natural aging process and as the result of exposure to excessive noise. The subjective effects of noise are then dealt with and the most common measurement units cur-

8

rently in use are defined and their development and areas of application described. Criteria are defined in terms of these units at levels which have been shown to be acceptable from the point of view of annoyance, hearing damage, speech interference, etc. Practical cases using I.S.O. procedures as examples have been included to demonstrate the techniques.

Chapter 4 describes noise measurement instrumentation and general measurement and analysis techniques, beginning with simple sound level meters and filter sets and progressing through more comprehensive instruments to analysis systems intended mainly for laboratory applications. The requirements for a basic sound measuring system and the specifications which it must meet are briefly described. The choice of portable instrumentation for noise measurements extends from simple sound level meters for A-weighted measurements, through comprehensive types capable of providing a frequency analysis or measuring impulsive noise, to new types with digital reading of L_{eq} or L_{AX} by continuous calculation.

Laboratory measurement and analysis equipment is described in some detail with sections on real-time analyzers, recording devices and signal storage techniques. The principle of the condenser microphone and the choice of a microphone to suit the frequency range, dynamic range, and type of sound field being measured is discussed in some detail. A similar detailed treatment is given to the choice of analysis technique and analyzer.

At the end of the chapter, the necessity for careful calibration of the set-up is stressed and procedures are outlined which should produce the best possible measurement and minimise the undesirable effects of background noise and reflections from observer and instrument. It is hoped that the reader will then be in a position both to choose the instrumentation necessary to suit his measurements and obtain those measurements with the greatest possible confidence of good accuracy.

Chapter 5 and 6 contain examples of typical noise measurement practice in several areas of importance in noise control and community annoyance respectively. In each case measurements have been carried out to the relevant standards where applicable, (although it should be remembered that the standards in different countries may differ in important details), and serve to illustrate the way in which measurements may be made, the type of information which can be extracted from them, and the conclusions which can be drawn.

Section 5.1 describes sound power measurements in detail and it is stressed that this is the only practical way in which the absolute output of a noise source can be quantified. Section 5.2 deals with noise in the workplace and its control, with examples from both factory and office environments, while 5.3 describes ways of utilizing noise (or vibration) measurements from machinery as a basis for noise reduction, as a quality control parameter, or for condition monitoring. Section 5.4 introduces Audiometry and section 5.5 deals with the particular problems associated with the measurement of transient signals.

The measurements of chapter 6 have all been carried out recently, to International Standards and accepted noise measurement practice, and can be considered representative of conditions and problems encountered by the practising noise engineer in the field. The section 6.4 on Construction Noise has been included in the light of recent suggestions and recommendations in several countries including the U.S.A., Britain and Germany.

A recent review of various national and international standards is given in chapter 7. Many specialist areas of noise measurement require that equipment and measurements meet certain standards. These must be examined before measurements are made and adhered to. Deviations from standards may invalidate the data obtained.

A general reference list of books and periodicals follows this introduction, but a list of relevant papers is provided at the end of each chapter (or section) so that the reader with a particular interest may begin to delve into that subject, via the references, in some depth.

It is hoped that this handbook will assist the newcomer and experienced noise engineer alike to avoid the pitfalls of noise measurement and enable him to carry out, correctly and accurately, valid measurements which represent the actual acoustic situation.

General References

ALEXANDRE, A., BARDE, j-Ph., LAMURE, C. and LANGDON, F. J.:   *Road Traffic Noise.* Applied Science Publishers, England 1975.

BERANEK, L. L.:   *Noise and Vibration Control.* McGraw-Hill Book Company Inc. 1971.

BERANEK, L. L.:   *Noise Reduction.* McGraw-Hill Book Company Inc. 1960.

BURNS, W.:   *Noise and Man.* John Murray 1968

CHAVASSE, P. et al.:   *Bruit et Vibrations.* Institute National de Securité. Paris 1957.

CROCKER, M. J. and PRICE, A. J.:   *Noise and noise Control.* Vol. 1. CRC Press 1975.

GERHARDSSON, G.:   *Buller.* Bonniers Uggleböcker 1971.

GÜNTER, B. C., HANSEN, K. H. and VEIT, I.:	*Aktuelle Probleme der Technischen Akustik.* Lexika-Verlag 7031 Grefenau 1/Württ.
HARRIS, C. M.:	*Handbook of Noise Control.* McGraw-Hill Book Company, Inc. 1957.
KINSLER, L. E. and FREY, A. R.:	*Fundamentals of Acoustics.* Wiley 1962.
KRYTER, K. D.:	*The Effects of Noise on Man.* Academic Press. 1970
KURTZE, G.:	*Physik und Technik der Lärmbekämpfung.* Verlag G. Braun, Karlsruhe 1964.
N.B.S. Handbook 119:	*Quieting: A Practical Guide to Noise Control.* U.S. Dept. of Commerce. National Bureau of Standards 1976.
National Physical Laboratory:	*The Control of Noise (Symposium No. 12).* H.M.S.O. London 1962.
PARKER, P. H. and HUMPHREYS, H. R.:	*Acoustics, Noise and Buildings.* Faber 1969.
ROBINSON, D. W. (Editor):	*Occupational Hearing Loss.* British Acoustical Society Special Volume No.1. Proceedings of a Conference held at the National Physical Laboratory. Teddington, London. March 1970.
SCHULTZ, T. J.:	*Community Noise Ratings.* Applied Science Publishers Ltd. London 1972.
TAYLOR, R.:	*Noise.* Pelican Books. London 1970.
WARRING, E. R. (Editor):	*Handbook of Noise and Vibration Control.* Trade and Technical Press Ltd.
YERGES, L. F.:	*Sound, Noise and Vibration Control.* Van Nostrand Reinhold Company 1969.

Journals

Acustica	Hirzel Verlag. Stuttgart.
Akusticheskii Zhurnal:	Published by the Academy of Science of the USSR, Moscow. (Also translated and published by the American Institute of Physics as, Soviet Physics, Acoustics).
Applied Acoustics:	Published Quarterly by Applied Science Publishers Ltd. London.

J.A.S.A. (Journal of the Acoustical Society of America):	Published by the American Institute of Physics, New York.
Journal of Sound and Vibration:	Published by Academic Press, London.
Journal of the Acoustical Society of Japan (Japanese):	Published by the Acoustical Society of Japan, University of Tokyo, Japan.
Journal of the Environmental Sciences:	Published by the Institute of Environmental Sciences, Illinois. U.S.A.
Kampf dem Lärm:	Published by Springer-Verlag, Berlin.
Noise and Vibration Bulletin:	Multi-Science Publishing Company Ltd., London.
Noise Control Engineering:	Published by the Institute of Noise Control Engineering. New York.
Noise Control, Vibration Isolation	Trade and Technical Press Ltd., London.
Revue d'Acoustique:	Published by Groupement des Acousticiens de Langue Francaise, Paris.
Sound and Vibration:	Published by Acoustical Publications Inc., Ohio. U.S.A.
Technical Review	B & K quarterly publication

2. THE PHYSICAL PROPERTIES OF NOISE

2.1. VIBRATIONS AND WAVES

Acoustic Noise is usually defined as unwanted sound; an undesirable by-product of society's normal day-to-day activities. In physical terms, sound is the mechanical vibration of a gaseous, liquid or solid elastic medium through which energy is transferred away from the source by progressive sound waves. Whenever an object moves or vibrates, a small proportion of the energy involved is lost to the surrounding medium as sound.

Let us consider a small particle of the medium, large enough to be representative of its physical properties, but small in relation to typical dimensions of the acoustic disturbance e.g. its wavelength.

If such a particle is displaced from its equilibrium position, it strikes its neighbour and thus causes that to move a similar small distance while rebounding itself. This neighbouring particle now strikes the next and so on, propagating the disturbance through the medium by successive oscillations of neighbouring elastic particles. None of these are transferred along with the wave; it is only the *energy* of the disturbance that is transmitted. The particles themselves oscillate for only an infinitesimal distance about their equilibrium positions along the direction of propagation of the sound wave, as shown in Fig. 2.1.

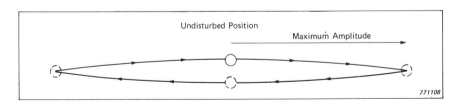

Fig.2.1. Motion of a particle during a single cycle

The time taken for the motion to be transferred between successive particles, and therefore the velocity of propagation of the disturbance, depends on the medium's elasticity according to the following equation

$$c = k \sqrt{\frac{E}{\rho}}$$

where k is a constant
       E is the modulus of elasticity of the medium
       ρ is the density of the medium

For air, under normal conditions, the medium with which we will be almost exclusively concerned, this velocity is approximately 344 m/s at 20°C.

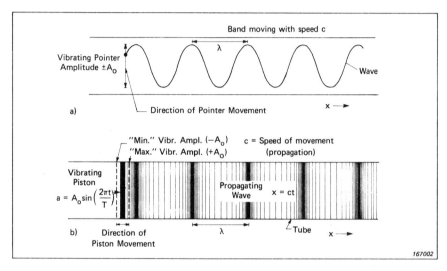

Fig.2.2. The transformation of vibrations into waves
a) By a vibrating pointer on a moving band
b) By a vibrating piston in a fluid medium

Fig.2.2b demonstrates what happens to the air along the path of propagation in an open-ended tube with a sinusoidally vibrating piston at one end. As the piston moves into the tube, the air is locally compressed and the compression is propagated along the tube at the speed of sound. After half the oscillation, the piston is about to move in the opposite direction, thus rarefying the air and propagating a rarefaction along the tube. Thus a pressure wave is transmitted at the same frequency and with the same characteristic waveform as the vibration of the piston which produced it. The speed of sound in air being fixed, the wavelength is defined only by the time interval between successive compressions, which is set in turn by the frequency of the disturbance.

14

Therefore,
$$\lambda = cT = \frac{c}{f}$$

Where λ is the wavelength
   T is the time between successive compressions
   c is the speed of sound in air
   f is the frequency of the disturbance

A reference nomogram relating wavelength to frequency for the speed of sound under normal conditions is plotted in Fig.2.3.

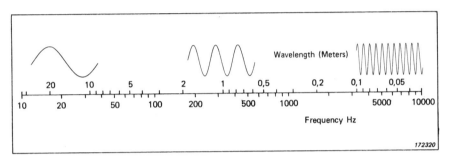

Fig.2.3. *Wavelength in air versus frequency under normal conditions*

We are dealing here with the simplest of all radiated waves, the plane, progressive wave, so called because it propagates away from the source in one direction only, the wavefronts always remaining parallel to each other. Because it cannot spread out into the medium, the only attenuation which is experienced is that due to transmission losses and dispersion caused by turbulence and temperature gradients within the medium itself. Although the magnitude of a sound wave can be determined in a number of different ways, it is usually more convenient to measure acoustic pressure rather than parameters such as particle displacement or velocity which are extremely difficult to measure in practice. These parameters are normally only required when measurements are to be made very close to the source in its near field. The particle velocity here is not necessarily in the direction of travel of the wave, and the sound pressure may vary appreciably at short intervals along the direction of propagation. Under these conditions the acoustic intensity is not simply related to the mean square of the sound pressure. In the far field, however, this relationship is true, and, because sound pressure level is an easy parameter to measure in practice, it has become the most common way of expressing the magnitude of an acoustic field.

15

2.2. SOUND POWER, ENERGY DENSITY AND INTENSITY

Sound Power

Any source of noise has a characteristic sound power, a basic measure of its acoustic output, but the sound pressure levels it gives rise to depend on many external factors, which include the distance and orientation of the receiver, the temperature and velocity gradients in the medium, and the environment. Sound power on the other hand is a fundamental physical property of the source alone, and is therefore an important absolute parameter which is widely used for rating and comparing sound sources.

Sound-energy Density

The acoustic energy contained in a unit volume of the medium is a fundamental parameter of any type of acoustic field. It is termed the energy density and is related to the acoustic pressure by the following equation

Energy Density
$$D = \frac{p^2_{rms}}{\rho c^2}$$

Intensity

The intensity, the acoustic energy flowing through unit area in the sound field (perpendicular to the direction of propagation of the wave if the field is not diffuse), in unit time, is different for various types of acoustic field.

For a free field in which the sound wave arrives only from the direction of the source

$$I = \frac{p^2_{rms}}{\rho c}$$

For a diffuse field, such as occurs in an ideal reverberant room, in which there is equal probability of sound arriving from any direction, the net intensity is zero. However, the intensity of sound passing through a plane of unit area from one side only is

$$I = \frac{p^2_{rms}}{4\rho c}$$

ρc is called the characteristic acoustic impedance of the medium, which for air at 20°C is 407 rayls (Kg m-2 sec-1)

16

2.3. THE PLANE SOURCE

Consider (see Fig. 2.4.) an elemental tube of the medium, with unit cross-sectional area and a length equal to the distance travelled by the sound wave in one second, i.e. numerically the speed of sound (c). If a piston source of power W is constrained by hard walls to radiate all its power into the elemental tube to produce a plane wave, the tube will contain a quantity of energy numerically equal to the power output of the source. Assuming no other losses, the intensity, i.e. the acoustic energy flowing through unit area anywhere along the tube in unit time, is independent of the distance from the source and numerically equal to its sound power. Apart from duct systems, plane waves and plane sources are rarely encountered in normal noise measurement situations.

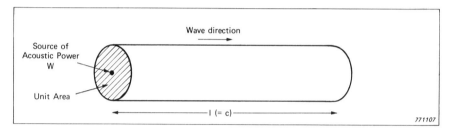

Fig.2.4. Acoustic Radiation into an elemental tube

2.4. THE POINT SOURCE

Sound sources can be considered as point sources if their dimensions are small in relation to their distance from the receiver, and many common noise sources, including industrial plant, aircraft, and individual road vehicles can normally be treated in this way. As shown in Fig.2.5 the ideal point source can be considered to produce a series of spherical wavefronts resulting from successive disturbances at the point source. For a pure sinusoidal disturbance, the distance between wavefronts representing the successive peak pressures will of course be the wavelength, a fact which is important when considering the effects of reflections within the sound field. As shown in Fig. 2.6., the sound energy spreads out equally in all directions so that as it travels further and further from the source its energy is received on an ever larger spherical area. If the medium is assumed to be non-dissipative then the entire power output of the source passes through a spherical shell of radius r. The intensity is therefore the Power of the source divided by the area of this shell. Thus we have

$$I = \frac{W}{4\pi r^2}$$

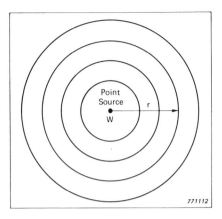

Fig.2.5. The propagation of spherical wavefronts from a point source

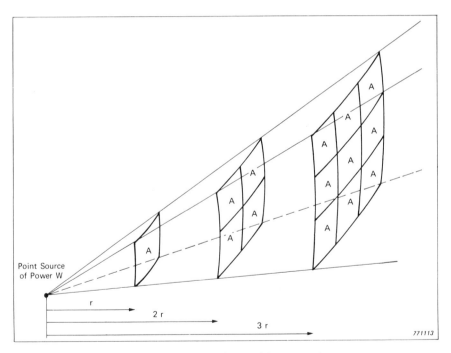

Fig.2.6. The dispersion of sound from a point source

It can be seen that the intensity is inversely proportional to the square of the distance between source and receiver, i.e. it attentuates 6 dB per doubling of distance.

2.5. THE LINE SOURCE

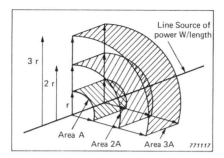

Fig.2.7. The dispersion of sound from a line source

A line source may be continuous radiation, such as from a pipe carrying a turbulent fluid, or may be composed of a large number of point sources so closely spaced that their emissions may be considered as emanating continuously from a notional line connecting them. In this category are included such factory sources as closely-spaced machines and conveyors, and two extremely important sources of environmental noise, namely roads and railways. A road which has a traffic flow high enough to be a noise nuisance can usually be considered as a line source rather than a succession of single events. Railways are often treated as line sources at the distances from the track which are usually the most important from the point of view of community annoyance. Very close to or very far from the track, the field is rather more complex. Consider the diagram in Fig. 2.7. of part of an infinite line source which has a constant power per unit length. The wavefront spreads out from the line in only one dimension perpendicular to its direction of travel, so that any two points at the same distance from the line are on the same wave front and have the same properties. The wavefronts therefore form concentric cylindrical surfaces about the line source as axis. The energy released from a unit length of the source in unit time passes through the same length of cylindrical surface at all radii. The intensity at a given radius is therefore the power emitted by this element, divided by the area of the cylindrical elemental surface. Thus:

$$I = \frac{W}{2\pi r \times 1}$$

The intensity is therefore inversely proportional to the distance from the source i.e. it attenuates 3 dB per doubling of distance.

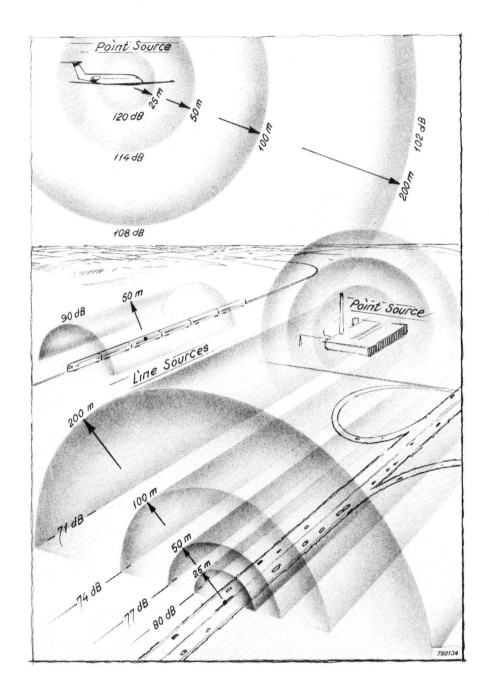

Fig. 2.8. Attenuation from point and line sources

2.6. PROPAGATION OF SOUND IN AIR

In addition to the reduction in intensity by distance, discussed in the previous sections, there are many other factors which can significantly affect the propagation of sound in a real medium like the atmosphere. Velocity and temperature gradients alter the direction of the wave, turbulence distorts it, and viscosity causes absorption. This latter effect is far greater for high than for low frequencies, so the atmosphere tends to act as a low pass filter, attenuating high frequencies, and thus distorting the frequency spectrum of a noise, as well as reducing its strength and changing its propagation path. In addition, most measurements are made near ground level where people live and work and where noise is invariably received and, with the notable exception of aircraft noise, produced. For this reason the reflection and absorption of the ground under the path between source and receiver is very important, and must be taken into account as a matter of course whenever studying the transmission of outdoor noise.

2.7. THE EFFECTS OF WIND

The atmosphere is in a state of continuous motion over the Earth's surface and is also a real fluid with all the normal physical properties including viscosity. Because the air is viscous the velocity of molecules at the ground must be zero and a boundary layer is formed near the surface, in which the wind speed gradually increases with height until the speed of the main air mass is attained. This region may be as much as several hundred meters thick so it can, and does, affect measurements made of most noise sources. When a sound wave impinges on a layer of air which has a different speed, the wave's direction of travel changes, as represented by the sound "rays" and vector constructions in Fig.2.9. This happens because the speed of sound depends only upon the medium in which it is propagated, so any movement of that medium must necessarily impose a similar movement on the sound wave as seen from the ground. If it has a component in the same direction as the wind, the ray representing the direction of propagation is therefore refracted towards the interface between the two different velocity regions when entering that with the higher speed, or away from the interface when entering a region of lower speed. The effects are simply reversed if the direction of sound propagation is opposite to that of the wind. Although the lower atmosphere is not a series of discrete layers with fixed velocities, but a transition region in which the velocity changes continuously with altitude, it can be seen from this simple approach how the sound rays will be continuously refracted as they progress through the boundary layer.

The overall effect as far as a stationary observer on the ground is concerned, is to bend the downwind sound rays back towards the Earth and bend the upwind rays away from it as shown in Fig. 2.10. A region of noise

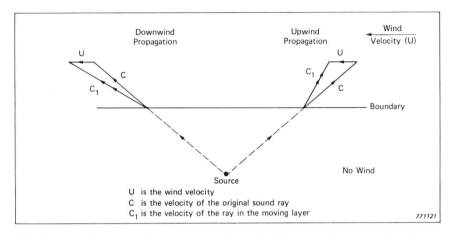

Fig.2.9. Sound propagation across a boundary between layers with different velocities

reinforcement is therefore formed downwind of the source and a sound 'shadow', a region of reduced intensity, occurs on its upwind side. Refraction effects can only occur because there is a wind gradient, i.e. because the wind speed varies with altitude, and are not the result of sound being convected along by the wind. The magnitudes of changes in sound intensity which can be attributed to this phenomenon are dependent only on the rates of change of wind speed with altitude. Attenuations in the shadow region may be as high as 30 dB but the increases which are due to reinforcement downwind of the source are usually rather less.

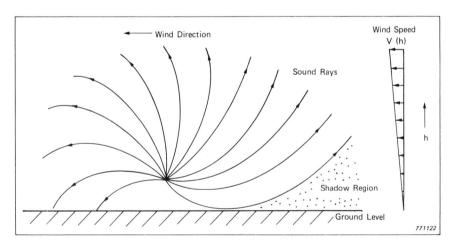

Fig.2.10. Sound refraction in a boundary layer

2.8. TEMPERATURE GRADIENTS

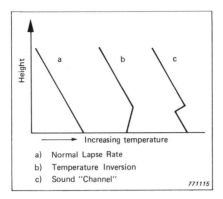

Fig.2.11. Typical atmospheric temperature gradients

The velocity of sound in air increases with temperature, and in a normal atmosphere the temperature itself decreases with height as in Fig. 2.11(a). A rising sound ray, on entering a layer with a lower temperature, undergoes a reduction in propagation velocity and is refracted away from the interface between the two layers. The result is that, in the absence of wind, the rays are continuously bent away from the ground surface as shown in Fig. 2.12(a) and a shadow region is formed beginning at a distance from the source which depends on the strength of the temperature gradient. As with wind gradients, the effects of temperature gradients are made less distinct by the inhomogeneity of the atmosphere in its normal state, with turbulence and local heat exchange scattering sound into the shadow regions.

Sometimes, however, the temperature gradient near the ground is positive, i.e. the temperature increases with height up to a point where it reverts to the normal lapse rate as in Fig.2.11(b). This situation is called a temperature inversion and leads to effects opposite to those described above for a normal lapse rate. A sound ray becomes refracted downwards towards the ground as it progresses through the warmer layer of air, reinforces the sound field at surface level around the source, and, as Fig.2.12(b) shows, no shadow region will be formed.

A double temperature gradient such as that in Fig.2.11(c) is rarely encountered, but can trap slightly-inclined sound waves in the inversion layer and channel them over considerable distances with only low attenuation.

23

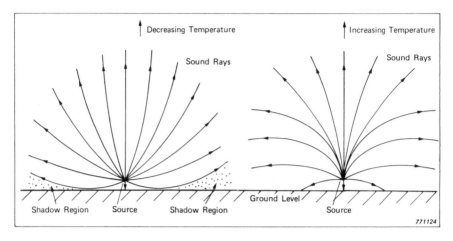

Fig.2.12. Refraction of sound in an atmosphere with
a) a normal lapse rate
b) an inverted lapse rate

2.9. HUMIDITY AND PRECIPITATION

The absorption of sound in air varies with frequency, humidity and temperature in an extremely complicated fashion; the only general trend being that it is higher at high frequencies, and shows a tendency to increase with temperature but decrease at higher relative humidities. If it is imperative to include these effects when carrying out research into distant noise sources, the current literature on the subject, and the available tables which contain the relationships between all the relevant parameters, should be consulted. The oft-mentioned ability of sound to "carry" in fog or light precipitation of any kind is not due to any changed physical property of the medium which is conducive to better propagation. Reduced human activity and still air conditions often combine to produce a lower than normal background noise level during these periods.

2.10. ABSORPTION BY NATURAL FEATURES

If the ground surface below a sound wave is perfectly flat and reflecting, the wave would propagate without any excess attenuation over that attributable to the spreading of the acoustic energy throughout an ever increasing volume. Even a man-made hard surface such as concrete is not perfectly reflecting, however, and most natural ground cover has significant absorption. This causes a significant reduction in intensity, which is most marked when source or receiver, or both, are near the ground and relatively distant. As would be expected, the attenuation is greater for high frequencies than for lower ones and depends to a large extent on the effective "roughness" of the surface, i.e. the ratio between the wavelength and the dimensions of the irregularities of the ground. The values are, therefore, low for ordinary grassland, but may rise to as much as 20 dB per 100 metres for long grass, corn or low shrubs and trees.

2.11. REFLECTION

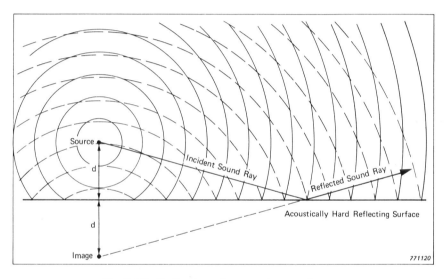

Fig.2.13. Reflections from a plane surface

When sound waves come in contact with a surface, part of the energy is reflected from it, part is transmitted through it and part is absorbed by it. The instantaneous sound pressure at any point in the field is therefore due to the direct radiation from the source, and the sound arriving indirectly after one or more reflections from the surfaces, where a part of its energy, however small, is absorbed. If absorption and transmission are low, and therefore most of the sound energy incident on the surface is reflected, it is said to be acoustically hard, and can be considered to reflect sound in much the same way as a mirror reflects light. The ray reflected from a flat rigid surface then takes up the position as shown in Fig. 2.13 and the sound ray and wave fronts can be considered as coming from the image. The reflected wave fronts and those arriving directly from the source reinforce or cancel each other where they cross, giving rise to problems when making noise measure-

25

ments in the presence of reflecting surfaces such as hard ground, roads, and building facades.

The effect of curved surfaces, parallel flat surfaces, and corners, on the sound field, is shown diagrammatically in Fig. 2.14. If the reflecting surface is curved then the rays will be focused when the surface is concave, and dispersed when convex. A ray entering a right angled corner will be reflected from it, after two reflections, back along a path different from, but parallel to, its incoming one. Parallel surfaces cause two important effects. Firstly, the formation of standing waves, which occur at frequencies such that an integral number of half wavelengths occur between the two surfaces, leading to a very large variation in sound pressure from node to antinode. The second effect, flutter echo, is caused by the continuous and regular reflection of a pulse from parallel surfaces with low absorption. These phenomena are undesirable in architectural acoustics (concert halls, lecture rooms etc.) and in acoustic testing chambers, where uniformity of the sound field is generally required.

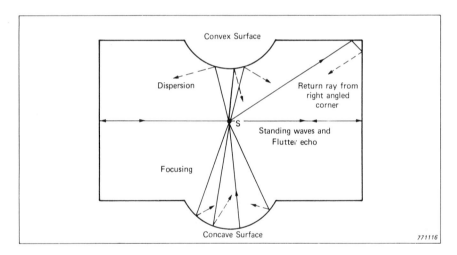

Fig.2.14. Reflections from surfaces of various shape

In any enclosed sound field there will be a region near the noise source in which its dimensions have an important effect, a region further away in which it is the direct sound which is dominant, and beyond this a region dominated by the reverberant sound, which builds up by continual reflection until the energy produced by the source is just balanced by the energy absorbed by the room surfaces, and an equilibrium state is reached. These regions are shown in Fig. 2.15. The "near field" is usually avoided in making noise measurements because simple relationships between the sound intensity and

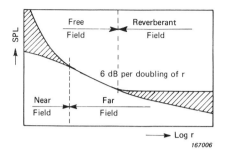

Fig.2.15. Sound pressure variation in a room, with variability indicated (F.M. Wiener)

other physical parameters, such as pressure and particle displacement, do not exist there. Measurements are usually only made here when detailed information about the radiation characteristics of the source are required for research and development purposes in the laboratory. The "far field" consists of two parts, the free field, where sound, as the term suggests, behaves as if in the open air, without reflecting surfaces to interfere with its propagation, and the reverberant field, which is dominated by reflections and therefore occurs in most enclosures. A diffuse field: i.e. one in which a large number of reflected waves from all directions combine so that the average energy density is the same throughout the field, is desirable for sound power measurements and for determining the sound insulation properties of materials. Reverberant rooms used for these measurements are often constructed as in Fig.2.16 with highly-reflecting non-parallel walls, or provided with diffusers in order to achieve a suitably diffuse field.

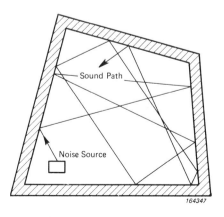

Fig.2.16. A reverberant room designed to obtain a diffuse field

2.12. ABSORPTION

Whenever a sound wave meets a surface, some small amount of its energy is lost. The absorption of a surface is a function of many parameters, including its effective roughness, its porosity, its flexibility, and in some cases its resonant properties. The efficiency of an absorbing surface is expressed as a number between zero and 1, called the absorption coefficient. Zero represents no absorption, i.e. perfect reflection, which is never encountered in practice, and 1 represents perfect absorption. Most mechanisms of absorption are frequency dependent, so the spectrum of the noise concerned has to be known to judge its effect, both in rooms and in the open air. Absorption techniques really come into their own with regard to Architectural Acoustics and the control of reverberation and diffusion in halls, rooms and offices. Absorbent materials can, however, be put to good use to reduce overall levels in noisy factories, and to provide acceptable conditions near particularly noisy machinery by reducing reflected noise from adjacent hard surfaces.

2.13. DIFFRACTION

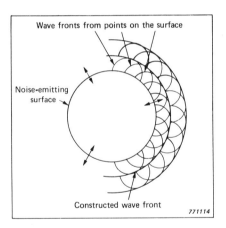

Fig.2.17. Huygen's method of wavefront construction

When a sound wave encounters an obstacle which is small in relation to its wavelength, the wave passes round it almost as if it did not exist, forming very little shadow. But, if the frequency of the sound is sufficiently high and the wavelength is therefore sufficiently short, a noticeable shadow is formed. These phenomena can be explained by first introducing Huygen's method of wavefront construction, which states that a source may be considered as an infinite number of point sources covering its surface, and radiating in all directions. At an instant in time, each point emits a sound wave and these

28

combine to form an overall wavefront as in Fig. 2.17. Similarly, each point on a wave front can be considered as a new sound source, so the next position of the wave front can be constructed from the last. Extending this concept to the two cases of Fig. 2.18(a) and 18(b) we can see what happens when the wave fronts from a distant source impinge on the edge of, or an opening in, an otherwise infinite wall.

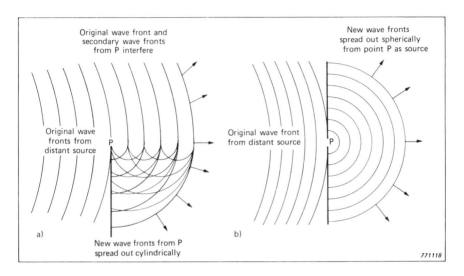

Fig.2.18. Effects of diffraction at low frequencies

In the case of the situation in Fig.2.18(a) the wall edge can be considered as a source of secondary wavelets radiating away from it in all directions according to Huygen's principle. These secondary wavelets combine to form wavefronts which spread out cylindrically in the quadrant behind the wall, in the so-called shadow region. For the second case the opening becomes, in effect, a new point source of sound, radiating hemispherically into the space beyond the wall, but with a lower intensity (depending on the size of the opening) than the incident sound.

A large ratio of wavelength to obstacle size causes the diffraction pattern as shown in Fig.2.18(a) and 2.18(b). A small value leads to the formation of a more distinct shadow behind a barrier, Fig.2.19(a), or a beam of sound through an opening as shown in Fig.2.19(b). The greatest attenuation behind a barrier occurs if the angle between the ray from the source to the barrier top, and the line from there to the receiver, is as small as possible. Practically, this means that the barrier should be as near as possible to either the source or the receiver for greatest effect. When taking measurements of noise sources in the field, unobstructed situations are always to be preferred unless the barrier effect is of direct interest.

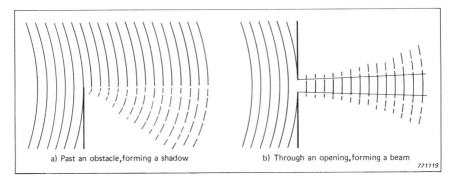

a) Past an obstacle,forming a shadow   b) Through an opening,forming a beam

Fig.2.19. Effects of diffraction at high frequencies

2.14. SCALES FOR NOISE — THE DECIBEL

Propagation through any elastic medium takes place in the form of a wave, and the most important quantity characterising its magnitude is its root mean square amplitude, A_{rms}. Suitable units and scales for expressing this value must now be considered. Normally, the sound pressure rather than the intensity of a sound field is the parameter used, expressed as force per unit area in units of dynes per square centimeter (bar) in the CGS system or in units of newtons per square meter (Pascals) in the S.I. system. As the Pascal has now been internationally adopted as the unit of pressure, it will be used exclusively throughout this book.

The normal method of measuring pressure on a linear scale unfortunately gives rise to certain problems when related to the performance of the human ear. The quietest sound at 1000 Hz which can be heard by the average person has been found to be about 20 μPascals and this value has been standardised as the nominal hearing threshold for the purpose of sound level measurements. At the other end of the scale the threshold of pain occurs at a sound pressure of approximately 100 Pascals, a ratio of more than a million to 1. The direct application of linear scales to the measurement of sound pressure would therefore lead to the use of enormous and unwieldy numbers.

30

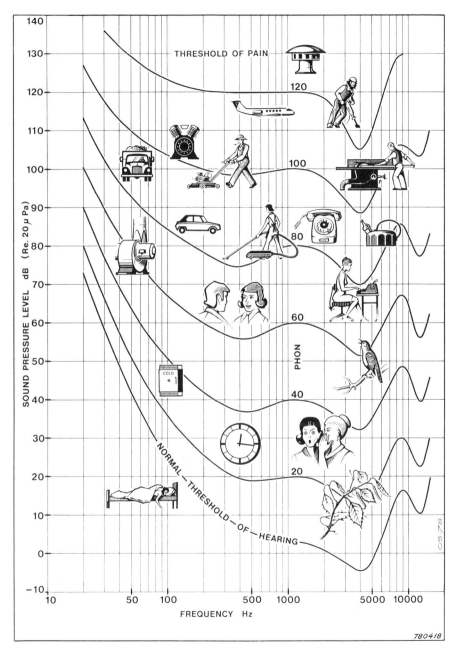

Fig.2.20. Typical sound pressure levels of common noise sources

Additionally, the ear responds not linearly but logarithmically to stimulus. For these reasons it has been found more practical to express acoustic parameters as a logarithmic ratio of the measured value to a standard value. This reduces the numbers to manageable proportions and the resulting unit, called the Bel (after Alexander Graham Bell) is defined as the logarithm to the base ten of the ratio of two acoustical powers, or intensities. But, this unit was found in practice to be rather too large, and a unit of one tenth of a Bel, the decibel, is now in general use. As the acoustic intensity, the power passing through a unit area in space, is proportional in the far field to the square of the sound pressure, a convenient scale for acoustic measurements can be defined as

$$\text{Sound Pressure Level} \quad Lp = 10 \, log_{10}\left(\frac{p}{p_0}\right)^2 = 20 \, log_{10}\frac{p}{p_0} \qquad (1)$$

where p is the sound pressure being measured. p_0 is the reference sound pressure, usually 20μPa. and the word level is added to sound pressure as an indication that the quantity has a certain level above some predefined reference value.

Any measurement may be expressed in decibels, whatever its units, as long as the absolute reference value for the unit used in the logarithmic ratio is quoted. Use of the decibel scale thus reduces a dynamic range of sound pressures of a million to 1 to a more manageable range of sound pressure levels of only 0 to 120, zero indicating the reference minimum threshold and 120 the approximate threshold of pain. This is far more convenient and easier to deal with as the values lie within a range easily conceived by the layman and one unit, i.e., 1 decibel is about the smallest value of significance. The illustrated graph of Fig.2.20 shows many well-known sounds appropriately placed with regard to the sound pressure level at which they are normally heard and their major frequencies.

Acoustic Power is also usually measured in decibels because of the enormous range of powers encountered in typical noise problems. The power level is defined as ten times the logarithm to the base ten of the ratio of the source power to the reference power, usually taken as 10^{-12} watt, mathematically this becomes

$$\text{Sound Power Level} \quad L_W = 10 \, log_{10}\frac{W}{W_0} \qquad (2)$$

where W   is the power emitted
and W_0 is the reference power (10^{-12} watt).

The approximate power outputs of a range of a few regularly encountered noise sources are indicated in Fig. 2.21. This demonstrates well the problems of magnitude and dynamic range which are always involved when making noise and acoustic measurements.

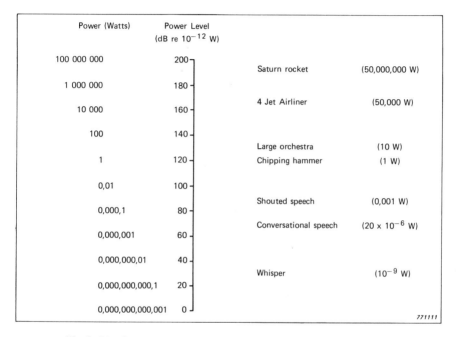

Fig.2.21. Sound Power output of some typical noise sources

Dealing with Decibels

The following short table shows the subjective effect of changes in noise levels.

CHANGE IN LEVEL dB	SUBJECTIVE EFFECT
3	just perceptible
5	clearly perceptible
10	twice as loud

Several important facts must always be borne in mind when dealing with decibel quantities, but if these are fully understood then their use and manipulation should cause no more problems than the more familiar linearly ex-pressed quantities. Zero decibel level does not mean an absence of noise, it merely implies that the level in question is equal to the reference level. One of the most important concepts which must be grasped firmly by newcomers to noise measurement is that, because of the logarithmic units, normal addi-tion and subtraction cannot be used directly on decibel quantities. Two sound sources, each producing a sound pressure level of 60 dB when measured in the absence of the other, will not produce 120 dB when both are emitting at the same time. To arrive at the correct level one must consider the two in-stantaneous sound pressures from the two sources at a point in space. If these two individual pressures are $p_1(t)$ and $p_2(t)$, then the total pressure is

$$p_{tot}(t) = p_1(t) + p_2(t)$$

and the mean square sound pressure, the time average of $p^2_{tot}(t)$ is

$$\overline{p^2_{tot}} = \frac{1}{T} \int_0^T [p_1(t) + p_2(t)]^2 \, dt$$

therefore
$$\overline{p^2_{tot}} = \overline{p_1^2} + \overline{2p_1 p_2} + \overline{p_2^2} \qquad (3)$$

where a bar over the term denotes a time-averaged quantity. In most cases of independent noise sources we can assume that they are not coherent and therefore that significant interference of one wave front by another does not occur, so that the time average cross-term represented by $p_1 p_2$ is zero.

then
$$\overline{p^2_{tot}} = \overline{p_1^2} + \overline{p_2^2}$$

but
$$p_1 = p_2$$

therefore
$$\overline{p^2_{tot}} = 2\overline{p_1^2}$$

so if we have two similar sources then we have doubled the mean square pressure, and from equation (1) we have

$$SPL = 10 \, log_{10}\left(2\frac{p_1^2}{p_0^2}\right)$$

$$= 10 \, log_{10}\left(\frac{p_1^2}{p_0^2}\right) + 10 \, log_{10} \, 2$$

$$= 10 \, log_{10}\left(\frac{p_1^2}{p_0^2}\right) + 3$$

i.e. New SPL = old SPL + 3 dB

Doubling the number of sources therefore raises the sound pressure level by 3 dB, a further doubling to four times the number raises it by 6 dB, and so on.

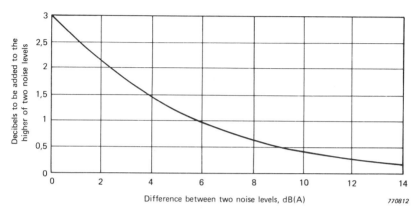

Fig.2.22. Noise level addition chart

The addition of sound pressures of different levels and from many different sources can be carried out by first reducing the measured values to actual pressures, combining these to find the effective mean square and then taking the logarithm, as described in some detail in appendix B. A simple graph for the case of two sources only is shown in Fig. 2.22 in terms of a correction which is to be added to the highest of the two levels, depending on their difference. This may also be used to estimate the combined effect of more than two sources by summing them two at a time. If the assumption that sources of equal intensity are uncorrelated is not made, then the term p_1p_2 is not necessarily zero and positions of reinforcement and cancellation will occur. In the extreme case of constructive interference between two tones of the same frequency.

$$p_1 = p_2$$

Therefore
$$p_1p_2 = p_1{}^2$$

and equation (3) becomes
$$\overline{p^2{}_{tot}} = \overline{4p_1{}^2}$$

Now
$$10\,log_{10}\,4 = 6$$

so the level will rise by 6 dB
For destructive interference $p_1 = -p_2$
and in this case equation (3) becomes

$$\overline{p^2{}_{tot}} = \overline{p_1{}^2} - \overline{2p_1{}^2} + \overline{p_1{}^2} = 0$$

35

so the level will fall, theoretically, by ∞. In practice of course the regions of reinforcement will be a little less than 6 dB and the regions of cancellation will certainly not fall by more than 20 or 30 dB at the very most. It is recommended that appendix B is studied at this point in order to gain experience on the manipulation of quantities expressed in decibels. The ability to think clearly and effectively in terms of decibels is invaluable to the understanding of most of the Standards and the techniques involved in acoustics and noise measurement.

2.15. CHARACTERISTICS OF NOISE SIGNALS

All sound signals are characterised by certain basic physical parameters which are relatively simple for fixed amplitude and frequency signals but become increasingly complicated if the frequencies and amplitudes vary with time. Perhaps the simplest form of sound wave, with a sinusoidally varying amplitude and constant frequency, (a pure tone) is shown in Fig. 2.23. The time history repeats itself exactly with a repetition period T, corresponding to the generating frequency f, and possesses the fundamental characteristics which apply to all types of signals. Phase is of little importance in the analysis of individual noise signals, which are usually composed of many frequency components combined in random phase. However, it is a useful concept in considering reflecting or absorbing surfaces, standing waves, and the vibration of structures, where the phase difference between many signals is particularly important.

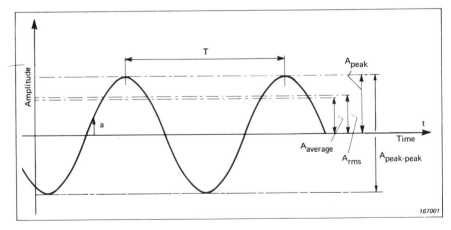

Fig.2.23. Sinusoidal signal showing various measures of signal amplitude

The amplitude of a sinusoid may be expressed by any of the quantities shown in the diagram and all are simply related to each other in the case of this particular simple signal. The root mean square (r.m.s.) value of any signal is proportional to its energy content and is therefore one of the most important and most often used measures of amplitude. It is defined

$$A_{rms} = \sqrt{\frac{1}{T} \int_0^T a^2(t) \cdot dt}$$

Where T is the relevant time period over which the averaging takes place
and a is the instantaneous amplitude

Other measures of amplitude are

$$A_{average} = \frac{1}{T} \int_0^T |a| \cdot dt$$

and A_{peak} which is the maximum amplitude reached by the signal in the repetition period.

For any signal, a measure of its wave shape can be indicated by two factors

$$\text{Crest Factor} \quad F_c = \frac{A_{peak}}{A_{rms}}$$

$$\text{Form Factor} \quad F_f = \frac{A_{rms}}{A_{average}}$$

For a sinusoid *only* these values are simply related as follows,

$$A_{rms} = \frac{\pi}{2\sqrt{2}} A_{average} = \frac{1}{\sqrt{2}} A_{peak}$$

so that F_c = 1,414 ($\doteqdot$ 3 dB)
and F_f = 1,11 ($\doteqdot$ 1 dB)

Unfortunately most sounds are not sinusoids and more often than not vary both in amplitude and frequency content with time. Simple mathematical relationships between A_{rms} , $A_{average}$ and A_{peak} do not exist for these complex signals but still retain their importance as descriptors of the signal. The quantity A_{peak} is not strictly applicable to truly random noise but in practical measurements, especially when dealing with shocks, impulsive noise, and short events, it is an extremely important factor.

A signal typical of those encountered in practice is shown in Fig. 2.24(d) and clearly it cannot be described by the three simple quantities, the maximum amplitude, frequency, and, where relevant, the phase, because it is composed of more than one frequency. The signal may be viewed as a combination, however complex, of a large number of superimposed sinusoids, the concept of Fourier Analysis. A pure sine wave contains one frequency and can therefore be represented in the frequency domain as a single line as in Fig. 2.24(a). If we were to add two sine waves, one being 3 times the frequency of the other, we would obtain the distorted wave of Fig. b, which is represented in the frequency domain by two lines. Analysis of a far more complex but still periodic function, such as the square wave of Fig. c, yields an infinite number of lines in the frequency domain at the odd harmonics of the repetition frequency of the signal. The spectra of all the functions mentioned so far have been harmonically related discrete lines and are therefore termed periodic, as they repeat themselves exactly at regular and predictable intervals. Most practical noise is non-periodic, however, and contains a large number of frequency components which are not harmonically related, forming a continuous spectrum as in Fig. d. A special case of the non-periodic signal is white noise, which has a completely flat spectrum and is of particular importance in both theory and practice.

The internal combustion engine is a typical source which produces periodic noise containing many harmonics of its rotational speed. However, the noise from a vehicles tyres at high speed and that from falling water are non-periodic; both have a continuous and almost flat spectrum. In practice the majority of noise consists of a mixture of both types of signal.

The process of signal analysis is of vital importance in every branch of noise measurement, analysis and control. On one hand the frequency content of a noise affects its perceived loudness, and therefore the annoyance to which it gives rise, and also the amount of speech masking. On the other hand, the provision of an adequate acoustic environment and the reduction of noise at source or during transmission, demand a knowledge of both the source spectrum and the properties of frequency-dependent insulating and absorbing materials. This information is necessary for effective design and can only be obtained from a frequency analysis. For a fuller discussion of these techniques please refer to the companion publication "Application of Brüel & Kjær equipment to Frequency Analysis".

38

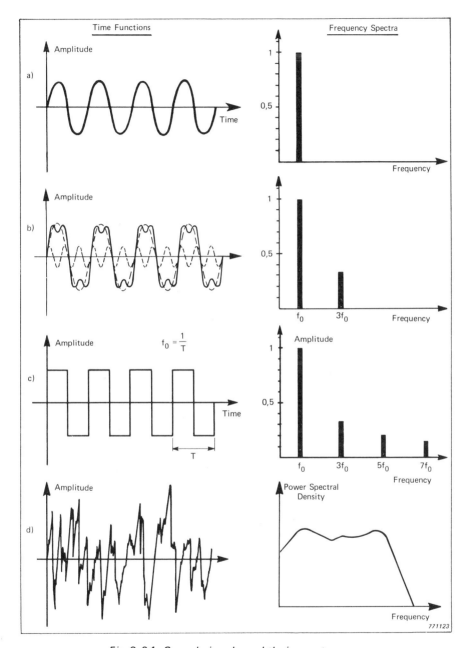

Fig. 2.24. Sound signals and their spectra
a) pure sinusoid (simple and periodic) c) square wave (complex but periodic)
b) combination of two sinusoids   d) random noise (complex and non-periodic)

39

3. PSYCHO-ACOUSTICS AND NOISE CRITERIA

3.1. THE HEARING MECHANISM

Hearing is necessary for many desirable things; for communication, the enjoyment of music, and to locate sound sources, as well as the means by which we receive undesirable noise. The reception and analysis of sound is a complicated process which is still not completely understood, and the ear itself is a complex instrument capable of excellent discrimination over a wide range of frequencies and sound intensities. The purpose of this chapter is to summarise the operation of the ear, the main methods of loudness determination, and certain noise units and criteria which are used for environmental noise control and assessment.

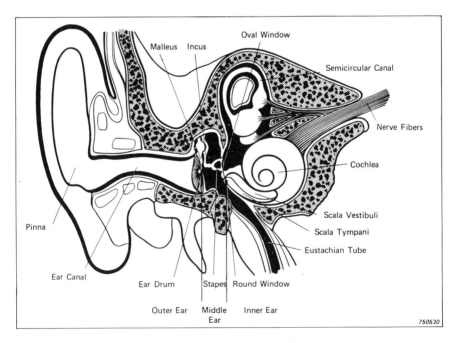

Fig.3.1. The main parts of the ear

The human ear consists of three main parts, as shown in diagram 3.1. The outer and middle ear collect the airborne sound waves and pass them to the liquid-filled inner ear, which acts as a transducer, converting mechanical vibration signals into neural impulses which transfer the acoustic information to the brain. The outer ear, consisting of the pinna and the ear canal, collects the airborne sound waves and channels them through the auditory canal, finally setting the eardrum into vibration. The middle ear, which acts as an impedance matching device, has three small bones operating as a set of levers with a mechanical advantage of approximately 3 : 1. These transfer the vibration of the eardrum to the inner ear.

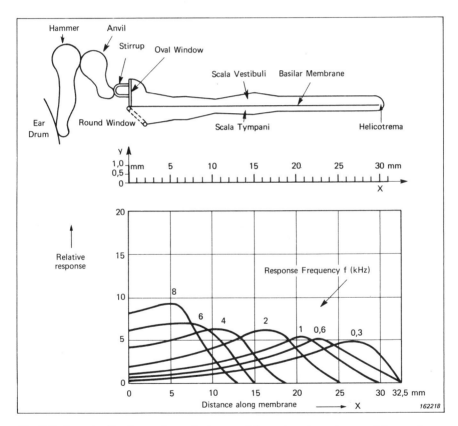

Fig.3.2. Longitudinal section of the cochlea showing the positions of response maxima

The final link between the acoustic event and the neural impulse occurs in the inner ear, which consists of two separate systems, the semi-circular can-

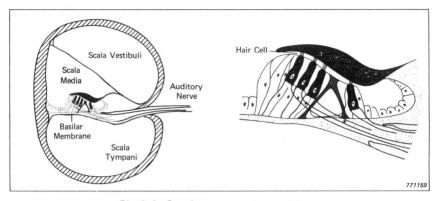

Fig.3.3. Section across the cochlea

als which are concerned primarily with balance, and the cochlea which is concerned with hearing. The liquid-filled cavity of the cochlea is divided into two longitudinal canals by the basilar membrane, which extends along the cochlea's entire length except for a small gap called the helicotrema at the far end. See Fig.3.2 and 3.3, which show a longitudinal section of the unfurled Cochlea and a section across it. When the stirrup, responding to an acoustic stimulus, moves the oval window, the resultant fluid disturbance passes along the upper canal, past the helicotrema, into the lower canal, and ultimately the round window deflects to accommodate it. During its passage through the canals the disturbance distorts the basilar membrane, on whose upper surface, as Fig.3.3. shows, there are thousands of extremely sensitive hair cells which register this distortion and transform it into nerve impulses which are ultimately transmitted to the brain. The frequency sensitivity varies with distance along the basilar membrane, the maximum response at high frequencies occurs near the oval window and that at low frequencies near the helicotrema. By this system of canals, levers, membranes, and hair cells, the ear is able to detect sounds over enormous ranges of frequency and intensity. The highest frequency sound the healthy human ear can hear is 1000 times the frequency of the lowest, and the loudest can have a sound pressure one million times that of the quietest that can be heard (an intensity ratio of 10^{12} :1).

Unfortunately, no simple relationship exists between the measured physical sound pressure level and the human perception of the same sound. The loudness of a pure tone of constant sound level, perhaps the simplest acoustic signal of all, varies with its frequency, and that of a short pulse will vary with its duration as well, even though the sound pressure may be the same in every case. The treatment of acoustic noise and its effects is therefore a complicated problem, which must take a wide variety of parameters into account to achieve good correlation between measurements and the resultant human perception or reaction.

42

3.2. MASKING AND THE CRITICAL BANDS

We are very rarely exposed to just an isolated sound. The sound in which we are interested normally occurs with several others, usually referred to as background noise. The reception of sound, and especially the intelligibility of speech, may be impaired or masked if the frequency components of the background noise are sufficiently loud compared with those of the sound we wish to hear. Further difficulties arise because the physical parameters of the masking and the masked noise may vary widely. Either noise may be narrow band, wide band, a pure tone, steady, intermittent, or impulsive etc., thus generating a large number of possible combinations. A lot of research has been carried out to try to identify the effects of some of these parameters and several areas of general agreement have been reached.

1. A narrow band of noise causes more masking than does a pure tone of the same intensity centred at the same frequency.

2. At low levels, masking is confined to a fairly narrow band around the masking noise's centre frequency. As the level of the masking noise increases so does the frequency range over which it has an effect.

3. The masking effect is not symmetrical about the centre frequency of the masking noise. Frequencies above the centre frequency are more easily masked than those below.

These general effects are shown in the simplified diagram of Fig.3.4. The ability of the ear to detect small changes in frequency and intensity, and perhaps more importantly, methods of quantitative description have, of course, been well known for many years. That the ear can also be considered to act as a set of overlapping constant percentage bandwidth bandpass filters has, however, only been the result of relatively recent research. These hypothetical filters apparently have normal practical filter characteristics.

Increasing the bandwidth of a noise beyond a critical value does not lead to increased masking of a pure tone at its centre frequency. This concept of a critical bandwidth means that only the energy near the frequency of the sound to be masked contributes significantly towards its masking, and forms a basis for explaining other phenomena such as loudness and auditory fatigue. According to Zwicker one critical band corresponds to a distance of approximately 1,3 mm along the basilar membrane (defined as 1 Bark) and bears a direct relationship to the response maxima along it. This led to the definition of critical bands and their associated bandwidths as in Fig.3.5. The critical bandwidth over a wide range of frequencies, especially at the high end of the range, approximates to 23% i.e. 1/3 of an octave, so this is often used to justify the use of 1/3 octave band analysis in noise measurement as a good approximation to the way in which the ear itself actually works.

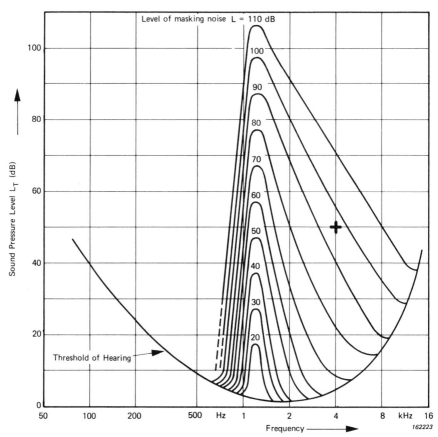

Fig.3.4. Masking effect of a narrow band noise centred at 1200 Hz at various
levels (after Zwicker). A 50 dB 4 kHz tone (marked +) can be heard if
the masking noise level is 90 dB, but is masked if its level rises to
100 dB

Critical Band (Bark)	1	2	3	4	5	6	7	8
Centre Frequency (Hz)	50	150	250	350	450	570	700	840
Bandwidth f (Hz)	100	100	100	100	110	120	140	150
Critical Band (Bark)	9	10	11	12	13	14	15	16
Centre Frequency (Hz)	1000	1170	1370	1600	1850	2150	2500	2900
Bandwidth f (Hz)	160	190	210	240	280	320	380	450
Critical Band (Bark)	17	18	19	20	21	22	23	24
Centre Frequency (Hz)	3400	4000	4800	5800	7000	8500	10500	13500
Bandwidth f (Hz)	550	700	900	1100	1300	1800	2500	3500

Fig.3.5. Table of critical bands (Frequenz-gruppen)

44

3.3. LOUDNESS AND ITS DETERMINATION

The human perception of loudness of pure tones and other noise types has been exhaustively investigated and various sets of equal loudness level contours proposed. These curves are the result of a large number of different psycho-acoustical experiments, and each is therefore valid only for the particular experimental conditions of the test itself. The sound source may, for example, be a pure tone or a frequency band of various width; the subject may be in a free or reverberent field; a stimulus may be applied to one or both ears by means of sound sources in the room, or directly by earphones. The curves finally obtained are usually the result of smoothing and averaging the statistical properties over large groups of people with normal hearing in the age group 18 to 25 years. Fig.3.6 shows the loudness level contours which have been internationally standardized for pure tones heard under standard conditions, and demonstrates how the subjective loudness, of a pure tone of given physical sound pressure level, varies with frequency. Tests were carried out by presenting the tone to be judged to the subject, who adjusted a 1000 Hz reference tone until it appeared to have the same loudness. 1000 Hz is thus the reference for all loudness measurements, and all contours of equal loud-

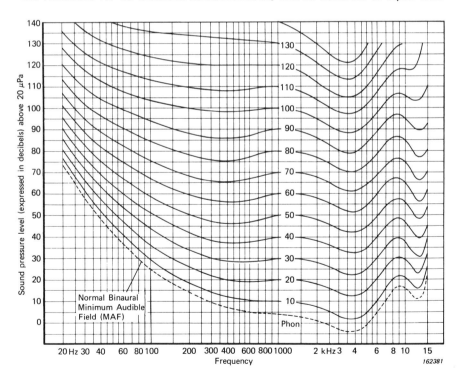

Fig.3.6. Normal Equal Loudness Contours for pure tones

ness level, expressed in Phons, have the same numerical value as the sound pressure level at 1000 Hz. A 50 dB tone at 1 kHz thus has the same loudness level, 50 phons, as a 73 dB tone at 50 Hz or a 42 dB tone at 4000 Hz, the ear's most sensitive frequency. Generally, then, it can be seen that the loudness level of a pure tone at a given sound pressure level falls off at low frequencies and at very high frequencies, and is a maximum at approximately 4 kHz. In addition, at very high sound pressure levels, tones of all frequencies tend to have similar loudness. The ear's assessment of loudness is therefore very non-linear in relation to both frequency and absolute sound pressure level, but for a given noise, a rise of 10 dB in sound pressure level corresponds approximately to a doubling of subjective loudness. A scale proportional to perceived loudness, the sone scale, has been developed to represent this subjective parameter. It is shown in graphical form in Fig.3.7 and is mathematically given by

$$S = 2^{\left(\frac{P-40}{10}\right)}$$

where P = loudness level in phons and S = the loudness in sones. On this scale 1 sone is defined as the loudness of a sound of loudness level 40 phons, so 30 phons is 0,5 sones, 50 phons is 2 sones, 60 phons is 4 sones etc.

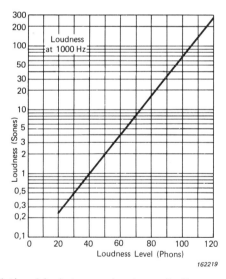

Fig.3.7. The relationship between loudness in Sones and loudness level in Phons

The loudness of more complex sounds, e.g. 1/3 octave band noise, may be determined by the comparison method in the same way as the now-standardised pure tone loudness curves. This is not always practicable, especially when making assessments in the field, and it was recognised that a method which substituted calculation for comparison could be much more easily and widely used. A procedure was therefore developed by Zwicker which uses 1/3 octave bands as its basic data, corrected for the effects of masking, and enables the loudness of complex broadband noises, (which may include pure tones) to be evaluated for both free field and diffuse conditions. Another method, due to Stevens, is simpler to use but rather more restricted in its areas of application. It can only be used for diffuse sound fields with a flat spectrum and makes use of octave bands, again corrected for the masking effects mentioned in the last section. Both the Zwicker and Stevens loudness calculation procedures are discussed in detail together with examples of their application in Appendix C, and both methods have been accepted by ISO as standard loudness calculation procedures.

3.4. LOUDNESS OF SHORT DURATION SOUNDS

In the previous sections, the loudness of a sound as perceived by the ear was shown to be dependent on both its amplitude and its frequency. If, in addition, the sound stimulus is of relatively short duration (less than about 200 msecs.), its loudness is reduced compared with the same sound heard continuously. The shorter the duration becomes, the less loud the sound appears to be. Many experimenters have investigated this phenomenon, and research on the subject has recently been given a boost by the desire to define more closely the relationship between sounds of short duration and both hearing damage and annoyance.

The results of Fig.3.8 were obtained from psycho-acoustic experiments in

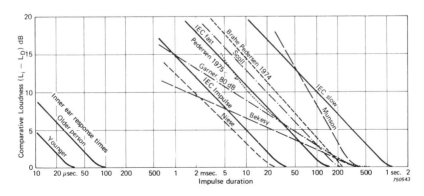

Fig.3.8. Results from different researchers of the subjective perception of short impulses compared with the standardized sound level meter characteristics and inner ear response times

47

which tone-burst impulses of different durations were compared with steady tones. The ordinate of the figure is the sound pressure level difference, $(L_i - L_D)$, between the level of the impulse, L_i, and the steady sound level, L_D, which was judged equally loud. The abscissa is simply the pulse duration. As long as its duration is greater than a certain length, the loudness of a pulse is judged to be equal to that of a steady sound of the same sound pressure level, i.e. $(L_i - L_D) = 0$. For shorter pulses, however, the loudness decreases with pulse length. The break-point corresponds to the effective averaging time of the ear, and the slope of most of the curves show that an increase of 3 dB in sound pressure level (a doubling of pulse intensity) is necessary to maintain the same perceived loudness when the pulse duration is halved. As the product of intensity and time is an energy, the ear appears to act as an energy-sensitive device, as far as the perception of loudness is concerned. The impulse characteristic of sound measuring systems has been standardised on this basis, (see Fig.3.8) the time constant being designed to give a measure of the *loudness* of single impulses. For the correct measurement of actual peak levels for purposes other than loudness evaluation, an instrument is required which is capable of detecting and holding peaks with rise times of less than 50 microsecs.

3.5. AGE-RELATED HEARING LOSS — PRESBYCUSIS

The normal aging process leads to hearing losses which tend to be small up to the age of 30 years or so and increase rapidly as old age is reached. Low frequencies below say 1 kHz are relatively little affected, but the loss increases steadily with frequency as demonstrated by the results of two independent surveys shown in Fig. 3.9 which both show the same trends al-

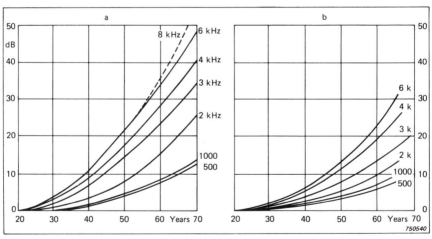

Fig.3.9. Average normal age-related hearing loss
a) According to Spoor   *b) According to Hinchcliffe*

though they are slightly different in detail. Not all this loss may be directly attributable to aging; some of it may be due to the noise which bombards modern man from all sides in his normal day to day activities. But such non-occupational hearing loss contributions, (dubbed 'sociocusis') are very difficult to quantify. Measurements of the hearing thresholds of Nomadic tribesmen living in exceptionally quiet rural conditions indicate their age-related hearing loss to be far smaller than that of comparable groups in industrialised countries, although this may be due at least in part to the vast difference in other, non-acoustic, factors.

A correction at each frequency must be applied to audiograms to take account of this age-dependent characteristic, in order to be able to arrive at the amount of hearing damage which can fairly be attributed to the effects of noise exposure.

3.6. NOISE-INDUCED HEARING LOSS

Steady Noise

If the ear is exposed to a high level of noise for a short period, a test of the sensitivity of that ear taken immediately afterwards reveals a small hearing loss known as a temporary threshold shift. The hearing threshold is the lowest sound pressure level which can be detected by the subject, and this may rise by up to 20 dB at certain frequencies after even a relatively short exposure. That is, a sound would have to be much louder than it was before the exposure to be heard afterwards. Fortunately, the phenomenon is temporary in nature, the ear recovering its original sensitivity after a relatively short time, any permanent threshold shift being too small to measure.

However, as the level and/or the exposure time increase, so too does the temporary threshold shift and the length of time the ear takes to recover from it. As long as the exposure times are relatively short and the intervals between them are long, then the permanent effects are not significant. Unfortunately, a large number of people work in factories and workshops where the noise levels are consistently high; and when the exposure takes place regularly for up to 8 hours every day, year after year, the effects cease to be temporary. A permanent hearing loss develops which in time may become severe enough to make normal conversation difficult to follow, and ultimately lead to chronic disability. The damage is by this time permanent and irreversible, for no amount of "rest" will lead to any significant recovery.

The form which a loss of hearing takes is remarkably independent of the mechanism which brings it about. There is almost always an initial dip in the audiogram at approximately 4 kHz., whatever the frequency content of the noise exposure which caused the damage, and the greatest shift is invariably

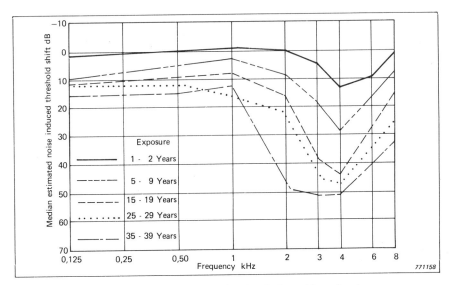

Fig.3.10. The development of noise induced hearing loss

at a frequency above that of the noise. This is characteristic of noise-induced hearing loss, and occurs for both temporary and permanent threshold shifts.

Permanent damage begins, as does the temporary, with a drop in sensitivity around 4 kHz., and as the exposure time increases, the shift becomes greater and extends gradually down to include the lower frequencies. The course which this takes is very clearly shown in Fig.3.10, which is taken from a classic survey of jute weavers in Dundee, Scotland. The workforce was particularly stable, many of them having worked at the same factory, and in some cases at the same loom, for up to 50 years. During this time virtually the same machinery was in continuous use and the noise had therefore remained remarkably constant. This provided an excellent opportunity to obtain all the necessary information at one time and in one place. The sample even included people who had left the industry or retired after a significant period of exposure and therefore had had a long time for any recovery process to have ended. Of particular interest is that the disability shown in Fig.3.10 rarely exceeds 20 dB below 1 kHz, and is less severe at frequencies of 6 kHz and above than it is between 1 kHz and 5 kHz, which is the frequency range of most importance to the understanding of speech.

Impulsive Noise

Impulsive noise is particularly important both as the cause of annoyance and as a significant hazard to hearing. It occurs widely in industry and construction where it arises from impact-producing operations such as rivetting, bottling, and materials handling, and also from the explosive release of energy, e.g. firearms, explosive forming, blasting, and cartridge guns. Otherwise apparently harmless objects such as toy pistols, clicking toys and fire-works are also capable of emitting dangerously high levels of impulsive noise.

Based on audiometric studies and close examination of the physical charac-teristics of impulsive sources, some factors important in causing damage have been identified. These include peak level, duration, rise time, and in the case of repeated events or reverberent fields, the repetition rate or reflection intensity respectively. The problem is further complicated because the loud-ness of a pulse reduces with its length below a certain critical duration (see Fig.3.8). Acoustic impulses of extremely short duration, which may be intense enough to contribute to hearing damage, may sound relatively quiet to the observer, and therefore the possibility of a hearing hazard may be overlooked. Normal sound level meters are designed for steady-state condi-tions and cannot respond with the very rapid rise times of impulsive sounds, and will in general underestimate the extent of a potential hearing hazard. To measure the absolute sound pressure level of an impulsive noise correctly, it is necessary to use a precision meter with a very rapid rise time (50 μsec. or less) and a peak hold facility, so that the true maximum peak level can be iden-tified and the value retained. However, if a measure of the subjective loud-ness only is required, a Precision Impulse Sound Level Meter with the inter-nationally agreed time constants and characteristics should be employed.

The noise specialist should always approach a noise measurement aware of the need to check for characteristics in the noise which might necessitate the use of special instruments or techniques of measurement or analysis. Im-pulsiveness is perhaps the most important of these, and will be mentioned in specific instances in later sections.

3.7. NOISINESS AND ANNOYANCE — SUBJECTIVE RATING SCALES FROM BASIC ACOUSTIC MEASUREMENTS

The previous sections of this chapter have dealt with the mechanism of hearing and the determination of loudness. The latter concept is well under-stood, and prediction methods, although still the subject of discussion and re-finement, are firmly established in the relevant standards. This is hardly the case, however, for noisiness and annoyance. Although certain qualities of a sound have been identified as increasing subjective reaction to it, the effects of non-acoustic stimuli and the high variability in the response of individuals to an identical acoustic event, have made the prediction of annoyance rather more difficult.

When assessing community reaction to noise there is obviously a need for a scale which relates subjective community response to some readily mea-sured property of that noise, preferably in terms of a single number descrip-tor. A point can then be chosen as the criterion above which the noise expo-sure is deemed to be unacceptable. Subsequently, similar measurements can be made where a noise problem exists, compared with the established criteria, and reliable predictions made as to its acceptability. What is meant by acceptable varies with the context. In the case of community noise the criterion for acceptability may be a certain level of dissatisfaction with airport operation, in the case of educational buildings or courtrooms, the ability to understand speech, or in the case of factories, the avoidance of noise-induced hearing loss. The aim of much noise research has therefore been to identify the physical characteristics of noise and combine them, in a variety of ways, into a noise unit which predicts subjective response consistently and accurately.

Many characteristics have now been identified as being important to the generation of annoyance. As the intensity of a noise increases, it is judged to be more annoying, i.e. the annoyance and loudness are simply related, and high frequencies, above 1000 Hz are more annoying than lower frequencies. In addition, if the noise is intermittent, irregular or rhythmic, or contains impulses or recognisable pure tones, it may be considerably more annoying than a steady noise of the same intensity, or even of the same perceived loudness. To take account of all these factors, and many others, in a single noise unit is clearly a formidable task, especially when the large variability of individual responses and a wide range of noise types has to be considered.

Some rating scales involve a simple single measurement, some require a knowledge of the spectrum, others require temporal statistics, and still others are formed by amalgamating all these parameters. It is important, therefore, when choosing a noise rating unit for a particular application to consider carefully whether the increase in predictive precision, if any, in adopting a more complicated method is likely to repay the large amount of extra measurement and computation necessary. It should also be recognised that scales developed to rate one particular type of noise may give wildly inaccurate predictions when used to rate another, especially if their spectral or temporal characteristics differ significantly.

These considerations divide rating methods naturally into two groups, the first of which, the scale, describes only the physical characteristics of the acoustic stimulus itself. This scale may be a simple A-weighted sound level, a more complicated measure of the statistical noise variation, or may form the basis of a calculated scale that predicts subjective response with regard to, for example, speech interference or perceived noisiness.

The second group, the procedure, attempts to standardise methods and to assess the non-acoustic, but still relevant, external factors which may affect community response in the social context in which the noise occurs. Most procedures stipulate the scales used to rate the noise, the way in which measurements are made, and penalties and relaxations, in terms of small changes, in dB, to the measured noise, to allow for such factors as the characteristics of the noise, time of day, and type of neighbourhood.

A brief introduction to some of the more widely used rating scales, approximately in order of increasing complexity, follows.

3.7.1. Overall Sound Pressure Level

This simple measure of the unweighted sound over the audible frequency range (usually taken to be 20 Hz to 20 kHz) is rarely used because of its poor correlation with subjective response.

3.7.2. A-weighted Sound Level: and other frequency weightings

This quantity is measured directly by a calibrated microphone and amplifier or sound level meter incorporating an electrical filtering network which modifies the frequency response to follow approximately the equal loudness curve of 40 phons. The A-weighted sound level, expressed in dB(A), has been shown to correlate extremely well with subjective response and shown up consistently well in comparisons with other noise scales. This fact, together with the ease with which measurements using a sound level meter can be

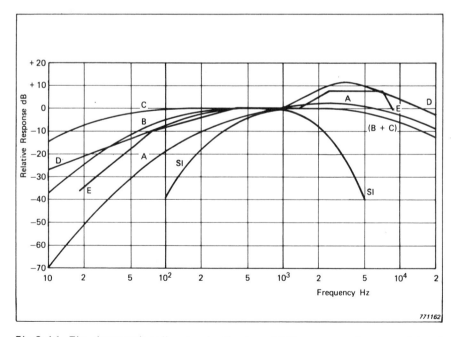

Fig.3.11. The internationally standardized weighting curves for sound level meters and recently suggested E and SI weighting

made, has led to its adoption in many national and international codes and standards. Because individual response to noise varies so widely and because noise scales are so highly correlated with each other it is often argued that A-weighted sound levels are as good as any other method of subjectively rating noise.

The other frequency weightings which are internationally standardised and in current use are shown in Fig.3.11. The B-weighting and C-weighting more or less follow the 70 and 100 phon contours respectively. The D-weighting approximately follows a contour of perceived noisiness, and is used for single event aircraft noise measurement, which is discussed at greater length in section 6.2.

Several other recently suggested weightings for application to specific areas of measurement are shown in Fig.3.11. Various D-weightings have been proposed by several authors for estimating perceived noise level, and the E- (or Ear) weighting by Stevens. The SI-weighting suggested by Webster for the assessment of speech interference, concentrates heavily on the predominant speech frequencies.

The A-weighting is by far the most widely used of these scales and can be incorporated into small, portable instruments with all the necessary characteristics to measure steady sound levels. The A-weighted sound level of a fluctuating signal can be sampled to yield statistical information such as the L_{eq} or L_N, the level exceeded for N % of the measurement period, and these measures may in turn form the basic data for more complex noise scales.

3.7.3. L_{eq} — Equivalent Continuous Sound Level

L_{eq} is the A-weighted energy mean of the noise level averaged over the measurement period. It can be considered as the continuous steady noise level which would have the same total A-weighted acoustic energy as the real fluctuating noise measured over the same period of time, and is defined as

$$L_{eq} = 10 \ log_{10} \frac{1}{T} \int_0^T \left(\frac{p_A(t)}{p_0} \right)^2 dt$$

where   T   is the total measurement time

           $p_A(t)$ is the A-weighted instantaneous acoustic pressure

and p_0 is the reference acoustic pressure (20μPa)

L_{eq} is used as the basis for calculating L_{NP} and L_{DN}, and is used in its own right in American, German and other national and international standards for rating some forms of community noise. An important use of the unit is in the assessment of hearing loss risk where it has gained wide acceptance among national and international bodies.

3.7.4. L_{DN} — The Day-Night average sound level

An L_{eq} with a 10 dB weighting for noise occurring during the night-time period from 22:00 to 07:00. The scale has been suggested for community noise assessment by the US Environmental Protection Agency as an improvement on the basic L_{eq} to take into account the increased annoyance caused by noise at night.

3.7.5. L_{NP} — the Noise Pollution Level

The rating comprises two terms, the first a measure of the equivalent continuous sound level, and the second representing the increase of annoyance caused by fluctuations in that level. It is defined as follows:

$$L_{NP} = L_{eq} + K\sigma$$

where L_{eq} is the A-weighted equivalent continuous sound level during the measurement period.

σ is the standard deviation of the instantaneous level during the same period.

K is a constant tentatively set at 2,56 by the originator of the scale, D.W. Robinson of the British National Physical Laboratory. This was the best fit with data then available from British studies of subjective response to aircraft and traffic noise.

3.7.6. TNI — Traffic Noise Index

The basic unit of measurement is again the A-weighted sound level, measured outdoors during a 24 hour period. The two statistical levels L_{10} and L_{90}, those exceeded for 10 and 90 percent of the time respectively, are determined. The L_{90} can be considered as an average background level into which the L_{10}, as an average peak level, intrudes. It is defined as follows

$$TNI = 4(L_{10} - L_{90}) - 30$$

The term (L_{10} — L_{90}) has been called the "noise climate" by some authors and the final arbitrary constant is included to yield more convenient numbers. As in the case of the Noise Pollution Level, emphasis is placed on the fact that signifcant annoyance is attributable to the variation of the noise level with time, as well as to some average measure of its amplitude.

3.7.7. PNL — Perceived Noise Level

PNL is a rating for single aircraft flyovers, based on a concept of perceived noisiness which originally assumed the judgement of a jury, and resulted from extensive subjective experiments to determine the relationship between "noisiness", "annoyance" and the physical characteristics of aircraft noise. Now it invariably implies an extensive calculation procedure, and has been applied to other than the jet aircraft noise for which it was first designed. The calculations are based on a frequency analysis in third-octave-bands measured every one half second or less, which are weighted and summed to give a perceived noisiness value (in Noys) for each time interval. This value is converted to give the Perceived Noise Level (in PNdB), by means of a standard table. Corrections may be made to this value to account for the increased annoyance attributable to the duration of the flyover and the tonal content of noise from rotating engine parts, forming a more refined unit, the Tone-Corrected, Effective Perceived Noise Level, (expressed in Tone-corrected EPNdB.)

These procedures are discussed further in section 6.2 and in detail in the relevant national and ISO publications. Aircraft noise measurement is an increasingly sophisticated and complicated subject and it is essential for anyone planning such measurements to study the current codes and literature in order to be aware of new techniques and changes in procedure.

3.7.8. NNI — The Noise and Number Index

Specifically for aircraft noise, it was developed during the period of the Wilson Committee Report on Noise in Great Britain. It takes into account both the average peak noise level, measured in PNdB, uncorrected for either duration or pure tones, and the number of events occuring during the measurement period. The unit is defined as follows

$$NNI = L_{apn} + 15 \, log_{10} \, N - 80$$

Where N is the number of aircraft flyovers during the measurement period. The constant 80 is subtracted to bring the index to zero for conditions of no "annoyance" which were identified for single event noise levels of approximately 80 PNdB. Positive numbers are then an indication of potential annoyance. Average peak noise level is defined as follows

$$L_{apn} = 10 \, log_{10}\left(\left(\frac{1}{N}\right)\sum_{i}^{N} 10^{\frac{L}{10}}\right)$$

where   L is the peak noise level in PNdB.

The rating was used for airport planning procedures in Great Britain, and formed the basis of a scheme under which residents in the vicinity of London (Heathrow) Airport were able to obtain grants towards the installation costs of noise insulation for their homes.

3.7.9. L_{AX} — Single Event Noise Exposure Level

This is defined as the constant level which, if maintained for a period of one second, would deliver the same A-weighted noise energy to the receiver as the actual event itself. This is, then, basically an L_{eq}, which is normalised to a time period of one second.

Mathematically, $L_{AX} = 10 \, log_{10} \int_{-\infty}^{\infty} \left(\frac{p_A(t)}{p_{ref}}\right)^2 \cdot \frac{dt}{\tau_{ref}}$

Where $p_A(t)$ is the instantenous A-weighted sound pressure
p_{ref} is the reference pressure, 20 micropascals
τ_{ref} is the reference time, i.e. 1 second

In practice the following is often used

$$L_{AX} = 10 \, log_{10} \int_{t_1}^{t_2} 10^{\left(\frac{L_A(t)}{10}\right)} \cdot dt$$

Where $L_A(t)$ is the instantaneous A-weighted sound pressure level
t_1 and t_2 define the time interval in which the level remains within 10 dB of its maximum during the event.

The usefulness of this concept becomes most apparent when dealing with an environment in which a number of different types of noise event occur. These may differ because of the operating conditions or individual characteristics of the same general type of source, such as aircraft, or the occurrence of two or more totally different types of noise source. In either case a knowledge of the normalised single event exposure level, L_{AX} , for each type of event, further categorised in terms of operating conditions where applicable, has many advantages. When describing any noisy environment in terms of the Equivalent Continuous Sound Level, L_{eq}, or designing a mathematical model for prediction purposes, the L_{eq} , and other units based on it, such as L_{dn} , can be readily calculated from the various L_{AX} s, as follows.

$$L_{eq} = 10 \ log_{10} \frac{1}{T} \sum_{i=1}^{n} 10^{\left(\frac{L_{AX_i}}{10}\right)}$$

where   n is the total number of events in time T
L_{AX_i} is the single event noise exposure level for the i'th event

It has, therefore, the advantage that the units used to describe both the individual sources and the overall environment are fully compatible, although it is implicit in the method that all sources are adequately subjectively rated by their equivalent A-weighted energy alone. The new draft International Standard Procedure for describing aircraft noise heard on the ground, specifically includes L_{AX} as a suitable simplified unit for application to aircraft noise surveys intended for environmental assessment rather than certification purposes. It has also been recently applied to other circumstances, some of which have been referenced at the end of this chapter.

3.8. COMMUNITY NOISE ANNOYANCE — CRITERIA AND RATING PROCEDURES

When interest in community noise annoyance first developed, the relationship between physical noise measurements and the response of an "average" population was based on its tolerance of nominally steady noise levels which could be readily measured. Controls, where they were instituted, were of a simple type, often only stipulating that a criterion noise level should not be exceeded, with perhaps a lower value to be observed at night. More recently, however, much work has been done to determine parameters which adequately describe the annoyance caused by the variability of fluctuating or intermittent noise levels, their duration, and the time of their occurrence.

Standards now exist which implicitly take all these temporal characteristics into account, although the type of noise source which can be rated by these Standards differ from country to country. For example, the British Standard BS 4142 is intended only for the assessment of noise from Industrial Premises, the International Standards Organisation Recommendation 1996 encompasses all community noise except that from aircraft, while California's Community Noise Equivalent Level, which is an A-weighted L_{eq} with additional penalties for evening and night-time exposure, is intended for application to all types of community noise.

Most procedures consist of two elements, a measured noise level, suitably corrected for the "annoyability" of its characteristics and called the rating noise level, and a criterion level, corrected for external and social factors, with which it is ultimately compared and assessed.

Where National standards exist in a particular country, the area of application, and other details of the procedure, should be in accordance with the standards of that country. The differences between national standards may be extremely significant for some types of noise, for example ISO 1996 recommends the use of the "fast" meter characteristic and defines the background level as the A-weighted L_{95}, whereas BS 4142 recommends "slow" and defines the background as the L_{90}. Although the difference between L_{90} and L_{95} will not generally be significant, meter readings taken on fast and slow settings may differ appreciably for rapidly fluctuating sounds. Recommended corrections both to the basic criterion and to the measured noise levels may also differ in numerical value. The time of day (and sometimes also the time of year), type of neighbourhood, the use to which an area of land or building is put, and, where indoor standards are concerned, the building sound insulation, are all considered when assessing the acceptability of a given noise exposure. These parameters are taken into account in the form of corrections which are made to the basic criterion and form a measure of an area's tolerance to noise in general. A measure of the tolerability of the particular noise to be rated is formed by imposing penalties on the noise itself if it contains pure tones or impulses, which are easily identified and which lead to increased annoyance.

The basic criteria may be set at an absolute level, especially for planning purposes involving large new developments, which completely alter the character of an entire area and dominate its noise climate. If a relevant background noise level can be measured this should always be used in preference, because complaints are likely whenever it is exceeded by a certain margin, regardless of its absolute level. The ISO recommendation "Assessment of noise with respect to Community Response",which will be used as an example of a typical procedure, suggests that a basic outdoor noise criterion of 35 to 45 dB(A) be applied in residential areas where measurements of the existing background noise levels are not available. Corrections recommended for different types of district are:

Type of district	Correction to basic criterion dB (A)
Rural residential, zones of hospitals, recreation	0
Suburban residential, little road traffic	+5
Urban residential	+10
Residential urban with some workshops or with Business or with main roads	+15
City (business, trade, administration)	+20
Predominantly industrial area (heavy industry)	+25

Further corrections, which concern the time of the day are:

Time of day	Correction to basic criterion, dB (A)
Day time	0
Evening	− 5
Night time	−10 to −15

780127

In the case of rooms, the above values may be converted into internal criteria by the application of the following approximate corrections for the insulation of facades with windows:

Window conditions	Correction, dB (A)
Windows open	−10
Single window shut	−15
Double windows shut or non-openable window	−20

780126

If measured values for facade insulation are available these should be substituted. In addition, the criterion should not be set below 20 dB(A). For noise in non-residential rooms the following internal criteria are proposed.

Type of room	Noise criterion dB (A)
Larger office, business store, department store, meeting room, quiet restaurant	35
Larger restaurant, secretarial office (with typewriter)	45
Larger typing halls	55
Workshops (according to intended use)	45−75

780130

The second element in the Comparison, the rating sound level, is the sum of the measured level of the noise to be assessed and all the corrections which take into account identifiable characteristics, duration, and fluctuation. The noise can be measured directly with a sound level meter if it is steady or intermittent, whatever its spectral or impulsive content. If the noise variation with time is more complicated, the L_{eq}, as defined in the previous section, should be obtained. Corrections for impulsiveness, spectral character, and duration should be applied as below, to determine the rating sound level.

60

Characteristic features of the noise		Correction dB (A)
Peak factor	Impulsive noise (e.g. noise from hammering)	+ 5
Spectrum character	Audible tone components (e.g. whine) present	+ 5
Duration of the noise with sound level L_A in percent of the relevant time period	Between: 100 and 56%	0
	56 and 18%	− 5
	18 and 6%	−10
	6 and 1,8%	−15
	1,8 − 0,6%	−20
	0,6 − 0,2%	−25
	less than 0,2%	−30

780128

The rating sound level may now be compared with the corrected criterion to gauge the impact of the noise on the environment and assess the probable intensity of community reaction according to the following scale.

Amount in dB(A) by which the rating sound level exceeds the noise criterion	Estimated community response	
	Category	Description
0	None	No observed reaction
5	Little	Sporadic complaints
10	Medium	Widespread complaints
15	Strong	Threats of community action
20	Very strong	Vigorous community action

780129

The above Example is based on measurements of the A-weighted sound level, but a frequency analysis may be preferable for some rating purposes and is essential for the evaluation of noise control measures. The measured noise spectrum is then compared with a group of rating curves in order to identify the bands which are most intrusive. These curves are approximately the same shape as those of equal loudness and several slightly differing groups exist, including the American Noise Criteria (NC) curves and the International Standards Organisation Noise Rating (NR) curves. Typically, measurements are made in octave bands, corrected as explained previously, and compared with the NR curves, the NR criterion being taken as 5 lower numerically than the equivalent criterion set in dB(A) if such comparisons are necessary. A practical example of the use of these curves is given in Section 5.2.

3.9. HEARING DAMAGE RISK CRITERIA

Occupational Noise has only recently been widely acknowledged as a potentially serious health problem, but it is certainly not a new phenomenon. Hearing impairment was observed in Blacksmiths and attributed by observers to the noisiness of their work as early as 1830. In many areas, especially in productive industry, it seems to have been accepted in the past, by both management and work force, as an unavoidable, if undesirable part of the job. To some extent this still appears to be the current attitude, either because the harmful effects of high noise levels are not fully recognised, or because to the layman improvements appear difficult or even impossible. Fortunately, this need not, indeed should not, be the case, and the benefits to both employee and employer of a quiet and pleasant working environment are becoming increasingly appreciated.

The diverse effects of noise in factories and offices, and methods for its control to achieve a comfortable environment conducive to efficiency are discussed at greater length in section 5.2; here we are only concerned with noise in relation to permanent hearing loss. In general this will not be a problem in shops and offices where levels are unlikely to be high enough to contribute towards hearing impairment.

For steady noise, good correlation has been demonstrated between hearing damage risk and A-weighted sound level measurements, and this unit is now universally employed when rating noise for this purpose. Useful on-the-spot measurements can therefore be made using simple sound level meters, especially when defining likely problem areas during the early stages of a hearing conservation program. Frequency analysis techniques, on the other hand, are generally unavoidable when noise control measures are being considered and designed.

Although a maximum peak noise level, which should never be exceeded in a place of work, is quoted in most standards, the more important recent concept is that of the maximum allowed noise dose which takes into account both the time-varying noise level and its duration. This dose is the A-weighted equivalent noise level limit, or L_{eq}, to which an employee may be subjected for a normal working week of 40 hours, (or sometimes a day of 8 hours) before he runs a significant risk of permanent hearing loss. This is of course a statistical limit applied over the whole population, the susceptibility of individuals to hearing damage will therefore vary widely for a given dose. The allowable dose varies slightly between countries but is usually 85 or 90 dB(A) and is referred to as the criterion (or 100%) noise dose. The advantages of expressing the noise dose in this manner is that 100% will always represent the criterion dose whatever the measurement duration and however it is accumulated. An employee may spend some time in a noise environment in excess of the criterion value as long as he also compensates for it by spending enough time in a quieter area to maintain his total noise dose below that permissible.

The trade-off between noise level and permitted exposure time is still the subject of some divergence of opinion. The International Standard, which will be used as an example here, allows 3 dB increase in noise level per halving of exposure duration but the American Occupational Safety and Health Act (OSHA) permits 5 dB, as do the Canadian Provinces and some European countries. In addition there are differences between the standards of different countries which make a study of the relevant document before assessing the risk imperative. The overriding limit varies in value as well as in the manner in which it is measured, as also does the peak impulse allowed, and some countries, e.g. the USA also stipulate the maximum daily "dose" of impulses. A brief summary of some national standards follows.

National Standards on Occupational Noise Exposure Limits

EEC member state	Steady noise level (dB(A))	Time exposure (h)	Halving rate (dB(A))	Over-riding limit (dB(A))	Impulse peak SPL (dB)	Impulses (no./ day)
Germany	90	8	–	–	–	–
France	90	40	–	–	–	–
Belgium	90	40	5	110	140	100
Luxembourg	–					
Netherlands	–					
UK	90	8	3	135*	150	–
Irish Rep.	90	–	–	–	–	–
Italy	90	8	5	115	140	–
Denmark	90	40	3	115	–	–
Others						
Sweden	85	40	3	115	–	–
Norway	–					
USA (Fed.)	90	8	5	115	140	100
Canada (Fed.)	90	8	5	115	140	–
Australia	90	8	3	115	–	–

780124

* UK over-riding limit 135 dB (SPL), on 'fast' response   (After Hay)

The ISO standard will be used as an example to demonstrate the method of assessing an employee's noise dose. A composite index is built up from a number of partial indices which represent the various noise exposures which an employee experiences during his work. His exposure may vary either because of changes in noise levels during different processes at his work place, or because of his own movement between different areas of the factory. Before embarking on measurements to determine the exposure, the following points should be noted.

1. The rating method is not applicable to impulsive noises consisting of noise of a duration less than 1 sec., or single high level transients of a very short duration, for example, from gunfire.

2. "Noises for which the sound level is less than 80 dB(A) may be disregarded" once all corrections have been taken into account.

3. "If the total weekly duration is less than 10 min, the minimum value of 10 min should be used".

4. "For impulsive noise consisting of series of noise bursts of approximately equal amplitudes (for example noise from rapidly repeated hammering or riveting) an approximation to the partial noise exposure index may be based on a value 10 dB(A) higher than the measured sound level".

The impulsive quality of much industrial noise and the acoustic impulse itself are the subject of extensive research at present to determine why this type of noise should be particularly damaging and to develop methods of rating it effectively. The harmfulness of impulsive sound appears to depend on many physical parameters of the signature including the peak pressure, duration, rise time and pulse shape. Most standards currently only take the first of these, or an easily measured approximation to it, into account. Analysis of short duration sounds and impulsive noises is discussed in Chapter 5.

To illustrate the method let us suppose that the measured noise levels for a normal working week at a particular place in a workshop were distributed, the class intervals being 5 dB, in the following manner

S.L. dB (A)	Monday	Tuesday	Wednesday	Thursday	Friday	Total
100	0,5	0	0,5	0	0	1
95	1	1	2	1	1	6
90	2	2	2	2	3	11
85	3	2	2,5	4	3,5	15
80	1	2	1	0,5	0,5	5
75	0,5	1	0	0,5	0	2

The corresponding partial noise-exposure indices are then obtained from Fig.3.12:

dB(A)	100	95	90	85	80	75
P.N.E.-index	25	45	25	15	0	0

64

Duration per week		Partial noise exposure indices								
		Sound level in dB(A) (Class midpoint)								
h	min	80	85	90	95	100	105	110	115	120
	10					5	15	40	130	415
	12					5	15	50	160	500
	14					5	20	60	185	585
	16					5	20	65	210	665
	18					10	25	75	235	750
	20					10	25	85	265	835
	25				5	10	35	105	330	1040
	30				5	15	40	125	395	1250
	40				5	15	55	165	525	1670
	50				5	20	70	210	660	2080
	60			5	10	25	80	250	790	2500
	70			5	10	30	90	290	920	2920
	80			5	10	35	105	330	1050	3330
	90			5	10	40	120	375	1190	3750
	100			5	15	40	130	415	1320	4170
2				5	15	50	160	500	1580	5000
2,5				5	20	65	200	625	1980	6250
3				10	25	75	235	750	2370	7500
3,5			5	10	30	90	275	875	2770	8750
4			5	10	30	100	315	1000	3160	10000
5			5	15	40	125	395	1250	3950	12500
6			5	15	45	150	475	1500	4740	15000
7			5	20	55	175	555	1750	5530	17500
8			5	20	65	200	630	2000	6320	20000
9			5	25	70	225	710	2250	7100	22500
10		5	10	25	80	250	790	2500	7910	25000
12		5	10	30	95	300	950	3000	9490	30000
14		5	10	35	110	350	1110	3500	11100	
16		5	15	40	125	400	1260	4000	12600	
18		5	15	45	140	450	1420	4500	14200	
20		5	15	50	160	500	1580	5000	15800	
25		5	20	65	200	625	1980	6250	19800	
30		10	25	75	235	750	2370	7500	23700	
35		10	30	90	275	875	2770	8750	27700	
40		10	30	100	315	1000	3160	10000	31600	

Fig.3.12. Partial noise exposure indices

The Composite Noise exposure index is then 25 + 45 + 25 + 15 = 110 and the equivalent continuous sound level read from Fig.3.13 is just over 90 dB(A). This indicates that a worker at this position runs a risk of hearing impairment and that to reduce his noise dose he should be issued with ear defenders, his work should be reorganised to include periods in quiet areas or, better still, the noise should be reduced at source, thus benefitting everyone in the workshop.

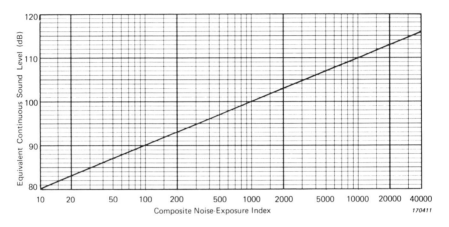

Fig.3.13. Relationship between Equivalent Continuous sound level and Composite Noise Exposure Index

Although adequate for a situation in which the employee is stationary, or where the partial noise exposures are both easily defined and few in number, the above process becomes unweildy and tedious when applied to a great many typical jobs in industry. The noise level at a particular place in a factory may vary frequently and over a wide range, and the worker's job may also involve extensive movement around the factory into different noise environments. For these cases, a simple sound level meter cannot be used, and a more sophisticated instrument is required which can be carried by the worker and which integrates the noise level continuously during the entire working day to give the total noise dose. This instrument, the noise dose meter, measures the A-weighted sound level and, because the damage to hearing has been found to increase with both intensity and duration, it is then "amplitude weighted" and integrated to take these factors into account. The noise dose thus determined is usually expressed in terms of a percentage of the criterion dose and enables workers in danger of exceeding this to be recognised immediately.

3.10. SPEECH INTERFERENCE CRITERIA

Speech Intelligibility is an important factor to be considered in the design of working environments because most work involves verbal communication to a greater or lesser extent. Moreover, in activities as diverse as air traffic control, complex production processes, and lecturing, where good communication is essential, the intelligibility of speech is vitally important. The two main methods of communication, by face-to-face conversation and by telephone or other electroacoustic device, require slightly different approaches. Speech has a wide range in both frequency and power. The vowels may have a sound power as high as 50 μwatt, soft consonants only 0,03 μw, while the maximum sound power from the male voice may be as much as 2000 μwatts. The instantenous sound pressure also varies during normal speech by up to 30 dB, the peak levels exceeded for 1% of the time being greater than the long-term RMS by about 12 dB. The high-frequency low-energy transient consonants are the chief contributors to the intelligibility of speech, and noise will therefore have the greatest masking effect if its spectrum is significant in the frequency range above 500 Hz.

In addition to the factors mentioned above, the perception of speech can also be affected by reverberation effects, the voice quality, information content and, in communications systems, signal clipping and the frequency response of the system itself. In extreme cases it may also be possible to gain a measure of the speech intelligibility performance of a system or an auditorium by carrying out actual judgement tests with panels of listeners. In the more usually encountered situations, however, it is often possible to assess speech intelligibility using only relatively simple physical measurements of the masking noise and a small amount of subsequent calculation. Early work by French and Steinberg resulted in a method which used weighted frequency bands of the measured noise, chosen according to their importance to the understanding of speech, to calculate a measure of the interference caused. This is called the Articulation Index (AI) and is expressed as a number from 0 to 1,0, indicating 0% to 100% intelligibility. An AI less than 0,3 is generally rated as unsatisfactory, between 0,3 and 0,5 acceptable, between 0,5 and 0,7 good, and over 0,7 as excellent.

Later methods were based on measured levels in the three octave bands centred on 500 Hz, 1 kHz and 2 kHz. These were found to be the most important for understanding speech, and the resulting arithmetic average of the three band levels is called the (Preferred) Speech Interference Level. (PSIL). It is usually compared with an average value for the voice level, ignoring the large variability of individual voice powers, and has now become the most widely used rating for speech interference assessment. It is a good indicator of the ability of a noise to mask speech and has the advantage of being readily ascertained using only a portable sound level meter with octave band facilities. Fig.3.14 shows the relationship between ease of face-to-face conversa-

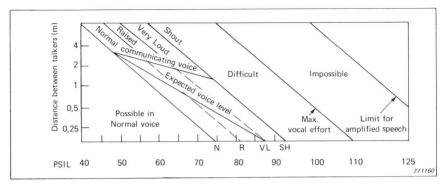

Fig.3.14. Communication limits in the presence of background noise (after Webster)

tion, ambient noise level in PSIL, and separation distance in metres. A recent ISO Technical Report argues for the redefinition of PSIL to include the octave band level at 4 kHz and suggests the following revised table for satisfactory intelligibility.

Speech Interference level dB	Maximum distance at which normal conversation is considered to be satisfactorily intelligible m	Maximum distance at which conversation in raised voice is considered to be satisfactorily intelligible m
35	7,5	15
40	4,2	8,4
45	2,3	4,6
50	1,3	2,6
55	0,75	1,5
60	0,42	0,85
65	0,25	0,50
70	0,13	0,26

Selected Bibliography

BARKHAUSEN, H.:   *Ein neuer Schallmesser für die Praxis.* Techn. Physik 1926, 599: Z. VDI 1927. 1471.

BEKESY, G. v.:   *Übersicht über die innere Hörphysiologie.* Elektr. Nachr. Technik. 1935. 71.

BEKESY, G. v.:   *The variation of Phase along the Basilar Membrane with Sinusoidal vibrations.* J.A.S.A. Vol.19 No.3 May 1947 pp.452-460.

BEKESY, G. v. and ROSENBLITH, W. A.:   *The mechanical properties of the ear.* Handbook of Experimental Psychology. Wiley & Sons. New York 1951. 1975.

BERGLUND, B., BERGLUND, U. and LINDVALL, T.:   *Scaling Loudness, Noisiness and Annoyance of Community Noises.* J.A.S.A. Vol. 60, No.5. Nov. 1976 pp. 1119—1125.

BERRY, B.F.:   *The Concept of a single event noise exposure level, L_{AX}, and its use in the description of the overall noise environment* Proceedings of the Institute of Acoustics 5—2 1977

BOTSFORD, J. H.:   *Current Trends in Hearing Damage Risk Criteria.* Sound and Vibration. Vol. 4. No.4. April 1970

BOTSFORD, J. H.:   *Using Sound Levels to Gauge Human Response to Noise.* Sound and Vibration. Vol. 3. No.10. Oct. 1969.

British Acoustical Society Meeting April 1972:   *Impulsive Noise.* Proceedings of the B.A.S. Vol. 1. No.3 Summer 1972. Papers 72.34-72.38.

BROCH, J. T.:   *Loudness Evaluation.* B & K Techn. Rev. No. 2 — 1962.

BRYAN, M. E. and TEMPEST, W.:   *Industrial Audiometry.* University of Salford Audiology Group.

BS. 4142 1967:   *Method of Rating Industrial Noise Affecting Mixed Residential and Industrial Areas.* British Standards Institution.

BURNS, W., HINCHCLIFFE, R. and LITTLE, J. S.:   *An Exploratory Study of Hearing and Noise Exposure in Textile Workers.* Annals of Occupational Hygiene. Vol. 7. No.4. Dec. 1964. pp.323—333.

BURNS, W. and ROBINSON, D. W.:   *Hearing and Noise in Industry.* Her Majesty's Stationary Office. London 1970.

.

69

CHADWICK, D. L.:	*Noise Induced Deafness.* The Practitioner. Vol. 191. No.1146. Dec. 1963. pp. 733—741.
COHEN, A., ANTICAGLIA, J. and JONES, H. H.:	*"Sociocusis" — Hearing loss from Non-Occupational noise Exposure.* Sound and Vibration, Nov. 1970. pp. 12 — 20.
COLES, R. R. A., GARINTHER, G. R., HODGE, D. C. and RICE, C. G.:	*Hazardous Exposure to Impulse Noise.* J.A.S.A. Vol. 43. No.2. February 1968.
COLES, R. R. A. and RICE, C. G.:	*Towards a criterion for impulse noise in Industry.* Annals of Occupational Hygiene. Vol. 13. 1970. pp. 43—50.
DIN 45641:	*Mittelungspegel und Beurteilungspegel zeitlich schwankender Schallvorgänge.*
ERMISCH, W.:	*Lärmschwerhörigkeit in der Fachliteratur 1961 bis 1965.* Lärmbekämpfung. Bd. 11. Heft 4 — 1967. 5.75.
FELDTKELLER, R. und ZWICKER, E.:	*Das Ohr als Nachrichtenempfänger.* S. Hirzel Verlag. Stuttgart. 1956.
FLETCHER, H.:	*Speech and Hearing in Communication.* Toronto, New York, London: Nostrand 1953.
FLETCHER, H. and MUNSON, W. A.:	*Loudness, its definition, measurement and calculation.* J.A.S.A. 5 (1933). pp. 82—108.
FOSBROKE, J.:	*Practical Observations on the Pathology and Treatment of Deafness, No. II.* The Lancet. Vol. 1. 1830-31. pp. 645—648.
FRANKEN, P. A. and JONES, G.:	*On Response to Community Noise.* Applied Acoustics. Vol. 2. No.4. October 1969.
FRENCH, N. R. and STEINBERG, J. C.:	*Factors governing the Intelligibility of Speech Sounds.* J.A.S.A. Vol. 19. 1947. pp. 90 — 119.
GLORIG, A., WARD, W.D. and NIXON, J.:	*Damage-Risk Criteria and Noise-Induced Hearing Loss.* Proce. Conf. Control of Noise. HMSO, London 1962.
GRIFFITHS, I. D. and LANGDON, F. J.:	*Subjective Response to Road Traffic Noise.* J. Sound Vib. Vol. 8. 1968.
GUIGNARD, J. C. and JOHNSON, D. L.:	*The Relation of Noise Exposure to Noise Induced Hearing Damage, Sound and Vibration.* January 1975. pp. 18—23.

HAY, B.:   *Occupational Noise Exposure — the laws in the*
                            E.E.C. Sweden, Norway, Australia, Canada and the
                            U.S.A. Applied Acoustics (8), 1975.

HELMHOLTZ, H.:   *Die Lehre von den Tonempfindungen, Braunschweig.*
                            1913.

HINCHCLIFFE, R.:   *Population Studies Concerned with Presbycusis.* Ind.
                            J. Otolaryng. Vol. 20. 1968. pp. 52.

I.S.O.:   Recommendation R. 131: *Expression of the Physical*
                            and Subjective Magnitudes of Sound or Noise.

I.S.O.:   Recommendation R. 226: *Normal Equal Loudness*
                            Contours for Pure Tones and Normal Threshold of
                            Hearing Under Free-Field Listening Conditions.

I.S.O.:   Recommendation R. 266: *Preferred Frequencies for*
                            Acoustical Measurements.

I.S.O.:   Recommendation R. 454: *Relation between the Loud-*
                            ness of Narrow Bands of Noise in a Diffuse-Field and
                            in a Frontal Incident Free-Field.

I.S.O.:   Recommendation R. 532: *Procedure for Calculating*
                            Loudness Level.

I.S.O.:   Recommendation R. 1996-1971: *Assessment of*
                            noise with respect to Community Response.

I.S.O.:   Recommendation R. 1999-1975: *Assessment of oc-*
                            cupational noise exposure for hearing conservation
                            purposes.

I.S.O.:   Recommendation R. 2204-1973: *Guide to the meas-*
                            urement of acoustical noise and evaluation of its ef-
                            fect on man.

I.S.O.:   Recommendation R. 3352-1974: *Assessment of*
                            noise with respect to its effect on the intelligibility of
                            speech.

KOSTEN, C. W. and   *Community Reaction Criteria for External Noises.*
Van OS, G. J.:   Proc. Conf. Control of Noise. HMSO. London 1962.

KERRICK, J.S.,   *Multiple Ratings of Sound Stimuli.* J.A.S.A. Vol. 45.
NAGEL, D. C. and   1969.
BENNET, R. L.:

KLOSTERKÖTTER, W.:   *Lärmwirkungen: Ergebnisse und Aufgaben der mediz-*
                            inischen Lärmforschung. Kampf dem Lärm. Jg. 15.
                            Heft 6. Dezember 1968. S. 141.

KROAK, W., EMEL, H., FUDER, F. and KROCHT, L.:	*Risk of Hearing Damage caused by steady state and Impulsive Noise.* J.S.V. Vol. 6. No.3. 1974. pp. 347—59.
KRYTER, K. D.:	*Impairment of hearing from Exposure to Noise (and following Critiques).* J.A.S.A. Vol. 53. No.4. 1973. pp. 1211—1252.
KRYTER, K. D. and PEARSONS, K. S.:	*Some Effects of Spectral Contents and Duration on Perceived Noise Level.* J.A.S.A. Vol. 36. No.6. June 1963.
LÜPCKE, A. v.:	*Der Bewertungsfaktor bei der Beurteilung von Geräuscheinwirkungen.* Lärmbekämpfung. Bf. 11. Heft 5 — 1967. S. 101.
McKENNEL, A. C.:	*Aircraft noise annoyance around London (Heathrow) Airport.* The Government Social Survey, Central Office of Information Report SS337. April 1963. (Appendix B).
MØLLER, A. A.:	*Noise as a Health Hazard.* Ambio, Vol. 4. No.1. 1975. pp. 6—13.
NIESE, H.:	*Beitrag zur Relation zwischen Lautstärke und Lästigkeit von Geräuschen.* Acustica Vol. 15. 1965.
PARKIN, P. H., PURKIS, H. J., STEPHENSON, R. J. and SCHLAFFENBERG, B.:	*London Noise Survey.* Building Research Station Report Code 67-266. H.M.S.O. Jan. 1968.
PARKIN, P. H.:	*On the Accuracy of Simple Weighting Networks for Loudness Estimates of some Urban Noises.* J.S.V. 1964. Vol. 2. No.1. pp. 86—88.
PASSCHIER-VERMEER, W.:	*Steady-State and Fluctuating Noise. Its effects on the Hearing of People.* Occupational Hearing Loss. British Acoustical Society. Special Volume No.1. London 1971. pp. 15—33.
PATTERSON, Roy D. and HENNING, G. B.:	*Stimulus variability and auditory filter shape.* J.A.S.A. Vol. 62. No.3. 1977.
PORT, E.:	*Über die Zeitabhängigkeit der Lautstärkeempfindung.* Diss. Tech. Hochschule. Stuttgart 1962.
PORT, E.:	*Über die Lautstörke einzelner kurzer Schallimpulse.* Acustica. Vol. 13. 1963.

PORT, E.:	*Zur Lautstärkeempfindung von pulsierenden Geräuschen.* Acustica. Vol. 13. 1963.
REICHARDT, W.:	*Zur Trägheit der Lautstärkebildung.* Acustica. Vol. 15. 1965.
ROBINSON, D. W.:	*The Concept of Noise Pollution Level.* NPL Aero Report Ac 38. London, March 1969.
ROBINSON, D. W.:	*An Outline Guide to Criteria for the Limitation of Urban Noise.* C.P. No. 1112. Her Majesty's Stationary Office. London 1970.
ROBINSON, D.W.:	*Practice and Principle in Environmental Noise Rating* NPL Acoustics Report AC 81 April 1977
SCHOLES, W. E.:	*Traffic Noise Criteria.* Applied Acoustics. Vol. 3. 1970. pp. 2—21.
SPOOR, A.:	*Presbycusis Values in Relation to Noise Induced Hearing Loss.* Int. Audiol. Vol. 6. 1967. p. 52.
STEVENS, S. S.:	*Procedure for Calculating Loudness: Mark VI.* J.A.S.A. Vol. 33. No.11. 1961.
TAYLOR, W., PEARSON, J. C. G., MOIR, A. and BURNS, W.:	*Study of Noise and Hearing in Jute Weaving.* J.A.S.A. Vol. 38. No.1. July 1965. pp. 113—120.
U.S.E.P.A. Report:	*Information on levels of Environmental Noise Requisite to protect Public Health and Welfare with an Adequate Margin of Safety.* U.S. Environmental Protection Agency Report 550/9-75-004 Washington DC 20460.
VDI 2058 Blatt 2:	*Beurteilung von Arbeitslärm am Arbeitsplatz hinsichtlich Gehörschäden*
WARD, W. D., GLORIG, A. and SKLAR, D. L.:	*Temporary Threshold Shift from Octave-Band Noise Applications to Damage-Risk Criteria.* J.A.S.A. Vol. 31. No.4. April 1959.
WEBSTER, J. C.:	*S I L-Past, Present and Future.* Sound and Vibration. Vol. 3. No.8. August 1969
WEBSTER, J. C.:	*Speech Communication as limited by Ambient Noise.* J.A.S.A. Vol. 37. No.4. April 1965. pp. 692—699.

73

WEBSTER, J. C.:   *Effects of Noise on Speech Intelligibility.* Proc. of Con-
                          ference, Noise as a Public Health Hazard. Washing-
                          ton DC. June 13-14 1968. A.S.H.A. Reports 4. The
                          American Speech and Hearing Association. Washing-
                          ton DC 1969. pp. 49—73.

WILLINGHAM, O. R.:   *A Computer Analysis of a 10-year study of 6,209 Au-
                          diometric Tests of Employees of Various Noise Expo-
                          sures.* Professional Safety. Feb. 1976.

Wilson Report on   *Final report of the Committee on the Problem of
Noise: Noise.* Sir Allan Wilson, Chairman. Command 2056.
                          H.M.S.O. London July 1963.

ZWICKER, E.:   *Die Verdeckung von Schmalbandgeräuschen durch
                          Sinustöne.* Acustica 4, 1954. Beiheft 1. 415.

ZWICKER, E.:   *Über psychologische und methodische Grundlagen
                          der Lautheit.* Acustica 8, 1958. Beiheft 1. S. 237.

ZWICKER, E.,   *The critical bandwidth in loudness summation.*
FLOTTORP, G. and   J.A.S.A. 29. 1957.
STEVENS, S. S.:

ZWICKER, E.:   *Ein Verfahren zur Berechnung der Lautstärke.* Acus-
                          tica. Vol. 10. 1960. Heft 1.

ZWICKER, E.:   *Ein Beitrag zur Lautstärkemessung impulshaltiger
                          Schalle.* Acustica. Vol. 17. 1966.

ZWICKER, E.:   *Ein Beitrag zur Unterscheidung von Lautstärke und
                          Lästigkeit.* Acustica. Vol. 17. 1966.

ZWICKER, E.:   *Subjektive und objektive Dauer von Schallimpulsen
                          und Schallpausen.* Acustica. Vol. 22. No. 4. 1970.
                          p. 214.

ZWICKER, E.:   *Procedure for calculating loudness of temporally vari-
                          able sounds.* J.A.S.A. Vol. 62. No.3. Sept. 1977.
                          pp. 675.

4. MEASUREMENT INSTRUMENTATION AND TECHNIQUES

4.1. GENERAL CONSIDERATIONS

Before embarking on any noise measurement program, the object of the project must first be closely defined, the data necessary to achieve this object should be selected, and the measurement program organised to obtain it. Only at this stage should the detailed choice of instrumentation become of paramount interest, although the practicalities of the program should always be kept in mind. The characteristics of the noise itself are the most important consideration when choosing suitable instrumentation. The noise spectrum may be wide-band e.g. aircraft, traffic, narrow band, e.g. fans, or highly tonal, e.g. electric motors. Its level may be fairly constant, as in the case of continuous industrial processes, highly time dependent, as on construction sites or it may be intermittent, with intense noise separated by long quiet periods, e.g. near railways. Severe additional problems are encountered when measuring impulsive noise, e.g. gunshots, piling, pneumatic chippers, and industrial impact noise. The likely importance on the environment's acceptability of all these different source noise characteristics must be evaluated, and accordingly included in the measurement procedure.

The amount and type of analysis performed on the data also influences the choice of both instrumentation and measurement procedures. A basic research program generally requires an enormous amount of detailed, high quality data, subsequently analyzed in a multitude of different ways; whereas a noise control investigation normally requires much less detailed information, and the purpose of monitoring systems is often only to detect and record changes in relatively simple overall rating units.

An important factor when choosing equipment for field use, where most environmental and community noise problems naturally occur, is that it must be truly portable. This means, in effect, that it should be easy to set up and calibrate on site as well as independent of external power supplies and reasonably light in weight.

This chapter will develop the above points to ensure the best choise of instrumentation for a particular application and to ensure that the chosen instrumentation then gives the best possible results. To do this adequately, it is imperative that the different methods of describing and analysing a noise source by means of sound pressure measurements in the far field, are fully appreciated.

The simplest noise measurement is linear sound pressure level, which is independent of frequency, disregards the variation with time, and therefore ignores the two factors which are known to affect subjective reaction to noise as much as the level itself. It is therefore used only when vibration measurements are being made, or when data is being recorded for later laboratory analysis. The frequency response is then limited only by the instrumentation. However, by weighting the signal spectrum in a way which corresponds to the response of the human ear, it is possible to describe a measured sound pressure level by a single value which is more representative of its subjective effects.

Sound pressure levels are termed sound levels when weighted like this, and are expressed as dB(A), dB(B), dB(LIN) etc. to distinguish them. The weighting and reference level used e.g. 82 dB(A), (re 20 μPa) should always be stated whenever measurements are quoted, so that no confusion can arise when making later comparisons.

The A-weighted level has now become widely used, and many national and international standards are based either on direct A-weighted measurements, or on rating units derived from them which also take the time variation into account. Traffic noise, for example, is often expressed in terms of the A-weighted sound levels which are exceeded for a certain percentage of the measurement period, (L_N), or as an L_{eq} . Although these are essentially derived units, the advent of sound level meters with inbuilt digital processors has meant that they can now be read directly at the site, without the necessity for later laboratory analysis.

If a frequency analysis of the noise is required, measurements may be made in standard octave or one-third octave bands, depending on the application and desired resolution. Noise control curves for rating indoor noise from such sources as office machines and ventilation systems, for example, are defined in terms of octaves, while aircraft noise measurements to ascertain PNL (Perceived Noise Level), are made in one-third octave bands. For some purposes, especially where pure tones or irregular spectra are concerned, a very narrow band analysis may be necessary to separate out important frequency components.

4.2. BASIC MEASURING SYSTEMS

A wide variety of different systems, some consisting of a number of interconnected instruments, are available for the measurement of acoustic noise and cover most situations likely to be found in practice. Although very differ-

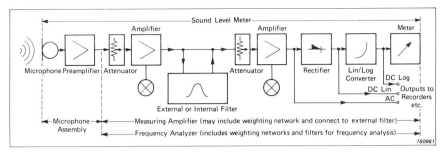

Fig.4.1. Block diagram of a noise measuring system

ent in detail, every system basically consists of a transducer, an analysis section and a read-out unit as shown diagramatically in Fig.4.1. The transducer is usually a microphone, though accelerometers, and even strain gauges, are sometimes used to help identify the actual mechanisms of noise emission from complex sources.

With a wide variety of circuits to condition, weight, and integrate the signal, the analysis section of the system is usually the most complex. In the simplest case it only weights the frequency spectrum of the input signal according to one of the standard networks, or filters it in octave one-third octave or narrow bands. Treating time rather than frequency as the important variable, the A-weighted level may be integrated to give L_{eq}, L_{AX}, or a complete statistical analysis may be computed continuously.

The output section often consists of a calibrated meter with a standardised response time, designed to meet the relevant IEC standards shown in Fig.4.2

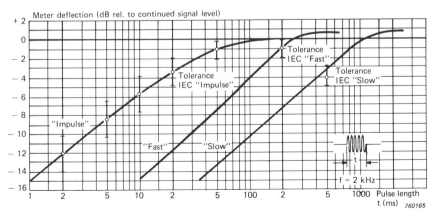

Fig.4.2. Response of meter to tone bursts of varying duration

and a level recorder to obtain a permanent record of the measured levels. However, recent rapid developments in electronics have made digital read-outs, alphanumeric printers, and cathode ray displays readily available for incorporation into noise measurement systems. Furthermore, the mini-computer or programmable desk top calculator can be employed to store and compare data from long term monitoring stations, or to perform complex calculations such as those required for aircraft noise certification.

4.3. PORTABLE MEASURING INSTRUMENTS

Perhaps the most convenient manner in which all the various elements necessary for a sound measurement system are brought together, is in the form of the portable sound level meter. Typical instruments range in complexity from a small compact instrument for simple A-weighted measurements, up to more comprehensive models with all the internationally standardised weighting networks. These may also have impulse measuring facilities, filters, or time-averaging circuitry to obtain L_{AX} and L_{eq}, but still be designed for hand-held operation. The simplest type, such as the Type 2219 shown in Fig.4.3.a, is designed for one-handed operation, to make the simple A-weighted measurements initially required in factories or offices to check noise levels, and to identify problem areas for later more intensive investigation.

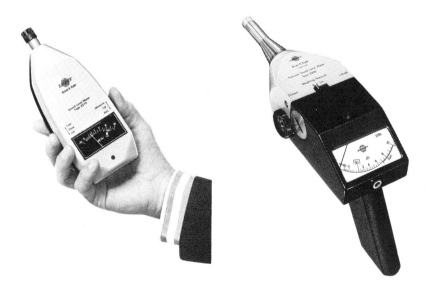

Fig.4.3. Examples of small portable sound level meters
a) Type 2219 Sound Level Meter
b) Type 2206 Precision Sound Level Meter

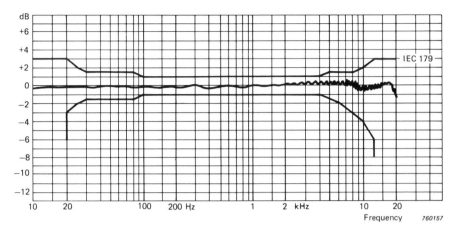

Fig.4.4. Free-field frequency response of a Sound Level Meter to sine waves with 0° incidence compared with the precision requirements of IEC 179

A more sophisticated lightweight hand-held instrument, the Type 2206 shown in Fig.4.3.b belongs to the very large group of sound level meters meeting the *Precision* requirements of IEC 179, the frequency response requirements of which are shown in Fig.4.4. All meters which fulfill these standards are supplied with a precision condenser microphone for which a wide range of accessories such as windshields, extension cables, nose cones, is available. The Type 2206 has A, C and linear networks and a thumb-operated push-switch to shift the measuring range quickly and easily by 10 dB. The indicating meter has "fast" and "slow" damping characteristics conforming to International Standards, the "slow" characteristics being intended for use when the fluctuations of the meter needle in the "fast" mode are too great (more than some 4 dB) to give a well-defined value for the sound level. An output socket is provided so that the signal can be connected either to a portable level recorder to obtain a permanent record of the noise

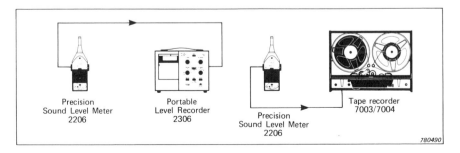

Precision
Sound Level Meter
2206

Portable
Level Recorder
2306

Precision
Sound Level Meter
2206

Tape recorder
7003/7004

Fig.4.5. Lightweight portable instrumentation for recording noise in the field

79

level, or to a tape recorder, for reproduction of the signal in the laboratory, when further analysis is required which is not possible in the field. See Fig.4.5.

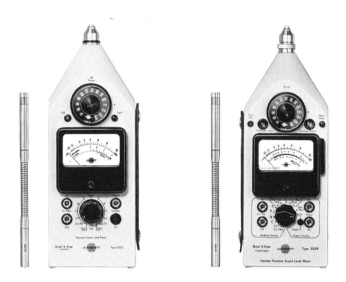

Fig.4.6. a) Precision Sound Level Meter Type 2203
b) Impulse Precision Sound Level Meter Type 2209

The Type 2203 shown in Fig.4.6(a) is a more comprehensive meter containing a B-weighting in addition to the A and C weighting networks. Filter Sets Type 1613 (octave) or 1616 (1/3 octave) can be attached directly to the base of the meter, electrical connections being made by means of a connecting bar, to convert it into a truly portable hand-held octave or one-third octave band analyzer.

If the sound to be measured consists of isolated impulses or contains a high proportion of impact noise, then the normal "fast" and "slow" time constants of the ordinary precision meter are not sufficiently short to give a meter indication which is representative of the subjective human response. To measure such signals properly, a more sophisticated instrument like the Type 2209 Impulse Precision Sound Level Meter shown in Fig.4.6(b) should be used. This contains the special circuitry necessary for detecting and displaying transient noise in a way which takes into account the human perception of impulsive sounds. These characteristics of the ear are described in a little more detail in chapter 3, and are standardised for the purpose of impulse sound level meters in IEC 179A and DIN 45 633-2. The instrument also has facilities for holding the impulsive value or peak value on the meter, which can be reset by a press switch after the reading is taken. A "D" frequency weighting is included, (specifically for aircraft noise measurements), as well as the other standard weightings, and the DC level or an AC signal can be output to external equipment. Fig.4.6 shows a Type 1616 1/3 Octave Band Filter Set attached to the instrument. An integrator and accelerometer, which are available as accessories, are fitted in place of the more usual microphone to carry out a frequency analysis of vibration.

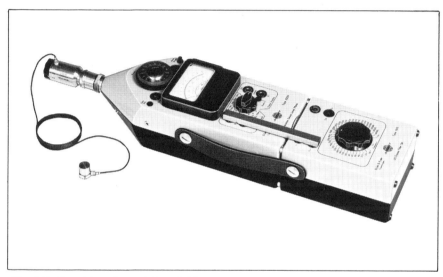

Fig.4.7. Precision Sound Level Meter Type 2209 and 1/3 Octave Filter Set Type 1616 fitted with integrator and accelerometer for vibration analysis

Octave or one-third octave filters can be combined with other accessories, such as an accelerometer and pistonphone, to produce a completely self-contained portable precision sound and vibration analysis set, as in Fig.4.8. Fig.4.9.a shows the Type 1621 Tunable Band Pass Filter, a completely self-contained instrument, which can be connected to the entire range of precision sound level meters in order to carry out frequency analysis in 23% (approx. 1/3 oct.) and 3% bandwidths. A narrow band analysis like this may be necessary to achieve sufficient resolution of a complicated spectrum to identify annoying pure tones. Typical frequency analyses carried out in the field and recorded on a Type 2306 Portable Level Recorder are reproduced in Fig.4.10. Fig.4.9b shows the Type 1623 Tracking Filter which has 6%, 12%, and 23% bandwidths and is tunable to ratios between 1/99 and 99/1 times the frequency of the tracking signal. This enables a signal to be analyzed with respect to a reference signal which is varying in frequency. When oc-

81

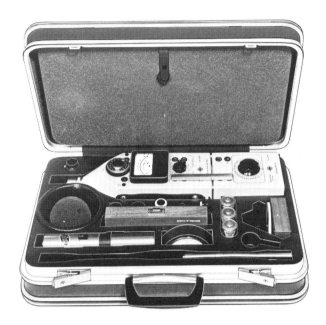

Fig.4.8. Case containing Meter and accessories for precision noise and vibration measurements (Sound and Vibration Set Type 3511)

Fig.4.9. a) The Tunable Band Pass Filter Type 1621
        b) The Tracking Filter Type 1623

tave analysis provides sufficient resolution, the Precision Sound Level Meter
and Octave Analyzer Type 2215 shown in Fig.4.11, a compact instrument designed for virtually one-handed operation, can be employed effectively. It contains 10 octave bands to IEC specifications, with centre frequencies from

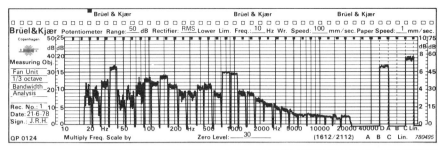

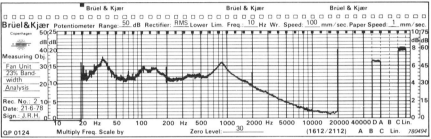

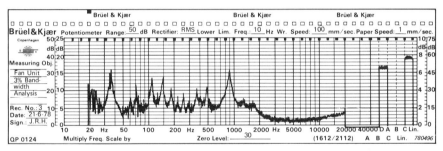

Fig.4.10. Frequency Analyses recorded in the field
a) 1/3 octave fixed band   b) continuous 23%   c) continuous 3%

31,5 Hz to 16 kHz, which can be used with or without the A-weighting network.

The previously described sound level meters are all traditional types with
analogue readout in the form of an indicating needle on a direct reading
scale. Digital techniques have permitted the addition of digital readouts and
more complex functions and facilities to the new generation of instruments.
One of these new hybrid types is the Impulse Precision Sound Level Meter
Type 2210 shown in Fig.4.12a, designed to fulfil the specifications for the internationally proposed type O laboratory reference standard instrument. A, B,
C, D, and linear weightings, the standardised "impulse", "fast", and "slow"
response characteristics, a peak detector with a 50 μsec risetime, and a "maximum hold" facility, which operates in all modes, are all incorporated in this

83

Fig.4.11. The Precision Sound Level Meter and Octave Analyzer Type 2215

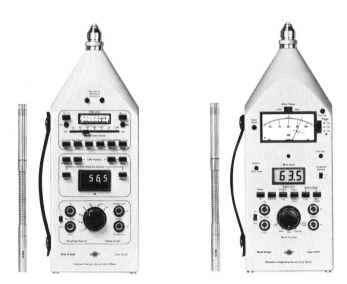

Fig.4.12. a) Impulse Precision Sound Level Meter Type 2210
b) Precision Integrating Sound Level Meter Type 2218

instrument. Gain control is automatic within a 90 dB range and read-out is via a digital display. Although designed to the most stringent of proposed standards regarding Sound Level Meters for laboratory use, it is entirely compatible with the usual range of other portable instruments, filters, accelerometers and ancillary recorders, to convert it for use as a field analyzer of sound and vibration. A digital output is provided for the connection of digital peripheral equipment, such as the Alphnumeric Printer Type 2312.

The Precision Integrating Sound Level Meter Type 2218 shown in Fig.4.12b combines a precision meter with analogue readout, and an L_{eq} meter with digital readout, in one instrument. L_{eq}, measured to the requirements of ISO R 1996, R 1999 and DIN 45641, and L_{AX}, the single event noise exposure level, (the L_{eq} normalised to a duration of one second), are available at the press of a switch. These facilities are particularly useful for the measurement of single events such as aircraft flyovers and vehicle drive-bys, and for on-the-spot assessment of fluctuating environmental noise expressed in L_{eq} e.g. construction, community, and occupational noise. Measurement time for L_{eq} can be preset and the elapsed time displayed, and the measurement may be terminated at any time at the discretion of the user.

Both these instruments have very large measuring and display dynamic ranges, which make them especially convenient for measuring widely fluctuating noise. The digital readout of the Type 2210 for example, has a 90 dB dynamic range. The digital display eliminates the uncertainties of visual averaging, and provides a repeatable value when measuring fluctuating noise levels.

The need to ascertain, for the purpose of occupational hearing conservation, the noise exposure of employees during their normal working day, has lead to the development of a new type of specialised integrating sound level meter from which the "noise dose" can be determined directly. The noise

Fig.4.13. Noise Dose Meter Type 4424/25 (protective cover removed)

dose is a measure of the total A-weighted sound energy received by an employee, and is expressed as a proportion of the allowed daily noise dose. It therefore depends not only on the level of the noise but also on the length of time that the employee is exposed to it. Often, both the noise in each work place, and the length of time spent there, vary widely so an instrument which can be worn by the employee himself is often preferable to the alternative method of measuring the noise in each place of work, deciding how long is spent there, and summing the individual exposures to be representative of the entire working day.

The noise dose meter, however, records the wearer's actual exposure, wherever he may be and however long he may be there. In addition it is small, compact, and light enough to be worn without hampering work, and can be interrogated at any time to check the current accumalated dose without affecting the measuring process. Two models are available. The Noise Dose Meter Type 4424 shown in Fig.4.13 is in accordance with ISO standards which require a halving of exposure time for each 3 dB rise in noise level, and Type 4425 is to American OHSA standards which require a halving of exposure time per 5 dB rise in level. The microphone may be used either in its normal position mounted directly on the main body of the instrument, or located remotely from it nearer the wearer's head if desired, as in Fig.4.14. The main body of the meter can then be carried in a convenient pocket, away from possible damage. A meter of this type need only be set up initially by a qualified person, and checked by him after the working day to ensure that the work cycle is acceptable from a hearing damage point of view.

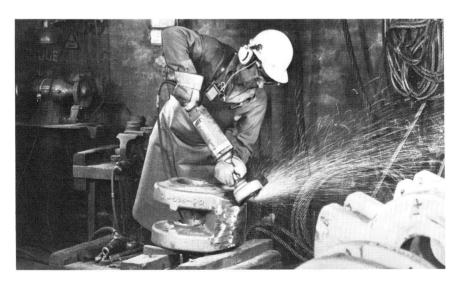

Fig.4.14. Dose meter in use in typical industrial environment

Fig.4.15. Photograph of the Noise Level Analyzer Type 4426

This removes the necessity for the continued presence of the specialist, the intervention of the employee, and the detailed analysis of each work area or noise source.

The natural next step is to an instrument which can perform on-the-spot statistical analysis, enabling the continuous variation of the noise level during the measurement period to be described by its statistical parameters. The Noise Level Analyzer Type 4426, shown in Fig.4.15, is a fully portable instrument which can be calibrated and used in much the same way as an ordinary sound level meter. But there the similarity ends, as the instrument samples the sound pressure level at preset intervals of 0,1 to 10 seconds, accepting up to 2^{16} (= 65536) samples and allowing up to 180 hours continuous recording at the lowest sampling rate. A dynamic range of 64 dB is available within a total instrument range (depending on the microphone type) from 26 to 140 dB.

Sound pressures from the microphone are A-weighted, and a variety of noise parameters, such as L_N, which may take any integer value between 1 and 99, L_{eq}, and the probability and cumulative distributions, are calculated continuously. L_{eq} may be calculated either from the instantaneous samples values according to I.S.O. standards, or from the peak values within the preceeding time interval, as required by DIN standards. All parameters may be read at any time from the digital display on the front of the instrument, simply by selecting the relevant function switch, without disturbing the measurement and calculation process. The A-weighted noise level or the number of accumulated samples may be read continuously from this display if desired. Tape recorded signals or those from other sources can be input, if this is required for analysis purposes, independently of the built-in A-weighting network.

In addition to the direct-reading digital display, a permanent record of the analysis can be obtained either on the Portable Level Recorder Type 2306, which can be electrically synchronised with the 4426 to plot the statistical distributions automatically, or on an Alphanumeric Printer Type 2312, which can be fitted in a weatherproof case together with the 4426 as shown in the photograph of Fig.4.16. The printer is controlled by the programmable output section of the 4426 which allows any combination of parameters to be output, at time intervals which may be preset by controls on the 2312.

This combination of instruments thus enables noise levels to be continuously monitored, and information written out at the required time intervals completely automatically, with no further intervention from the user. See also the later section on Traffic Noise.

Fig.4.16. Noise Level Analyzer Type 4426 and Alphanumeric Printer Type 2312 in use for on-site analysis of traffic noise

4.4. LABORATORY MEASUREMENT AND ANALYSIS SYSTEMS

All the instruments described so far have been powered by internal batteries and completely portable, though some of them can also be powered from the mains supply if required. If extensive periods of time are involved, if meas-

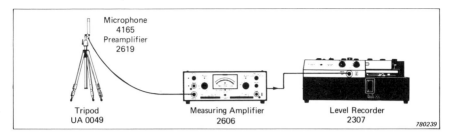

Fig.4.17. Simple mains powered noise measuring and recording instrumentation

urements can be made from secure premises, or if substantial work or analysis is to be carried out in the laboratory, then it may be preferable to use mains powered instruments. For the analysis of tape-recorded data, or experimental work in the laboratory, this will nearly always be the case. The arrangement of Fig.4.17 is perhaps the simplest of mains powered systems, consisting of a 1/2" Condenser Microphone Type 4165 and a Preamplifier Type 2619, powered directly from a Measuring Amplifier Type 2606, the output being recorded by a Level Recoder Type 2307. The amplifier has linear, A, B, C and D weighting networks, and the normal meter time constants found on sound level meters. For measurement of short duration signals and for mre demanding arrangements the more comprehensive Type 2607 which contains a wider range of averaging times and peak-hold circuitry, should be used.

Automatic analysis and recording of frequency spectra in standard octave and 1/3 octave contiguous bands from 2 Hz to 20 kHz can be easily carried out by adding ·the Bandpass Filter Set Type 1618 (see Fig.4.20) to the previous analysis arrangement, as in Fig.4.18. Because the filter switching can be controlled from the level recorder, the spectrum can be automatically recorded on pre-printed, calibrated paper. The speed and repeatability which automatic analysis allows, make it ideal for noise emission tests and quality con-

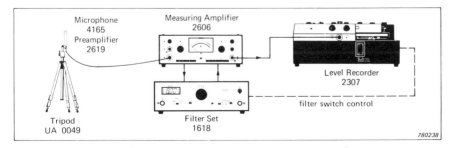

Fig.4.18. Arrangement for measurement and analysis of noise in fixed octave or 1/3 octave bands

89

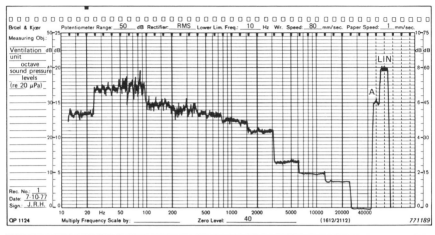

Fig.4.19. Octave and 1/3 octave band analyses of ventilation noise using the set up of Fig.4.18

Fig.4.20. Photograph of Band Pass Filter Type 1618

trol in the factory. Fig.4.19 shows typical examples of octave and 1/3 octave spectra of a ventilation unit recorded with this setup. For analysis at higher frequencies (up to 160 kHz), and for remote operation from other instruments via the proposed IEC standard interface, the more comprehensive Type 1617 Band Pass Filter Set is available.

Fig.4.21. Photograph of the Frequency Analyzer Type 2120

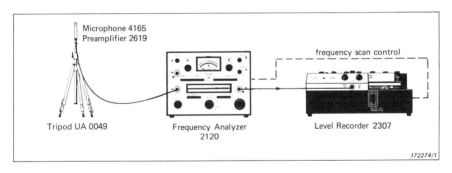

Fig.4.22. Arrangement for continuous constant percentage bandwidth analysis

The previous method measured and analysed the noise in contiguous bands, i.e. bands in which both the bandwidth and the centre frequency are fixed. The Frequency Analyzer Type 2120 shown in Fig.4.21 allows a continuous analysis to be made by sweeping through the desired frequency range. Analysis in 23% (approximately 1/3 octave), 10%, 3% or 1% bandwidths is possible with this instrument, and the arrangement shown in Fig.4.22 carries out and records the analysis automatically, the analyser being swept from the Level Recorder Type 2307. A typical frequency analysis of sound from 20 Hz to 2 kHz, is shown in Fig.4.23.

91

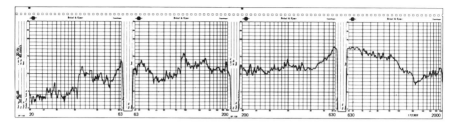

Fig.4.23. Frequency analysis of sound using the instrumentation of Fig.4.22.

Although a 1% bandwidth is narrow, a constant bandwidth, rather than a constant percentage bandwidth, analysis is often required. This is particularly true of noise and vibration problems associated with rotating machines and gearboxes, where the excellent resolution provided by narrow constant-bandwidth analysis is necessary to identify multiple resonances and harmonics, which occur at *constant frequency* intervals. The Heterodyne Analyzer Type 2010, shown in Fig.4.24, permits analysis in bandwidths from 3,16 to 1000 Hz in a total analysis range from 2 Hz to 200 kHz, split into 3 ranges 2 Hz to 2 kHz; 20 Hz to 20 kHz; and 200 Hz to 200 kHz; within which the instrument is continuously tunable. The frequency sweep may be made manually, or by electrical or mechanical synchronisation with a level recorder, as

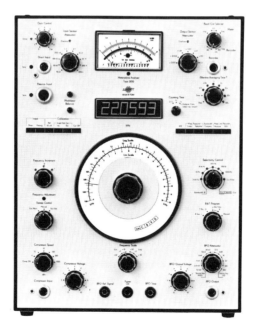

Fig.4.24. Photograph of the Heterodyne Analyzer Type 2010

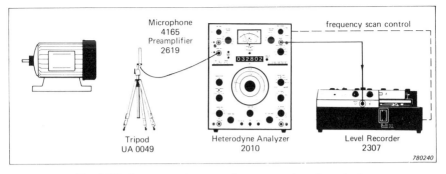

Fig.4.25. Instrument set-up for narrow-band analysis

in the arrangement in Fig.4.25, so that the analysis can be carried out completely automatically.

A feature of the 2010 is the B and T program, which allows analysis with constant B, constant T, and constant BT product, for constant statistical confidence, to be selected. The importance of this is dealt with later in this chapter. A typical frequency analysis showing the excellent resolution which can be obtained with this type of setup is reproduced in Fig.4.26.

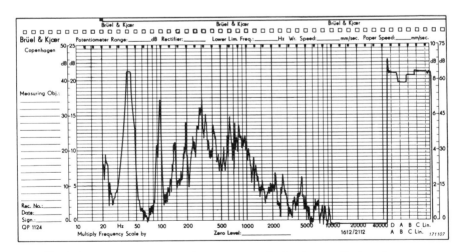

Fig.4.26. Recording of the frequency analysis of a small electric motor

93

4.5. REAL TIME ANALYSIS

The equipment described previously performed a frequency analysis by passing the data through a filter of the required bandwidth, and recorded the output as the analyzer was switched one filter after another, or swept continuously, through the frequency range of interest. Although it may be performed automatically, this sequential method requires a total time which is equal to the measurement time multiplied by the number of filters used, and is most suitable for the frequency analysis of signals which are steady or vary only slowly with time. For signals which vary rapidly in amplitude or in frequency content, a completely different technique must be employed, preferably one which is capable of analyzing all the data all of the time, so that rapid changes can be detected. This can be accomplished by presenting the signal simultaneously to the inputs of all the filters in the chosen analysis range, and feeding the outputs to a continuous display device such as a cathode ray screen, where they are displayed together as a complete spectrum. Modern instruments do this process digitally at high speed, and the displayed spectrum is renewed many times per second. Output can be to a range of analog instruments such as X-Y or Level Recorders, or via the IEC interface to digital data peripherals such as tape punch, printer, or desk-top calculator. The interfacing of a real-time analyzer to a suitably programmed calculator, thus provides a system for the very rapid automatic processing of acoustic noise data.

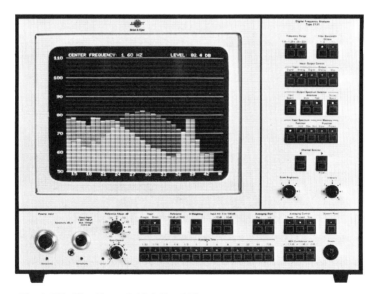

Fig.4.27. The Type 2131 Real-Time Digital Frequency Analyzer

Typical of instruments capable of fulfilling this role for octave and 1/3 octave band analysis is the Type 2131 Real-Time Digital Frequency Analyzer shown in Fig.4.27. Octave and 1/3 octave band analysis can be accomplished with or without an A-weighting network, and the linear or A-weighted sound levels are displayed alongside the frequency spectrum. By moving a switch-controlled cursor across the spectrum, a band can be chosen and its frequency and level in decibels is displayed at the top of the screen. Several useful features such as an alternating display for easy comparison of two spectra, and the ability to average linearly (as required in building acoustics) or exponentially (with a constant confidence level if desired) by present selection are incorporated. The 60 dB display range, a wide frequency range from 1,6 Hz to 20 kHz, and averaging times of 1/32 secs. to 128 secs. render the instrument suitable for most noise and vibration applications in the audible and infrasonic range. Normal B & K microphones and preamplifiers may be connected directly to the input section, and the entire system can be easily calibrated by normal techniques with either a pistonphone or acoustic calibrator. Output may be to an X-Y recorder or level recorder, which can be triggered electrically to record the spectrum automatically,

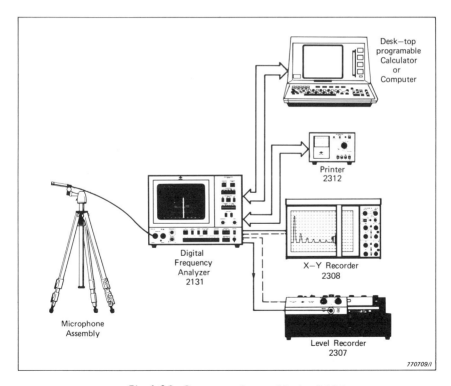

Fig.4.28. Output options with the 2131

95

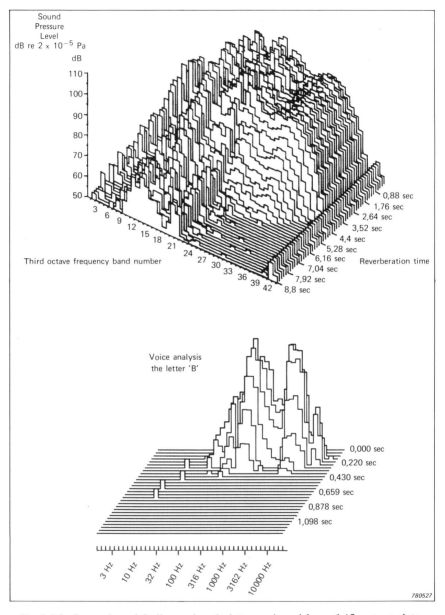

Fig. 4.29. Examples of 3 dimensional plots produced from 1/3 octave data

96

to an alphanumeric printer, or to a programmable desk-top calculator for further extensive calculations, e.g. perceived noise, sound power, loudness etc. The options are shown diagrammatically in Fig.4.28. A program package is available for desk-top calculators to enable them to carry out acoustical calculations, and to make plots. Typical three-dimensional plots showing the variation of spectra with time are reproduced in Fig.4.29.

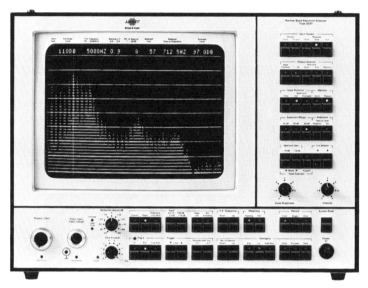

Fig.4.30. Narrow Band Spectrum Analyzer Type 2031

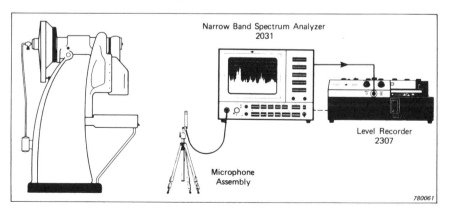

Fig.4.31. Set-up to analyze the noise from a punch press

For some applications, as discussed earlier, greater resolution is required than can be obtained from constant percentage bandwidth analysis, necessitating analysis in narrow bands. The Type 2031 Narrow Band Spectrum Analyzer of Fig.4.30 is an all-digital instrument with input and output sections enabling normal Brüel & Kjær microphones, amplifiers, and recording devices to be connected directly.

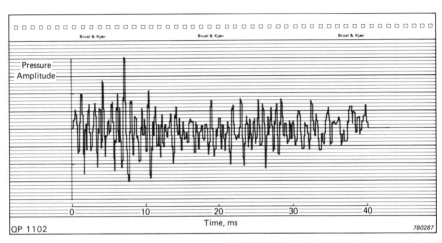

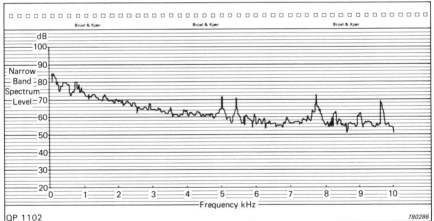

Fig.4.32. Noise from a punch press
a) Typical time function
b) Narrow Band spectrum

The measured time history is analyzed using Fast Fourier Transform techniques, producing a narrow band spectrum of 400 lines, in 11 ranges from 0 to 10 Hz, up to 0 to 20 kHz. The time history may be captured automatically and displayed directly on the screen. Transformations between the time and frequency domains are made at the press of a button, and any of the 400 discrete lines of the spectrum may be selected by the cursor, both the frequency of the selected band and its level being displayed at the top of the screen. Fig.4.31 shows a simple set-up used for analyzing punch press noise which is particularly impulsive in nature. The output was recorded automatically on a level recorder and a typical time record and spectrum extracted from the analysis is shown in Fig.4.32.

4.6. RECORDERS

Sound level meters and measuring amplifiers used in noise measurement have instrument meters or digital displays from which steady noise levels can be read directly. Often, however, data must not only be presented and noted, but also documented and stored for future reference and comparison. Noise levels which change with time, such as traffic noise, aircraft flyovers, etc. cannot be adequately described by a single measurement value, and it is often advantageous to have a record of the time history. Frequency analysis, using for example the Sound Level Meter and Octave Analyzer Type 2215, can be recorded semi-automatically and assessed on the spot using the Level Recorder Type 2306 as shown in Fig.4.33. Probability histograms can also be recorded on site directly from the Statistical Level Analyzer Type 4426.

Fig.4.33. Photograph of the Portable Level Recorder Type 2306

The Two Channel Level Recorder Type 2309 is available for applications which require simultaneous recording of two signals, such as vibration and the associated noise emission from machines, or sound insulation studies. Both these recorders are fully portable, being powered by a plug-in battery

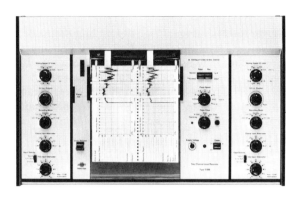

Fig.4.34. The Two Channel Level Recorder Type 2309

pack, and can be fitted with potentiometers to give either a 50 dB or 25 dB range. Four writing speeds from 16 to 250 mm/s and 8 chart speeds from ,01 to 30 mm/s can be selected. The Level Recorder Type 2307 shown in Fig.4.35 is a more comprehensive instrument with a wider range of facilities intended primarily for laboratory use. Writing speeds from 4 to 2000 mm/s, chart speeds from ,0003 to 100 mm/s and range potentiometers from 10 to 75 dB can be selected. The wide range of chart speeds allows recording of both sound levels for long term monitoring purposes, and expanded plots of actual signal waveforms. A polar plotter is built in and B & K filter sets and analyzers, including the real-time instruments, can be controlled either mechanically or electrically, so that the signal can be analyzed and plotted completely automatically on pre-printed, calibrated paper suitable for immediate documentation.

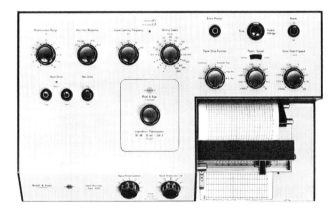

Fig.4.35. The Level Recorder Type 2307

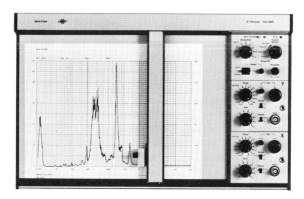

Fig.4.36. X—Y Recorder Type 2308

The X-Y recorder Type 2308 shown in Fig.4.36 is a mains powered DC in-strument for recording analyses, signal waveforms, and any graphical plot re-quiring two fully controllable axes. The sensitivity of each input can be ad-justed continuously and independently so that the plot size can be arranged to completely fill the paper. The writing table, which has an electrostatic hold, takes A4 paper.

Many applications, especially those concerned with noise monitoring, re-quire specific information to be recorded at regular intervals, so that varia-tions over a long period of time can be studied without the continued pres-ence of the observer. The Statistical Analyzer Type 4426 can be programmed

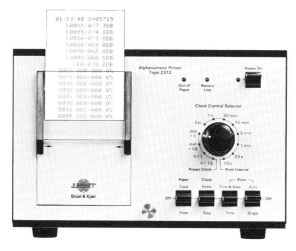

Fig.4.37. The Alphanumeric Printer Type 2312

to output a wide variety of parameters such as L_{eq}, L_{10}, etc. as well as a complete statistical analysis. The Alphanumeric Printer Type 2312 shown in Fig.4.37 accepts this data and prints it out on heat sensitive paper, at intervals which can be set on the instrument. The clock which controls the interval can be pre-set to record the day and actual time of the print-outs. The Impulse Precision Sound Level Meter Type 2210 may also be connected to the printer to record data automatically, for example from community noise surveys. Many modern real time analyzers incorporate a visual display which not only displays the analysis, but also presents important parameters, allows the operator to interrogate the stored data to obtain levels in particular bands, and enables manipulation of the incoming data. This latter facility is particularly useful when dealing with transient and impulsive signals.

4.7. SIGNAL STORAGE TECHNIQUES

It is often more convenient and sometimes absolutely necessary to record and store the noise data, so that it can be reproduced later for laboratory analysis. There are many reasons for doing this, the chief among them being:

(1) minimization of the time spent on site and the equipment employed there,
(2) analysis of the same data by a number of different techniques which could not necessarily be carried out in the field,
(3) the non-repeatability of certain types of noise event.

Unrepeatable events like sonic booms and explosions are of short duration and uncertain occurence, and once missed may prove difficult, expensive, or even impossible to reproduce.

The magnetic tape recorder is the most universally used instrument for bulk data capture and storage. To be suitable for noise measurement work it should be rugged, reliable, and portable, which means that it should be light and convenient to carry, battery operated, and easy to operate in the field. It must have a wide dynamic range, low wow and flutter, and a flat response over the frequency range of interest. This range is usually from 20 Hz to 15 kHz for acoustic noise measurement, but may extend to much lower frequencies for measurements of vibration or shocks, including sonic booms. For measurements confined to the normal acoustic range, a direct recording instrument such as the B & K Type 7004, with a frequency range from 20 Hz to 50 kHz, is probably the most efficient way of storing typical signals for subsequent spectral or statistical analysis. If the type of data to be recorded has important components down to very low frequencies, approaching DC, or if analysis is to be performed between signals from different transducers, for example correlation analysis, where the phase relationship of the signal is important, then the frequency modulated tape recorder Type 7003 shown in

Fig.4.38 is preferable. The characteristics of the signal to be recorded and the type of analysis should be considered carefully before a particular recording technique is chosen.

Fig.4.38. The Tape Recorder Type 7003

B & K instrumentation tape recorders are supplied with indicators to warn the operator when the input stage is overloaded. This is especially important when recording shocks or impulsive noise, which may reach very high short term peak levels, greatly in excess of the long term RMS value. High crest factor signals such as this should be checked with a meter possessing a peak hold circuit to alleviate this problem as far as possible. Whenever information is recorded, the recording must contain a reference level so that the analysis equipment can be set up correctly at a later time. This may be done using a sound level calibrator or pistonphone. It is important that once completed the gain controls of all the instrumentation are left in their original positions. If it is necessary to make adjustments after setting up in this way, information to this effect should be clearly recorded onto the tape. The recorder is fitted with a small microphone/loudspeaker, which overrides the first track and can be used for this purpose. It also enables recordings on any track to be played back directly after recording, in order to check that measurements have been correctly recorded and calibrated while still in the field, although on the spot measurements should always be made in order to have directly obtained values to compare with later analyses.

By recording at one speed and playing back the signal at another it is possible to shift the frequency range of the recordings. Low frequency recordings, say from vibration measurements, can be shifted into the frequency range of normal audio frequency analysis equipment, or short duration sounds may be slowed down considerably to be better able to study their actual waveform. To facilitate analysis of samples of the recording, a tape loop cassette is available. A system is shown in Fig.4.39 which can be used for the simultaneous recording of the noise from road traffic, and the vibration induced by it both in the roadway and in the elements of adjacent buildings. This system permits recording from virtually DC to 14 kHz at a tape speed of 15 in/s and allows correlation and cross spectrum analysis to be carried out on recorded signals.

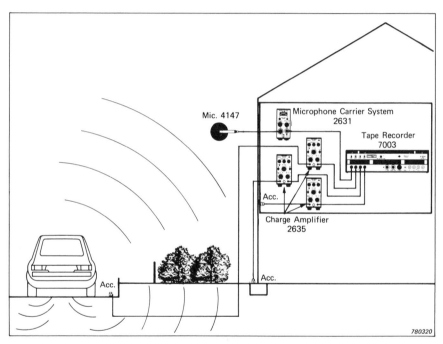

Fig.4.39. Simultaneous recording of noise and vibration from road traffic

Short duration and transient signals may also be recorded on the Type 7502 Digital Event Recorder, which is shown in Fig.4.40. This is a digital instrument which continually updates the input time history in a recirculating memory. In this way the stored information is always the signal which occurred in the sweep period up to the present time. The process continues until the instrument is triggered, either by the input itself exceeding a certain preset value, or by an external signal. The stored signal may then be repro-

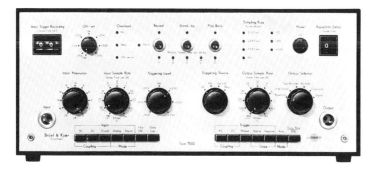

Fig.4.40. The Digital Event Recorder Type 7502

duced at a rate which can be set to give a wide range of frequency transformations. Ratios of 5000/1 and 1/200000 are made possible by suitable adjustment of both the input and output sample rates. In addition, the trigger point can be preset to occur at any time during the sweep period so that a chosen amount of data before the trigger point can be viewed. After capture the signal may be output for permanent storage to a paper tape punch, tape recorder, level recorder, or X-Y recorder to obtain permanent documentation. An arrangement suitable for the recording and narrow band analysis of the short duration acoustic signal is shown in Fig.4.41. It consists of a 1/2″ Microphone Type 4147 with an FM Microphone carrier system capable of recording frequencies from 0,01 Hz up to 18 kHz, and passes the data to a 7502. The captured impulse shown in Fig.4.42 is then input to the Heterodyne Analyzer Type 2010 and the resulting analysis recorded on the level recorder.

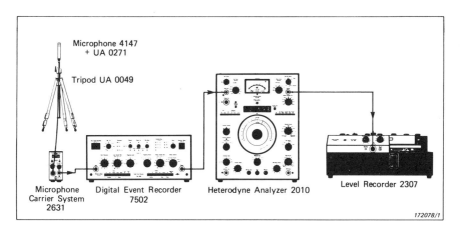

Fig.4.41. Set-up for recording and analysis of short duration acoustic signals

105

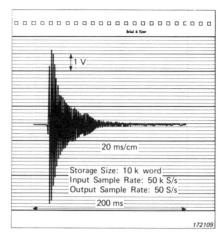

Fig.4.42. Recording of acoustic impulse

4.8. MICROPHONE SELECTION

The physical characteristics of noise can be described by many different parameters but the most practical quantity to measure, especially under field conditions, is the sound pressure. For this reason microphones have been developed to a high stage of refinement. The microphone chosen for a particular noise measurement will in general have to fulfil two rather different groups of conditions. Firstly it must operate satisfactorily over a range of environmental conditions such as humidity, temperature, air pollution and wind, and secondly, it must also meet the technical constraints, e.g. frequency response, dynamic range, directivity, and stability, necessary for accurate and repeatable measurements.

The *condenser* microphone is best able to meet all these conditions and has therefore become the most widely used type. It operates on the well-known principle that the capacitance of two electrically charged plates alters with their separation distance. One of these plates is an extremely light diaphragm, which moves in response to acoustic pressure variations, and the resulting change of capacitance is detected by the meter circuitry. Fig.4.43 shows a view of a typical condenser microphone with the most important components labelled. Because of practical design considerations, the size of the microphone is usually increased in order to achieve higher sensitivity. Unfortunately, this conflicts with the requirements for wide frequency range and omnidirectivity, both of which are better if the diaphragm is small compared with the wavelength of sound being measured.

106

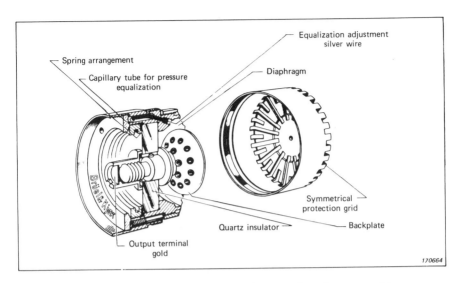

Fig.4.43. Sectional view of a condenser microphone cartridge

The frequency response of a microphone suitable for accurate acoustic noise measurements should be linear over the frequency range of interest. Usually this means the audible range of the human ear, i.e. from about 20 Hz to 15 kHz, but for special applications it may be extended below or above this range. Measurements of shocks, impulses or sonic booms, which contain important data down to very low frequencies, may be made using an FM Microphone Carrier System Type 2631 shown in Fig.4.44 and a special microphone such as the Types 4146 and 4147, to enable the frequency response to be extended down to some 0,01 Hz. Very high frequency and/or high sound level measurements can only be carried out with relatively small

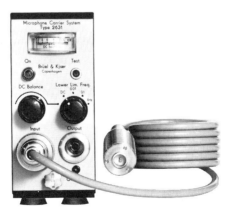

Fig.4.44. The FM Microphone Carrier System Type 2631

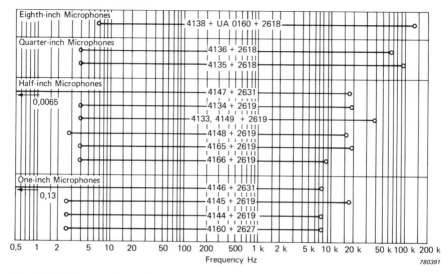

Fig.4.45. Comparison of the frequency response ranges (± 2 dB) of recommended microphone and preamplifier combinations

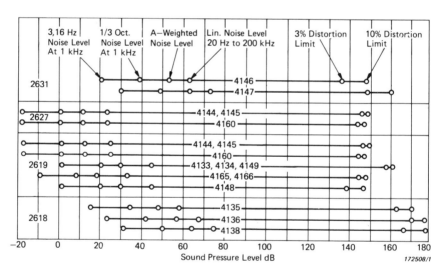

Fig.4.46. Dynamic ranges of B & K microphones and preamplifiers

microphones such as the 1/8″ Type 4138. Charts showing the dynamic range and frequency response of Brüel & Kjær condenser microphones are reproduced in Figs.4.45 and 4.46 the normal operating limits being indicated. The table of Fig.4.47 sums up their chief characteristics and applica-

108

Microphone type	Main area of application	Diameter	Associated preamplifier	Frequency range (± 2 dB)	Response	Sensitivity (mV/Pa)
4145	General sound level measurements including low sound levels	1"		2,6 Hz – 18 kHz	Free field	50
4144	Coupler measurements, audiometer calibration, calibration standard	1"	2619 or 2627	2,6 Hz – 8 kHz	Pressure	50
4146	Sonic boom measurements, acoustic pulse measurement, carrier type (carrier frequency 10 MHz)	1"	2631 (with 2619 same specs. as 4144)	< 0,1 Hz – 8 kHz	Pressure	12–60
4160	Primary calibration standard	1"	2627	2,6 Hz – 8,5 kHz	Pressure	47
4133	Free field general purpose, general sound level measurements, electro-acoustic measurements	1/2"		4 Hz – 40 kHz	Free field	12,5
4134	Pressure, general purpose, general sound level measurements, coupler measurements, probe microphones	1/2"	2619	4 Hz – 20 kHz	Pressure and random	12,5
4149	Best choice for polluted or humid environments, long term outdoor monitoring systems	1/2"		4 Hz – 40 kHz	Free field	12,5
4147	For sonic boom acoustic pulse and infrasonic measurements, carrier type (carrier frequency 10 MHz)	1/2"	2631 (with 2619 same spec. as 4134)	0,01 Hz – 20 kHz	Pressure and random	3,7–18
4148	Free field general purpose, for use with low polarizing voltage	1/2"	2619 with type 2804	2,6 Hz – 16 Hz	Free field	12,5
4165	General free field measurements including low levels	1/2"	2619	2,6 Hz – 20 kHz	Free field	50
4166	General random sound level measurements	1/2"	2619	2,6 Hz – 9 kHz	Pressure and random	50
4125	Low cost applications, low polarizing voltage	1/2"	2642	5 Hz – 12,5 kHz (± 3 dB)	Free field and random	10
4135	Free field sound level measurements model work, high levels	1/4"	2618 or 2619 + UA 0035	4 Hz – 100 kHz	Free field	4
4136	Random incidence, sound level measurements, boundary layer, pulses, coupler, measurements	1/4"		4 Hz – 70 kHz	Pressure and Random	1,6
4138	Very high frequency and very high sound level measurements, models, confined spaces, point source and receiver, sharp pulses	1/8"	2618 + UA 0160 or 2619 + UA 0036	6,5 Hz – 140 kHz	Pressure and random	1

770441

Fig.4.47. Table indicating the main characteristics and fields of application of Brüel & Kjær microphones

tions and should enable the optimum microphone choice to be made, with regard to dynamic range, frequency response, or type of sound field.

When choosing and using any microphone, the type of sound field to be measured should always be borne in mind. The response of the microphone is influenced at high frequencies by the reflections and diffraction caused by its own presence in the sound field, and is therefore dependent to some extent on the direction of the incoming sound. Two main types of acoustic conditions exist: diffuse and free field. If the field is diffuse the sound can be considered as equally likely to arrive at the microphone diaphragm from any direction. However, in a free field, the conditions which usually occur in the case of most outdoor and many indoor noise measurement situations, sound arrives from one direction only.

Special care should be taken to ensure that the characteristics and orientation of the microphone chosen are suitable for the type of sound field being investigated, otherwise the high frequency response will suffer. Microphone characteristics are usually expressed in one of three ways; the free-field, pressure, or random incidence response. A free-field microphone is designed to compensate for the disturbance caused by its own presence in the sound field, provided that the direction of propagation of the sound wave is perpendicular to the microphones' diaphragm. A pressure microphone has a uniform frequency response to the sound field as it exists, including its own disturbance, and should be used for coupler measurements, audiometer calibration, etc. A random incidence microphone responds uniformly to sound waves arriving simultaneously from any direction, and should therefore always be chosen when investigating diffuse fields.

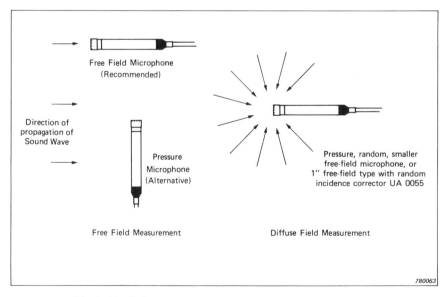

Fig.4.48. Orientation of microphones in the sound field

110

When measuring in a free field, a free-field microphone should be pointed in the direction of a noise source, and a pressure microphone should be held at right angles (grazing incidence) to the direction of propagation of the sound (see Fig.4.48).

Generally, the smaller a microphone is, the better its frequency response and omnidirectivity, but these advantages are paid for to some extent by a loss of sensitivity, as explained previously. To overcome this, a Random Incidence Corrector UA 0055 is available for the 1 inch free-field microphone Type 4145 to allow measurements to be made in diffuse fields at low sound

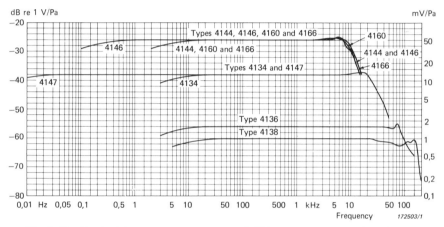

Fig.4.49. Typical frequency responses of different pressure microphones

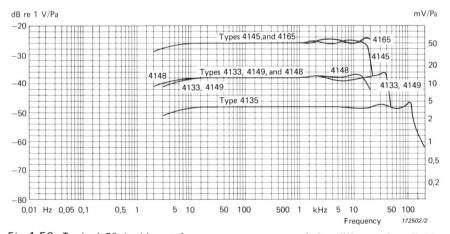

Fig.4.50. Typical 0° incidence frequency responses of the different free-field microphones

111

pressure levels. Nose cones perform a similar function for the 1/2 inch and 1/4 inch free-field microphones. Typical frequency response curves for the microphones in the Brüel & Kjær range are reproduced in Figs.4.49 and 4.50.

The microphone, once selected, must be connected to the rest of the system via a preamplifier which presents the microphone with the correct impedance, at the same time supplying its polarisation voltage from the preamplifier socket of a measuring amplifier or analyser, or from a special external power supply. This is 200 volts except for the Types 4125 and 4148 which have a polarising voltage of 28 volts. The Preamplifier has a low output impedance to enable the cable connecting it to the measuring instrumentation to be of a considerable length. Preamplifier Type 2619 is recommended for the 1 inch and 1/2 inch microphones, and Type 2618 for 1/4 and 1/8 inch types. The Type 2619 may be used with 1/2 inch Type 4148 if powered from the Microphone Power Supply Type 2804. The 1/2 inch Type 4125, intended for low cost applications, is used with Preamplifier Type 2642 and Microphone Power Supply Type 2810.

When a microphone is mounted on a Sound Level Meter, the case itself obstructs sound from certain directions and therefore makes the instrument's response more directional than that of a remotely mounted microphone, al-

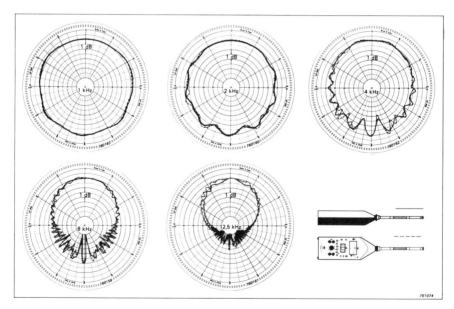

Fig.4.51. Directional characteristics of complete sound level meter in a free field

though these effects can be minimised by careful design of the meter shape. Fig.4.51 shows typical directional characteristics of a Type 2218 Precision Integrating Sound Level Meter, showing how the response becomes more directional with increasing frequency.

Inevitably, many outdoor measurements have to be taken in other than perfect conditions, very often in the presence of wind. In a moving airstream any microphone produces turbulence, which causes the diaphragm to deflect, and therefore to generate a spurious signal which is superimposed on the acoustic signal to be measured, giving rise to serious errors. Fig.4.52 shows the magnitude of the wind noise effects for different microphone orientations, with and without windshield, as a function of wind speed. The reduction of wind-induced noise which can be achieved by the use of a suitable windshield is quite marked at low windspeeds, below 40 km/hr, but rather less at higher velocities. In these conditions accurate measurements cannot be made in any case, and should not be attempted. The spectrum level of wind noise increases with decreasing frequency, so A-weighted measurements are less likely than others to be affected by this problem, as the wind noise tends

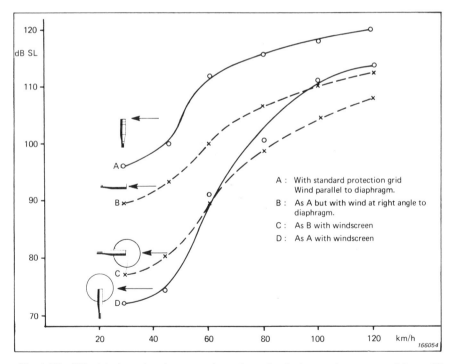

A : With standard protection grid
    Wind parallel to diaphragm.
B : As A but with wind at right angle to
    diaphragm.
C : As B with windscreen
D : As A with windscreen

*Fig.4.52. Wind-induced noise as a function of wind speed: measured by a 1″
microphone with and without a windscreen*

113

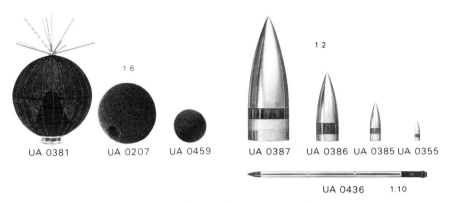

UA 0381   UA 0207   UA 0459   UA 0387   UA 0386 UA 0385 UA 0355

UA 0436   1:10

Fig.4.53. Microphone accessories

to be weighted out. For short term measurements using hand held portable sound level meters, a light foam windscreen, such as the Type UA 0207, shown in Fig.4.53 can be used. For permanent outdoor installations, a wire-framed cloth-covered windscreen UA 0381, as in the same figure, which can be fitted with spikes to prevent damage and interference by birds, is more suitable.

Fig.4.54. The Outdoor Microphone Unit Type 4921

114

For special conditions where the airflow is of high speed and in a well-defined direction, the nose cones shown in Fig.4.53 provide far less resistance to the flow, thus reducing the turbulence and wind-induced noise. For measurements in ducts, a turbulence screen, which gives good rejection of the flow noise while passing the acoustic signal to the microphone, should be fitted. A probe microphone kit for use with 1/2" microphones is also available.

For permanent outdoor installations in noise monitoring equipment, a complete outdoor microphone system such as the Type 4921 shown in Fig.4.54 should be seriously considered. This is supplied with a special quartz-coated half-inch condenser microphone Type 4149, protected by a windscreen with anti-bird spikes, and from rain penetration by rain cover UA 0393. This rain cover also contains a built-in electrostatic actuator which can be used to calibrate the microphone remotely. The assembly is mounted on a weatherproof case, which contains an amplifier, calibration oscillator, a dehumidifier for the air equalization system of the microphone, and a power supply.

4.9. FREQUENCY ANALYSIS TECHNIQUES AND THE SELECTION OF ANALYZER

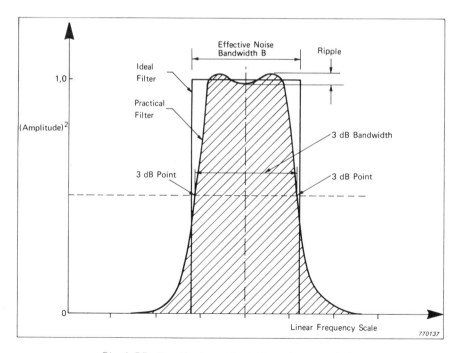

Fig.4.55. Practical vs. ideal filter characteristics

Very often in noise measurement we are interested in the amplitude of the signal at a particular frequency or in a range of frequencies, rather than just the overall linear or A-weighted sound level. The contributions to the overall signal made by the individual frequency band can be obtained by filtering it in bands, whose width depends largely on the ultimate use of the analysis results. The standardized weighting curves A, B, C and D, are of course, band-pass filters with a relatively wide bandwidth, whose cutoff rates at both ends of the spectrum are specifically designed to represent the response of the human ear. Normally, analysis is done in very much narrower bands, which should ideally pass everything within the passband concerned, and filter out all components of the origignal signal which lie outside it. In practice, however, the filter cannot have such a steep cut-off, and the usual filter shape is

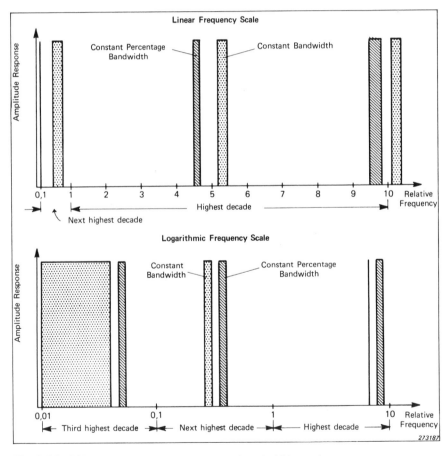

Fig.4.56. Difference between constant bandwidth and constant percentage bandwidth analysis

116

that shown in Fig.4.55, which has cutoff rates closely defined by the relevant international standards.

Two main types of frequency analysis are used in the analysis of noise signals; constant *percentage* bandwidth, and constant bandwidth. The effect which each method has on the width of the passband at different frequencies is clearly shown in the diagrams of Fig.4.56. In the first analysis method the filter bandwidth is a constant percentage of the centre frequency of the pass band, whatever its absolute value, and therefore increases as the frequency increases. In the second method, the filters have a constant bandwidth, say 100 Hz, completely independent of the centre frequency to which the filter is tuned. This technique permits very detailed analysis of the spectrum, which is especially required, for example, when analyzing noise emission prior to redesigning for noise reduction. Sources with many distinct harmonics, such as gear trains, those which emit pure tones, such as jet engines and electric motors, and the dynamic response of structures containing lightly-damped modes of vibration, can all be best analyzed by narrow band methods. On the other hand, acoustic noise measurements for purposes of estimating loudness, annoyance, and subjective response, generally do not require such detailed knowledge of the spectrum of the noise source. This is because the ear responds in a way similar to a constant percentage band analyzer with a 1/3 octave bandwidth, and loudness determination procedures have been largely based on this fact, see chapter 3.

Constant percentage bandwidth analysis is also normally used in procedures for the estimation of the subjective response of humans to environmental noise. Aircraft noise is generally analyzed into 1/3 octave bands, from

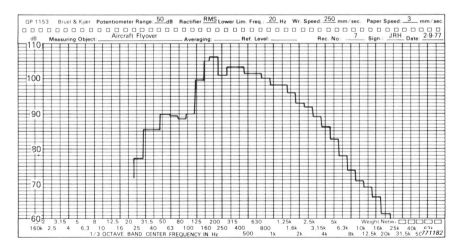

Fig.4.57. 1/3 octave spectrum of an overflying aircraft

117

which the perceived noise level, as recommended by the aircraft noise standards, is calculated. Noise levels in offices, lecture rooms, theatres, and other places of work and entertainment, are usually compared with noise criteria curves based on measurements in octave bands. Fig.4.57 shows an overflying aircraft 1/3 octave spectrum, which varies relatively slowly with frequency and therefore lends itself to constant percentage bandwidth analysis. Fig.4.57 shows the highly peaked spectrum of an electric motor, which is more realistically analyzed in narrow constant bands, so that the very rapid changes in the spectrum are revealed with the greatest possible precision. An important fact to remember is that the time taken for a sequential analysis depends on the bandwidth of the signal; a narrow-band constant bandwidth analysis will therefore take very much longer than the octave or 1/3 octave constant percentage bandwidth analysis more usual in environmental noise measurement.

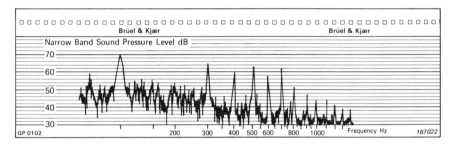

Fig.4.58. Highly peaked constant bandwidth spectrum from an electric motor

Sequential analyzers fall into two further groups, depending on whether the analysis is carried out in bands which have a fixed centre frequency, or in bands whose centre frequency sweeps continuously through the analysis range. These are called contiguous and continuous band analyzers respectively, the contiguous type being switched either manually or automatically from filter to filter through the analysis range. The table of Fig.4.59 gives the chief characteristicss of analyzers available from B & K.

The values which result from normal frequency analysis are obtained from a finite length of time record, giving rise to errors in the averaged values. The RMS value of the signal was given in chapter 2 as

$$A_{rms} = \sqrt{\frac{1}{T} \int_0^T a^2(t) \ dt}$$

where T is the averaging time used to determine the RMS value of the signal, and a is its instantaneous value. For noise which is statistically varying,

118

Instrument Type	Portable Filter Sets				Portable Analyzer	Laboratory Filter Sets				Laboratory Analyzers			
	1613	1616	1621	1623	2215	1617	1618	2020	2010	2120	2121	2031	2131
Analysis Type — Constant Percentage	Oct.	1/3 Oct.	3% 23%	6% 12% 23%	Oct.	Oct. 1/3 oct.	Oct. 1/3 oct.	—	—	1; 3; 10 23%	1; 3; 10 23%	—	Oct. 1/3 oct.
Analysis Type — Constant Bandwidth	—	—	—	—	—	—	—	3, 16, 316, 100 Hz	3, 16; 10 31,6; 100 316; 1000 Hz	—	—	0,25% of selected frequency range	—
Centre Frequency Range	31,5 Hz to 31,5 kHz	20 Hz to 40 kHz	0,2 Hz to 20 kHz	2 Hz to 20 kHz	31,5 Hz to 16 kHz	2 Hz to 160 kHz	2 Hz to 20 kHz	10 Hz to 20 kHz	2 Hz to 200 kHz	2 Hz to 20 kHz	20 Hz to 20 kHz	0 to 20 kHz	1,6 Hz to 20 kHz
Sweep Type — Contiguous	Log	Log	—	—	Log	Log	Log	—	—	—	—	Lin	Log
Sweep Type — Continuous	—	—	Log	Lin Log	—	—	—	Log	Lin Log	Log	Log	—	—
Sweep — Internal	Man	Man	Man	Man	Man	Man Auto	Man	—	Man	Man	Man	Auto	Auto
Control — External	—	—	Volt	Freq.	—	Pulse	Pulse	Freq.△	Volt-Mech	Mech	Mech	—	—
Battery — Int.	—	✓	✓	✓	✓	—	—	—	—	✓	—	—	—
Battery — Ext.	—	—	✓	✓	—	—	—	—	—	✓	—	—	—
AC Mains	—	—	—	—	—	✓	✓	✓	✓	✓	✓	✓	✓

△ Via Sine Generator Type 1023 or 1027

770569/1

Fig.4.59. Brüel & Kjær frequency analysis instrumentation

119

the RMS value obtained will only approach the true RMS value if this period T is infinitely long. This, of course, can never be the case, so we always have to accept an error in our measured values. However, by selecting a large enough value for T, the magnitude of these error fluctuations can be reduced. The second factor which affects the error superimposed on the true RMS value, is the passband width, and it can be shown that the relationship between the error, the bandwidth, B, and the length of the analysis record, T, is

$$\epsilon = \frac{1}{2\sqrt{BT}}$$

This is an extremely important result which has far-reaching effects in signal analysis. Its implications should always be borne in mind whenever frequency analysis is carried out. To obtain results of a certain accuracy, it is necessary to increase the time over which the data is averaged as the bandwidth of the analysis is decreased. A very narrow bandwidth analysis may have to be averaged over a very long time period to obtain sufficient accuracy. Before embarking on a lengthy analysis, it is therefore wise to determine the frequency resolution and accuracy which is required for a particular application, and arrange the averaging time to achieve this value. Narrow band sequential analyzers such as the Heterodyne Analyzer Type 2010 can be used to carry out an analysis with constant confidence by varying bandwidth and/or averaging time.

These basic requirements for accuracy apply equally to the new generation of real-time digital analyzers described in detail in an earlier section which, although working on entirely different principles of analysis, are still constrained by the same basic rules governing the averaging of data. In these instruments, data is analyzed in all the fixed bands at the same time, so the entire process takes only the time necessary to pass through one band. This may be made fast enough for all the available data to be analyzed in the time taken to produce it, thus analyzing in real-time.

The Type 2131 Digital Frequency Analyzer has the facilities for both linear averaging which gives equal weight to all points in the time history (averaging times from 1/32 to 120 secs), and exponential averaging, which gives more weight to recent samples than to previous ones. Exponential averaging may be carried out with constant statistical accuracy, the analysis in each band proceeding for the time necessary to reach a preset statistical accuracy.

Averaging times are also important in the recording of information on level recorders, which are widely used to record both measured noise levels and the result of frequency or statistical analyses. The averaging time with such instruments depends primarily on the writing speed and the potentiometer

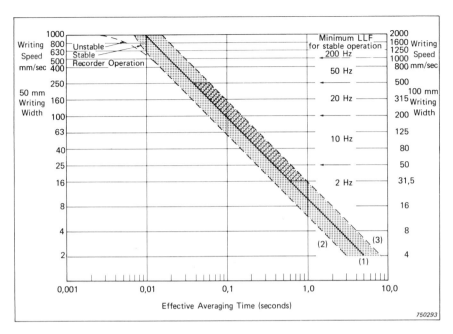

Fig.4.60. Averaging times of level recorders with tolerance limits

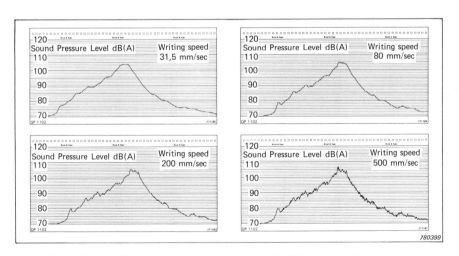

Fig.4.61. Aircraft flyover noise recorded at 4 different writing speeds but with other parameters unchanged

range, and should be determined by reference to Fig.4.60 curve (1). If the level recorder information is to be used to determine the level of a noise and

121

compare it with sound level measurements, then the chosen averaging time should correspond to either the "fast" or "slow" mode, whichever is used, of the sound level meter. Four time histories of the same noise using different writing speeds, but keeping all other parameters concerned with the level recorder constant, are shown in Fig.4.61. This clearly demonstrates the effect of different writing speeds on the smoothing of the recorded signal.

4.10 CALIBRATION

Microphones are individually calibrated at the factory, and the calibration chart, such as the one produced in Fig.4.62, delivered with the instrument. For laboratory purposes, techniques such as reciprocity calibration, for which a special apparatus is available (Type 4143), are usually used to determine a microphone's sensitivity over its entire frequency range. This sensitivity should be checked at regular intervals to ensure that the microphone remains within its specifications. For the purpose of obtaining calibrated measurements in the field, however, such complicated methods capable of obtaining the highest accuracy, are neither justified nor practical. Rather simpler techniques, which apply a known sound pressure level at fixed frequency to the microphone are usually sufficient to ensure that a properly calibrated tape recording or sound level meter measurement is made.

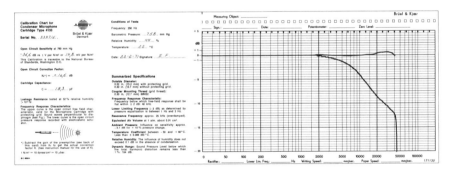

Fig.4.62. Microphone Calibration Chart

Two small battery driven portable calibrators working on slightly different principles are available to accomplish this conveniently under field conditions. The Pistonphone Type 4220 of Fig.4.63(a) is an accurate, reliable, and simple device, which employs a pair of independent pistons driven by a battery powered electric motor to produce a highly stable and distortion free sinusoidal sound pressure variation in the instrument's coupler cavity. It operates at 250 Hz and produces a sound level of 124 dB (re. 20 μPa) accurate to ± 0,2 dB. The sound pressure produced is proportional to the ratio of the volume swept by the pistons to the volume of the entire coupler cavity. Differ-

122

Fig.4.63. a) Pistonphone Type 4220
b) Sound Level Calibrator Type 4230

ent sizes and types of microphones can be calibrated at the same level with the same instrument because the coupler Volume, and therefore the calibration pressure within it, can be kept constant. To obtain the best results the microphone should be well sealed in the coupler opening. A change in atmospheric pressure alters the calibration level slightly, but a correction can be made using the barometer which is provided as a part of the instrument set.

The second calibrator is a smaller pocket unit, see Fig.4.63(b), which operates at 1000 Hz, making the calibration independent of weighting networks, which all have zero attenuation at this frequency. Calibration level is 94 dB re 20 μPa, with an accuracy of ± 0,25 dB. A stabilised oscillator feeds a piezoelectric driver element which vibrates a metallic diaphragm to create the sound pressure in the cavity.

The use of a calibrator is recommended for checking the accuracy of handheld indicating instruments, and must be used when tape recording data so that a known sound level of fixed frequency is available as a reference from which to calibrate any instruments which may be used in subsequent analysis. Accurate calibration of equipment used in the field has many advantages. It provides for the consistency in measurements, allows more accurate comparison of measurements made over long time intervals, brings to light any slight changes in the accuracy of instrumentation, and allows a re-analysis of data, if this is required at a later date. This care in the use of calibration for field measurements should be backed up by regular laboratory calibration using one of the more accurate techniques, in order to check the frequency response as well as the amplitude response of the equipment.

Fig.4.64. Calibration of sound level meter

4.11 BACKGROUND NOISE

The measurement of noise is often made difficult by the presence of a background noise level high enough to contribute to the level measured. Ideally, any noise measurement should only result from sound emitted from the source of interest, and not from any extraneous sources. If the offending extraneous noise is intermittent, it may be possible to carry out the measurements in the quiet intervals. The source may be moved to a relatively quiet area, or other significant contributors to the overall noise switched off temporarily while measurements are made. Sometimes, however, the measurements will have to proceed despite adverse conditions.

The effect which the background noise has on the noise level actually measured can be conveniently presented as a graph which is reproduced in Fig.4.65. This relates the correction to be subtracted from the total noise level measured, i.e. in the presence of the background noise, to the difference between the total and background noise levels. Before measurements are made, the background noise alone should therefore be checked and compared with the noise level with the noise source of interest operating. If this difference is greater than 10 dB, then the background noise can be considered to have negligible effect on the measurements of the noise source. If the level difference is found to be less than 3 dB, then the noise from the source is less than the background noise and the corrected level should only be regarded as an approximate measurement. If this is found to be the case, arrangements should be made to repeat the measurements in a quieter environment. If, however, the difference lies between 3 and 10 dB,

124

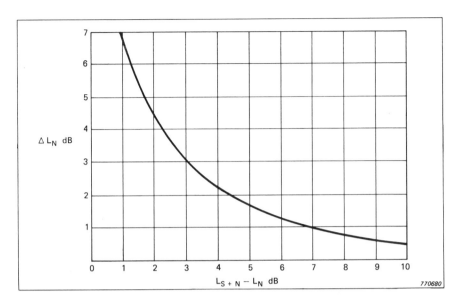

Fig.4.65. Background Noise correction curve

the graph can be used to obtain the correction, and a reasonable estimate for the level of the required sound source alone can be made.

When measurements are in 1/3 octave bands then the levels should preferably be at least 10 dB below the source noise in every band of interest. In really critical conditions however, it may be possible to extract useful information in important bandwidths, even if some of the other bands are dominated by the background noise. This is especially true if the overall noise levels are comparable, but the spectra of the source of interest and the background noise are vastly different.

4.12. THE EFFECT OF REFLECTIONS FROM OBSERVER AND INSTRUMENT

The presence of any object in the sound field has some effect on the sound pressure actually measured at the microphone. Reflections from the object alter the local field, and the type and amount of disturbance is therefore very dependent on the size, shape, proximity, and sound reflecting properties of the object, and on the angle of the incident sound wave. If the sound field is diffuse and is to be measured over a wide band, say as an A-weighted sound level, then these errors are not usually serious and the overall measurement accuracy is usually determined by the accuracy of the instrumentation itself. However, if measurements are to be made close to a source or in narrow

125

bands, it is possible for considerable measurement error to occur. For very precise measurements such as those carried out in anechoic chambers only the bare minimum of equipment, such as the noise source and microphone, should actually be present in the room. The microphone signal should be brought out by cable to the bulk of the apparatus, which should be housed outside the chamber.

For many noise measurements, however, it is more convenient for the observer to carry the sound level meter around with him and to read measurements directly from the indicating meter. Both the reflections from the meter body and those from the observer himself affect the measurement accuracy in this case. The effect of the meter body alone is negligible below 1000 Hz but the presence of the observer, especially if standing directly behind the meter, can cause significant errors in the range 300 to 1000 Hz. This position, i.e. placing the sound level meter between the observer and the field to be measured, can be viewed as a worst case. Improvements in accuracy can be made if the observer stands away from and to one side of the meter or by employing an extension cable so that the microphone can be remotely mounted on a tripod, as in Fig.4.66. This is certainly advisable in critical situations and where direct analyses are being made which employ large items of instrumentation which would otherwise be near the microphone position.

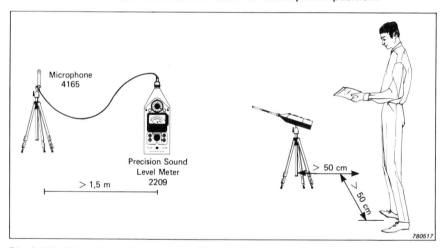

Fig.4.66. Minimising the undesirable effects of reflection when making noise measurements

4.13 MEASUREMENT PROCEDURE

The goal of noise measurement is to make valid, accurate, and thorough measurements which clearly represent the acoustic situation. The aim of this

126

section is to point out the many factors which are pertinent to the measurement of noise, and help show the way to the most effective use of equipment for its measurement and analysis. The following points should be taken into account before venturing out into the field:

1. Why are the measurements being made? Is it just a simple level that is really required? Is a narrow band analysis necessary to reach conclusions about possible noise control methods? Will a sophisticated analysis have to be carried out later in the laboratory in any case?

2. Do the measurements and the instruments have to meet certain standards, such as ISO, ANSI, DIN etc. with regard to instrumentation quality, measuring techniques, layout of measuring site etc.?

3. What type of noise is to be measured? Is it impulsive? Is it statistically varying? Does it contain significant pure tones? Will the frequency be required?

4. With the above three points in mind, choose the most suitable instrumentation to make the noise measurements required and to be able to produce the necessary results. This should take into account the frequency range of the measurements, the possible statistical analysis of those measurements, and whether special instrumentation is required, for example for sonic booms, shocks, or impulsive noise.

5. Having chosen the instrumentation, check and calibrate the entire arrangement.

6. Make a sketch of the instrumentation used and a note of the reference numbers of all the instruments.

7. Sketch the measurement situation, the position of the source, the microphone, and any reflecting or significant surfaces.

8. Note the meteorological conditions, including wind direction and strength, temperature, humidity.

9. Check the background noise level, either overall or in the same bands which will be required in the subsequent analysis.

10. Measure the noise, noting down the relevant equipment settings, such as dB(A), fast etc.

11. Keep a log, including any changes made to equipment settings and any unusual occurrences.

Selected Bibliography

B & K PUBLICATION   *Microphone Calibration for Accurate Sound Measurements*

B & K PUBLICATION   *Condenser Microphones and Microphone Preamplifiers, Theory and Application Handbook*

BROCH, J. T. and   *Recording of Narrow Band Noise.* B & K Techn. Rev.
WAHRMAN, C. G.:   No.4 — 1960.

BROCH, J. T. and   *Averaging Time of Level Recorders.* B & K Techn.
WAHRMAN, C. G.:   Rev. No.1 — 1961.

BROCH, J. T.:   *On the Description and Measurement of Sound Signals.* (English and German). Zeitschrift für Hörgeräte-Akustik. Heft 2 und 3 — 1962.

BROCH, J. T.:   *FM Magnetic Tape Recording.* B & K Techn. Rev. No.1 — 1967.

BROCH, J. T. and   *On the Frequency Analysis of Mechanical Shocks*
OLESEN, H. P.:   *and Single Impulse.* B & K Techn. Rev. No.3 — 1970.

BRÜEL, P. V.:   *Aerodynamically Induced Noise of Microphones and Windscreens.* B & K Techn. Rev. No.2 — 1960.

BRÜEL, P. V. and   *The Condenser Microphone and Some of its Uses in*
PARKER, W. J.:   *Laboratory Investigations.* Journal of the British IRE. Vol.26, No.3. September 1963.

BRÜEL, P. V. and   *Free-Field Response of Condenser Microphones.*
RASMUSSEN, G.:   B & K Techn. Rev. No.1-2 — 1959.

CHRISTENSEN, L. S.:   *A Comparison of I.S.O. and OSHA Noise Dose Measurements.* B & K Techn. Rev. No.4 — 1974.

CHRISTENSEN, L. S.   *Sources of Error in Noise Dose Measurements.* B & K
and HEMINGWAY, J. R.:Techn. Rev. No.3 — 1973.

FREDERIKSEN, E.:   *Long Term Stability of Condenser Microphones.* B & K Techn. Rev. No.2 — 1969.

HEDEGAARD, P.:   *General accuracy of Sound Level Meters.* B & K Techn. Rev. No. 4 - 1977. pp. 3 — 17.

HEDEGAARD, P.:   *Loudness Evaluation of Acoustic Impulses.* B & K Techn. Rev. No.1 — 1972.

HEDEGAARD, P.:   *The Free-Field Response of Sound Level Meters.* B & K Techn. Rev. No.2 — 1976. pp.3 — 24.

I.E.C.:   *Recommendation Publication 123: Recommendations for Sound Level Meters.*

I.E.C.:   *Recommendation Publication 179: Specification for Precision Sound Level Meters.*

I.E.C.:   *Recommendation Publication 225: Specifications for Octave, Half-Octave and Third-Octave Band Filters, Intended for the analysis of sounds and vibrations.*

I.S.O.:   *Recommendation R. 266: Preferred Frequencies for Acoustical Measurements.*

KITTELSEN, K. E. and   *Statistical Analysis of Sound Levels.* B & K Techn.
POULSEN, C.:   Rev. No.1 — 1964.

LIENARD, P.,   *Noise Measurements at High Levels and Calibration*
BENARD, M.,   *Methods.* Applied Acoustics. Vol. 3. No.1. 1970.
LAMBOURION, J. and

OLESEN, H. P. and   *Measurements of the averaging time of level recor-*
ZAVERI, K.:   *ders.* B & K Techn. Rev. No.1 — 1974.

RASMUSSEN, G.:   *A New Condenser Microphone.* B & K Techn. Rev.
                           No.1 — 1959.

RASMUSSEN, G.:   *Pressure Equalization of Condenser Microphones and Performance at Varying Altitudes.* B & K Tech. Rev.
                           No.1 — 1960.

RASMUSSEN, G.:   *Miniature Pressure Microphones.* B & K Techn. Rev.
                           No.1 — 1963.

RASMUSSEN, G.:   *The Free-Field and Pressure Calibration of Condenser Microphones using Electrostatic Actuator.* B & K
                           Techn. Rev. No.2 — 1969.

REINICKE, W.:   *Messung und Bewertung von Schallereignissen.* Der
                           Fernmelde-Ingenieur Heft 1. Jrg. 18. Bad Winsheim/
                           Mittelfranken 1964.

SCHNEIDER, A. J.:   *Microphone Orientation in the Sound Field.* Sound
                           and Vibration. Vol. 4. No.2. Febr. 1970.

SKØDE, F.:   *Windscreening of Outdoor Microphones.* B & K
                           Techn. Rev. No.1 — 1966.

STYHR HANSEN, K.:   *Details in the Construction of a Piezo-electric Micro-*
                           phone. B & K Techn. Rev. No.1 — 1969.

WAHRMANN, C. G.:   *Impulse Noise Measurements.* B & K Techn. Rev.
                           No.1 — 1969.

WAHRMANN, C. G.:   *On the Averaging Time of RMS Measurements.*
                    B & K Techn. Rev. Nos.2 & 3 — 1975.

WARRING, R. H.:   *Handbook of Noise and Vibration Control.* Trade and
                    Technical Press, Ltd. (England) 1970.

WINZER, G. E.:   *National Bureau of Standards Mobile Acoustical La-
                    boratory.* Sound and Vibration. Vol. 4. No.5. May
                    1970.

WOLFF, G.:   *Ausgewählte Fragen der Geräuschmessung.* Kampf
                    dem Lärm. Jg. 15. Heft 6. Dezember 1968. S. 153.

WOHRLE, K.:   *Die Messung von Impulsgeräuschen.* Lärmbekämp-
                    fung. Bd. 13. Heft 5. Oktober 1969.

YOUNG, R. W.:   *Can Accurate Measurements be made with a Sound
                    Level Meter Held in Hand?* Sound. Vol. 1. Jan.-Feb.
                    1962.

5. PRODUCT NOISE MEASUREMENT PRACTICE

INTRODUCTION

The variety of noise and vibration measurements can range from a simple sound level measurement to a detailed statistical or frequency analysis of the signal and may even involve further computation of the measured data to express the results in the desired units. The choice of the method depends of course on what the noise problem is and the ultimate use of the data that are to be obtained. Because there are a great number of different noise sources and various types of noise "environments" to which we are daily exposed, the selection of the appropriate measurement method to help overcome the noise problem should be given some careful consideration. To simplify the situation, however, it may be useful to distinguish between measurements on noise sources individually and measurements in noisy environments where the noise may be contributed by several noise sources simultaneously. There are obviously many cases where a clear distinction is difficult to make which will become evident from later sections. In Chapter 5 noise measurements are described which can generally be classified as measurements on individual noise sources (and audiometry) while Chapter 6 describes environmental and community noise measurements.

5.1. SOUND POWER DETERMINATION

5.1.1. General

Sound pressure level in decibels is a useful parameter to describe sound waves quantitatively. However, for describing the noise emission characteristics of a machine, it is not a satisfactory quantity in itself as it is dependent on the distance between the source and the observer as well as on the environment in which the measurements are made (sound wave reflections). On the other hand, the sound power levels emitted by machines and equipment and determined according to International Standards ISO 3740-3746 are essentially independent of the environment in which the data are obtained. The sound power level data are therefore to be preferred as they can also be used

i) to calculate the approximate sound level at a given distance from a machine operating in a specified environment (see Appendix D)

ii) to compare the noise radiated by machines of the same type and size as well as different types and sizes

iii) to determine whether the machine complies with an upper limit of noise specification

iv) in planning to determine the amount of transmission loss or noise control

v) in engineering work to assist in developing quiet machinery and equipment.

To describe completely the strength of a noise source two quantities are required, the sound power level and the directivity. The sound power level gives the total sound power radiated by the source in all directions and is usually measured in $1/3$ octaves, $1/1$ octaves or as A weighted. Directivity is a measure of the difference in radiation with direction around the source and is also measured for each frequency band. It can thus be seen that for a complete description, considerable data is required for a source with pronounced directivity such as a jet engine. Some noise sources are, however, nondirective i.e. they radiate nearly uniformly in all directions and are generally small in size compared to the wavelength of the sound they radiate.

As described in Chapter 2, section 2.11, the character of the radiation field of a typical noise source varies with distance from the source. In the vicinity of the source, i.e. in the *near field* the particle velocity is not necessarily in the direction of travel of the wave and the acoustic intensity is not simply related to the mean-square sound pressure. Further away from the source, i.e. in the *free field* (see Fig.2.15) the sound pressure reduces by 6 dB per doubling of distance and the particle velocity is primarily in the direction of propagation of the sound wave. Since the sound intensity is related to mean-square sound pressure for free field propagation (see Chapter 2, sec. 2,2) it is possible to determine the sound power in this region.

In the reverberant part of the field the sound pressure varies with position because the reflected waves are superimposed on the direct sound waves. However, when averaged over many positions, the sound pressure is essentially independent of distance from the source. When a great many reflected wave trains cross from all possible directions, the sound-energy *density* is nearly uniform and the field is said to be *diffuse*. Since the sound-energy density is directly related to mean-square sound pressure (Chapter 2, sec. 2,2) and the acoustic power of the source, it is again possible to use such a field for sound power measurements.

132

Fig.5.1.1. Factors influencing the choice of the method

		ISO 3741	ISO 3742	ISO 3743	ISO 3744	ISO 3745	ISO 3746
Size of source	Large sources — not movable				■		■
	Small sources — movable	■	■	■		■	
Character of noise	Steady — broad band	■					
	Steady — narrow band — discrete frequency		■	■	■	■	■
	Non-steady			□	■		
Classification of method	Precision	■	■			■	
	Engineering			■	■		
	Survey						■
Application of data	Noise control work	■	■	■	■	■	
	Type testing	■	■	■	■	■	
	Comparison : Machines different types	■	■	■	■	■	■
	same types						■
Information obtained	Octave band levels	■		■	■		
	1/3 octave band levels		■			■	
	A-weighted levels	□	□	■	■	■	■
	Other weightings			□	□	□	□
	Directivity Information	□			■	□	
	Temporal pattern	□	□		□	□	□
Test environment	Laboratory reverberation rooms	■	■				
	Special reverberation test room			■			
	Large rooms, outdoors				■		
	Laboratory anechoic rooms					■	
	In situ, indoors, outdoors				■		■

■ Information in accordance with International Standards
□ Optional Information

The International Standards Organisation (ISO) has published six standards 3741-3746 outlining different methods of sound power determination. The first three standards deal with measurements in a diffuse field while the last three are for free field environment as can be seen from Fig.5.1.1. To decide which of the standards is the most suitable for a specific application, ISO 3740 standard should be consulted which gives guidelines for the use of the basic standards. The selection of the appropriate standard depends on the size and character of the source, the application of the data, what type of environment is available and what accuracy is desired, see Figs.5.1.2 and 5.1.3. In the development of quieter machines for *noise control* work sound source levels in octave or 1/3 octave bands are usually required. Precision grade accuracy is preferable though engineering accuracy is frequently satisfactory. For *production noise testing* of equipment, overall weighted sound power level is usually sufficient, though the value of the data is increased if the power level distribution in frequency bands is also known. At least engineering grade of accuracy is desired. For *comparison of machines* which are different in type or size, the power spectrum is required for any compar-

133

International Standard No.	Octave bands (Hz)	125	250	500	1 000 to 4 000	8 000	A
	1/3 Octave bands (Hz)	100 to 160	200 to 315	400 to 630	800 to 5 000	6 300 to 10 000	
3741 3742		3	2	1,5		3	–
3743		5	3	2		3	2
3744		3	2	1,5		2,5	2
3745	(Anechoic room)	1	1	0,5		1	–
	(Semi-anechoic room)	1,5	1,5	1		1,5	–
3746		–	–	–	–	–	5

Fig.5.1.2. Uncertainty in determining sound power levels, expressed as the largest value of the standard deviation in dB as given by ISO 3740

International Standard No.	Classification of method	Test environment	Volume of source	Character of noise	Sound power levels obtainable	Optional information available
3741	Precision	Reverberation room meeting specified requirements	Preferably less than 1% of test room volume	Steady, broad-band	In one-third octave or octave bands	A-weighted sound power level
3742				Steady, discrete-frequency or narrow-band		
3743	Engineering	Special test room		Steady, broad-band narrow-band, discrete-frequency	A-weighted and in octave bands	Other weighted sound power levels
3744	Engineering	Outdoors or in large room	No restrictions: limited only by available test environment	Any	A-weighted and in one-third octave or octave bands	Directivity information and sound pressure levels as a function of time, other weighted sound power levels
3745	Precision	Anechoic or semi-anechoic room	Preferably less than 0,5% of test room volume	Any		
3746	Survey	No special test environment	No restrictions: limited only by available test environment	Steady, broad-band, narrow-band, discrete-frequency	A-weighted	Sound pressure levels as a function of time other weighted sound power levels

Fig.5.1.3. Various methods for determining sound power levels

ison to be meaningful, and engineering grade of accuracy is sufficient. However, the overall weighted level is sufficient if machines built to the same specifications are to be compared.

134

5.1.2. Measurement Procedures

FREE-FIELD ENVIRONMENT

Precision Method

The most accurate values of sound power levels of equipment can be determined in a free field environment achieved in anechoic chambers* or in the
open air. However, some sound sources are too heavy to be suspended or
are associated with a reflecting plane, in which case measurements are carried out in what is termed a semi-anechoic chamber where the equipment is
placed on a hard reflecting surface with absorption coefficient less than
0,06. In this case the spatial irregularity of the sound field may be increased
by the superposition of the sound field of the actual source and that of the image source, leading to a slightly lower accuracy of the measurement results.
It is important that the mounting base is prevented from vibrating and radiating an excessive amount of noise by the use of resilient layers.

The sound power in a free field can be found conceptually by adding the
products of the areas times the acoustic intensities for the areas on any hy-
phothetical surface that contains the source. Since equipment for measurement of acoustic intensity is generally not available, sound power inevitably
has to be determined indirectly by taking the spatial average of the sound
pressure squared measured on equal areas on the enclosing surface. ISO
3745 suggests three different methods of microphone positioning on equal
areas on the surface of a hemisphere centred at the acoustic centre of the
source. (In practice the geometrical centre of the source is used). The radius
of the hemisphere should be at least twice the major source dimension or
four times the average distance of the source from the reflecting plane,
whichever is the larger, and in any case not less than 1 meter.

1) The first method involves moving a single microphone from positions 1 to
   10 shown in Fig.5.1.4 or using an array of fixed microphones and sampling their outputs sequentially.

2) In the second method a single microphone is scanned at constant speed
   along horizontal circular paths successively. A minimum of five circular
   paths should be used as shown in Fig.5.1.5 where the annular area of
   the hemisphere associated with each path is equal. Alternatively, the microphone could be placed at the given respective heights successively
   while the sound source is rotated at constant speed using a turntable.

---

* See Technical Review No.2-1968

135

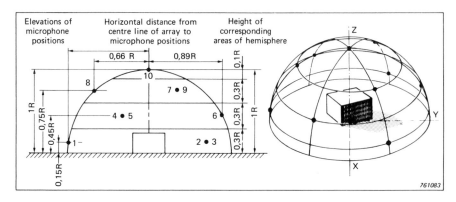

Fig.5.1.4. Microphone positions on equal areas on the surface of a hemisphere

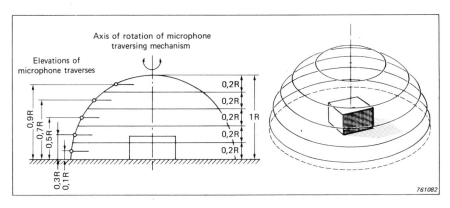

Fig.5.1.5. Coaxial circular paths for microphone traverses

3) The third method requires scanning a single microphone along a meridional arc, i.e. the microphone is traversed along a quarter of a circular arc about a horizontal axis through the centre of the source. At least eight microphone traverses at equal azimuthal angles around the source should be carried out, and may be achieved by rotating the source through 45° before each traverse.

From the sound pressure level measurements on a hemisphere over a reflecting plane, the sound power level L_w of the source can be calculated for each frequency band from the equation

$$L_w = L_p + 10\ log_{10}\left(\frac{2\pi r^2}{S_0}\right) + C$$

where

L_p = the mean surface sound pressure level over the test hemisphere in dB. Ref. 20μPa

r = radius of the hemisphere

S_0 = reference area 1m^2

C = correction term in decibels when the atmospheric temperature and pressure differ significantly from 20°C and 1000 mbar (10^{5}Pa) respectively.

When the mean surface sound pressure level has been determined it is possible also to determine the *directivity index* DI, which is of considerable interest in practice for directional sources, Fig.5.1.6. For measurements over a hemisphere the directivity index in decibels in the ith direction can be calculated from

$$DI = L_{pi} - L_p + 3$$

where L_{pi} is the sound pressure level in the ith direction at a distance r from the source.

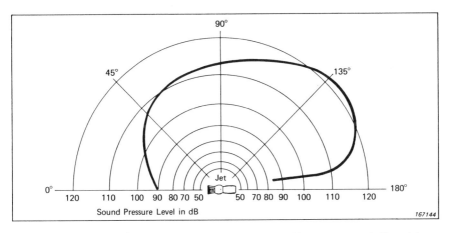

Fig.5.1.6. Radiation pattern of a noise source with pronounced directivity

137

In a measurement report it may be sufficient to include only the highest value of DI and the direction in which it occurs.

To determine the sound pressure level in 1/3 octave or 1/1 octave bands the simplest instrument that can be used is a sound level meter (with a filter set and extension cable) set on slow response. The average value of the meter deflection will approximate the mean squared sound pressure level if the fluctuations are less than 5 dB. When the fluctuations are greater, an L_{eq} meter, such as the Precision Intergrating Sound Level Meter Type 2218 should be used. By measuring the L_{eq} for equal time at each of the microphone positions or microphone traverses, the mean surface sound pressure level is directly obtained.

Fig.5.1.7 shows an instrumentation set-up for carrying out the measurements automatically. When multiple microphones are used, a multiplexer can be conveniently utilized to convey the signals to the Sound Power Processor Type 7507. In the 7507 the signals from each microphone in turn are frequency analyzed in parallel in 1/3 or 1/1 octave bands. The rms values of the filter outputs are sampled, converted to digital values, squared, and the results accumulated before switching to the next microphone. Hereby a true average of the surface sound pressure level is obtained. The numerical value of the constant $10 \log(2\pi r^2/S_0) + C$ is fed manually into the 7507 after which it calculates the sound power levels in each of the 1/3 or 1/1 octave bands or as A weighted. The results can be displayed digitally or can be fed to a level recorder or an Alphanumeric Printer Type 2312.

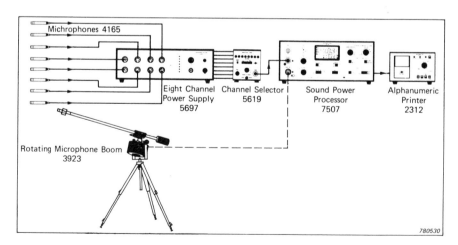

Fig.5.1.7. Arrangement for automatic measurements of sound power levels using an array of microphones or a rotating boom

138

The above methods involve use of multiple microphones or multiple microphone traverses. A method* which requires a single microphone traverse has been developed at Brüel & Kjær. It is similar to method 3, except that the microphone traverse is modified such that it moves with a constant vertical speed (instead of constant angular speed) and is therefore associated with equal areas per unit of time. The swing arm is attached to a string which via a pulley is lead to the roof of the anechoic chamber and then around a wheel attached to the mechanical drive of a Level Recorder, see Fig.5.1.8. Instead of carrying out eight scans as required by method 3, the test object is placed on a turntable and rotated while traversing the microphone. Thus the microphone effectively moves in a spiral path relative to the sound source.

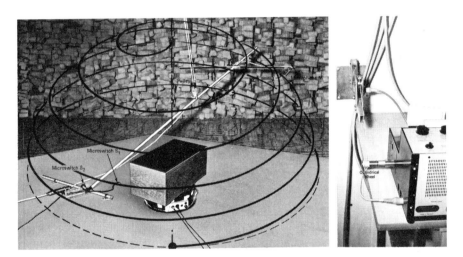

Fig.5.1.8. Set-up for scanning a microphone in a spiral path

The microphone traverse should be slow enough, so that the test object may be rotated at least five times during one traverse of the microphone. Fig.5.1.9 shows a laboratory set of instrumentation in which the Level Recorder Type 2307 plots the variation of sound pressure level whilst its motor drive scans the microphone. The microswitches activated by the scan arm start and stop the integration process of the Noise Level Analyzer Type 4426 which determines the mean surface sound pressure level. The Precision Integrating Sound Level Meter Type 2218 may also be used instead. For greater flexibility the output of the microphone can be fed to a Digital Frequency Analyzer Type 2131 where the frequency analysis is carried out in real time and the mean surface sound pressure level displayed on its screen in 1/3 or 1/1

---

* For detailed information of this method see Technical Review No.4-1976.

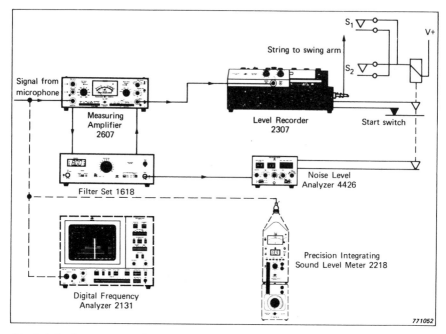

Fig.5.1.9. Instrumentation for determining the mean sound pressure level using a scanning microphone

octaves. A desk-top calculator may be connected to compute the values of sound power level or for getting a print out if several specimens have to be tested. (A program has been written for on-line determination of sound power for HP 9825A calculator.)

Engineering Method

Anechoic chambers are costly constructions and are not always available to the practicing engineer. However, sound power levels can be determined with engineering accuracy according to ISO 3744 in a flat outdoor area, or in a laboratory room which provides a free field over a reflecting plane. Also measurements on large machines (up to 15 m largest dimension) installed in factories and offices can be carried out in situ, where the contributions of the reverberant field to the sound pressures on the measurement surface are small compared with those of the direct field of the source. Satisfactory conditions can be obtained in large rooms as well as in smaller rooms with sufficient sound-absorptive material in their walls and ceilings.

On account of the various shapes and sizes of the test objects, the meas-

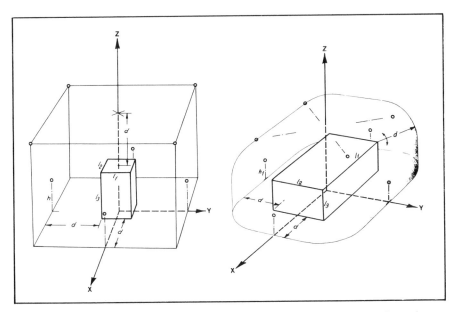

Fig.5.1.10. Microphone positions on a parallelepiped and a conformal surface

urement surface may be either a hemisphere, a rectangular parallelepiped, or a conformal surface which is the same as a rectangular parallelepiped except that the corners are round and formed by portions of cylinders and spheres, Fig.5.1.10. When environmental conditions permit, use of the hemispherical surface is usually preferred. The conformal surface in general is expected to give more accurate values of sound power level than the rectangular parallelepiped, but on the other hand more effort is required to position the microphones. However, for qualification of the measurement surface to be satisfactory, the environmental influences of the test room have to be evaluated. This is carried out by determining the ratio of the room absorption A to the *measurement* surface area S. The measurement surface is satisfactory if this ratio is equal to or greater than 6. The higher the value of this ratio the better is the environment. The total absorption of the room can be determined in each octave band from Sabine's equation

$$A = 0{,}16(V/T)$$

where   V   is the volume of the room
and   T   is the reverberation time in seconds.

If the above requirement is not fulfilled, a measurement surface with a smaller area should be chosen, but still be outside the near field of the source. Alternatively, the absorption in the room may be increased by using

141

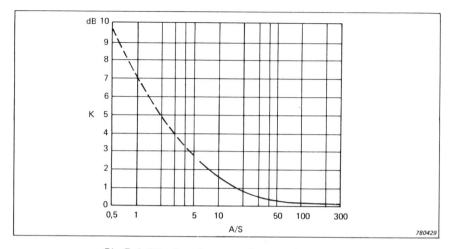

Fig.5.1.11. Envrionmental correction K in dB

additional sound absorptive material in the room and redetermining the ratio A/S. From evaluation of the environmental influence given by A/S, the magnitude of the *environmental correction* K in dB can be determined from the curve given in Fig.5.1.11. This environmental correction K must be subtracted from the mean surface sound pressure level. Thus the sound power level L_w can be calculated from

$$L_w = L_p - K + 10\ log_{10}\ \frac{S}{S_0}$$

where L_p is the mean surface sound pressure level
S is the measurement surface area
S_0 $= 1m^2$.

The directivity index can be determined in the same manner as described for the precision method.

The background sound pressure levels should ideally be at least 10 dB below the noise level of the specimen. For differences between 6 and 10 dB corrections given in ISO 3744 should be applied. (When the 7507 is used these corrections can be carried out automatically by measuring the background noise spectrum).

When the requirement A/S ⩾6 cannot be satisfied for any measurement surface which lies outside the near field of the source, a new test environment must be selected as the measurement uncertainties specified in this

142

standard would be exceeded. If this is not practicable, only "Survey method" of measurement described in ISO 3746 can be used.

Survey Method

For measurements according to this method no special environment is required, though the ratio of A/S must be greater than 1. The noise source may be of any size as long as the volume of the test room is large enough to permit the microphones to be located on either a hemispherical, or a rectangular parallelepiped measurement surface given in ISO 3746. The background A weighted noise level should be at least 3 dB below the A weighted sound level of the source. Only A weighted sound power levels may be obtained by this method. The measurement principles are basically similar to those of the engineering method described above.

DIFFUSE FIELD ENVIRONMENT

Precision Method

As mentioned in section 5.1.1 a diffuse field is another type of well-defined environment suitable for sound power determination. Such a field can be obtained approximately in a large highly reverberant enclosure which is relatively cheaper to construct than an anechoic chamber. Diffuseness of the field governs the accuracy of this method and is not always easy to achieve to a high degree especially at low frequencies and when the source radiates pure tones. The accuracies given in Fig.5.1.2 can, however, be obtained if the guidelines given in ISO 3741 are followed and the requirements for the test room qualification are fulfilled.

The minimum volume of the room depends on the lowest frequency of interest. For 125 Hz octave band (or 100 Hz 1/3 octave band) a volume of 200 m^3 is required for general purpose measurements. The volume should not be much larger as air absorption may cause an undesirable reduction in the uniformity of the reverberant field in the highest frequency bands. In order to avoid very close spacings between the frequencies of the normal modes of the room, the ratio of any two dimensions must not equal or closely approximate an integer if the room is rectangular. The ratios $1 : 2^{1/3} : 4^{1/3}$ are frequently used. If the room is not rectangular, no surfaces of the room should be parallel. Large rotating or oscillating vanes are sometimes used to increase the uniformity of the sound field in a room.

The equivalent absorption area of the test room affects the minimum distance to be maintained between the sound source and the microphone positions and also influences the sound radiation of the source. The absorption area should therefore be neither too large nor too small. To ensure an adequate reverberant field the average sound absorption coefficient of all the surfaces should not exceed 0,06. At frequencies below $2000/V^{1/3}$, where V is the volume of the room in m^3, additional absorption is desirable in order to increase the bandwidth of the resonance curves of the normal modes of the room. Yet the highest value of the average sound absorption should not exceed 0,16. The reverberation time in seconds should be greater than V/S where S is the total surface area of the test room in m^2. (If the above criteria are not fulfilled, the test room qualification procedure described in ISO 3741 should be followed).

When the sound source is mounted near one or more reflective planes, the radiation impedance may differ appreciably from that of free space and the sound power radiated by the source may depend upon its position and orientation. When carrying out the measurements it is good practice to mount the source near a corner of the room in a position that is typical of normal usage and at least 1,5 m away from any wall.

If a microphone is scanned it should be traversed at constant speed over a path of at least 3 m in length if the source emits broadband noise. The path may be a circle, a line, an arc or some other geometric figure. Alternatively an array of at least three fixed microphones or microphone positions spaced at least a distance $\lambda/2$ from each other (where λ is the wavelength of the lowest frequency of interest) may be used. The microphone traverse or array should not lie in any plane within $10°$ of a room surface and no point on the traverse or array should be closer than $\lambda/2$ to any wall. Although discrete averaging with the use of a fixed number of microphones is the more expensive method, it should be preferred as it will yield more accurate results. This is because the individual microphones can be spread as far apart as the room permits and a greater number of statistically-independent samples are obtained than when a single traversing microphone is used.

In a diffuse field the steady state sound energy in the room is equal to the difference between the sound energy transmitted by the source and that absorbed by the room boundaries. From here it can be shown that the sound power level L_w emitted by the source is given by

$$L_w = L_p - 10\,log_{10}\,\frac{T}{T_0} + 10\,log_{10}\,\frac{V}{V_0}$$

$$+\ 10\,log_{10}\left(1 + \frac{S\lambda}{8V}\right)^* + 10\,log_{10}\left(\frac{B}{1000}\right) - 14\,dB$$

* In a diffuse field where equal mean energy flows in all directions at all points, the sound energy is distributed into interference patterns at the reflecting boundaries. Thus the mean energy density is not uniform at all points in the field and the sound energy is concentrated near the walls of the room. To compensate for this, the term $10Log_{10}(1+S\lambda/8V)$ has been included in the above equation.

where L_p is the mean band pressure level (corrected for background noise level according to ISO 3741 if necessary).
 T   is the reverberation time in seconds, $T_0 = 1s$
 V   is the volume of the room in m^3, $V_0 = 1m^3$
 S   is the total surface area of the room in m^2
 λ is the wavelength at the centre frequency of the frequency band in meters
 B   is the barometric pressure in millibars.

When measuring the mean band pressure level, the integration should be carried out over at least 30s for requency bands centred on or below 160 Hz and over at least 10s on or above 200 Hz. There should also be a whole number of microphone traverses or array scans during the integration time. (The instrumentation required is the same as that for free field environment, except that a pressure microphone should be substituted for the free field one. When using the 7507, the constants describing the environment can be fed in manually for the respective frequency bands).

For obvious reasons, the directivity information of the sound source cannot be obtained in a diffuse field. When the sound source emits pure tones or narrow bands of noise the spatial variations in the sound pressure level exhibit maxima and minima, and generally greater effort is required in determining its mean value. Also the sound power radiated is more strongly influenced by the normal modes of the room and by the position of the source in the room. For such cases a greater number of source locations and microphone positions (or a greater path length for a moving microphone) is required, for which ISO 3742 should be consulted.

Engineering Method

When high precision is not necessary and the cost and labour involved in carrying out the measurements should be kept to a minimum, the method described in ISO 3743 should be followed. This method is applicable to small machines which can be installed in a special test room with prescribed acoustical characteristics. For the minimum test room volume of $70 m^3$ the maximum size of the source should be $0.7 m^3$.

In practice it may be necessary to adopt a room with hard surfaces (for example concrete walls) as a test room. The reverberation time of such a room is usually high at low and middle frequencies but approximates the prescribed value at the higher frequencies. It can, however, be reduced at low frequencies by the use of membrane absorbers (e.g. a wooden frame covered with hardboard and filled with mineral wool) while at middle and high frequencies perforated panels with mineral wool interiors will often be suitable. For the room qualification procedure the reverberation time of the room is de-

145

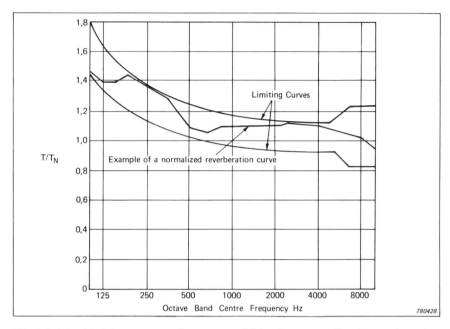

Fig.5.1.12. *Limiting curves between which the normalized reverberation time curve should fall*

termined in 1/3 octave bands and normalized with respect to the reverberation time at 1000 Hz. The normalized reverberation times are plotted against the 1/3 octave centre frequencies, and the curve thus obtained is centred within the limiting curves given in Fig.5.1.12. (The limiting curves shown in the figure are a function of the volume of the room and is here plotted for $70 \, m^3$). If the normalized curve cannot be centred within the limiting curves the reverberation times should be adjusted.

To determine the number of microphone and source positions as well as the calculation procedure for sound power by this method, ISO 3743 should be consulted. The measurement method however, is very similar to the precision method described earlier.

COMPARISON METHOD

The methods for diffuse field measurements described above are absolute methods. The comparison method which requires the use of a reference

146

sound source of known sound power output (fulfilling the requirements of ISO 3748*), has the advantage that the reverberation time of the room need not be measured. In this method the mean band pressure levels of the test specimen are measured (as described in the previous sections); the test specimen is then substituted by the reference sound source and the procedure repeated for the same microphone positions. The sound power level L_w of the test specimen can then be determined from the equation.

$$L_w = L_p + (L_{wr} - L_{pr})$$

where L_p is the mean band pressure level of the test specimen
          L_{pr} is the mean band pressure level of the reference source
          L_{wr} is the nameplate sound power level of the reference source.

(The use of Reference Sound Source is also recommended in ISO 3744, and 3746 as an alternative method for determining the environmental correction in the "qualification procedures for the acoustic environment".)

Fig.5.1.13. Reference and Electroacoustic calibrated sound sources

Fig.5.1.13 shows Reference Sound Source Type 4204 operating on an aerodynamic principle, and Type 4205 which is a calibrated electroacoustic sound source. Type 4204 has a fixed broadband sound power output and is calibrated in 1/3 and 1/1 octaves. The 4205 consists of two units, a generator and a loudspeaker unit HP 1001. The output from the generator may be wide band pink noise or it may be octave filtered noise using the seven built-in band pass filters. The output can be varied continuously and the sound power level emitted can be read off the meter scale. This feature is especially

---

* At present at the stage of draft.

useful when the machine under investigation may not be switched off as will be shown in the following. Because the sound source can be switched off instantly it can also be used for reverberation time measurements in connection with a sound level meter and a level recorder.

To illustrate the method the sound power level emitted by a tractor was measured according to ISO 3744 in open air over a reflecting plane. The tractor was then driven into a large hall, Fig.5.14 and measurements were carried out with the 4205 using the substitution and the juxtaposition methods. In the substitution method, the sound pressure levels with the tractor operating alone were measured at the microphone positions marked 'x'. The tractor was then replaced by the loudspeaker unit HP 1001 and the power emitted was adjusted until the same sound pressure levels were obtained at the same microphone positions. In the juxtaposition method, the loudspeaker unit was placed beside the tractor and both of them were operated simultaneously. The power emitted by the 4205 was adjusted until a 3 dB higher sound pressure level was measured than when the tractor was operating alone. In both the methods the power emitted by the tractor would be equal to that emitted by the 4205 and could be read off the meter scale. The results obtained for 1/1 octave analysis are shown in Fig.5.1.14 and can be seen to be in good agreement with those measured according to ISO 3744 in open air. To increase accuracy, the number of measurement positions should be increased. Because measurements are taken in the reverberant field of the room a reasonable distance away from the sources, the differences in the

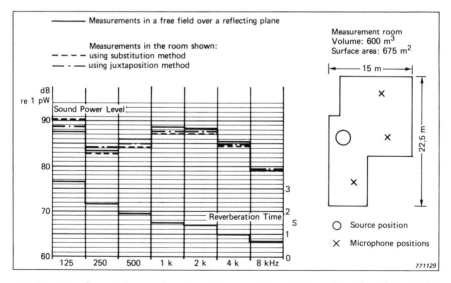

Fig.5.1.14. Sound Power Levels of the tractor and reverberation time of the large hall in 1/1 octave bands

directivity characteristics of the two sources have a minimum of influence on the results.

In Fig.5.1.15, the results of wide band analysis in terms of the A-weighted sound power levels are given. A difference of 1,5 dB is found between the free-field method and the substitution and juxtaposition methods. Ideally, either the spectra of the two sources should be similar or the reverberation time of the room should be uniform over the frequency range. If neither one of these conditions is reasonably fulfilled, the A-weighted values can be calculated from the octave band levels and A-weighted correction factors given in ISO 3741 Annex C. The results obtained by this method are also shown in Fig.5.1.15 and agree fairly well with the measured values, as the spectra of the 4205 and the tractor were very similar.

A Weighted Measurements of Sound Power Level		
Measurement Method	Measured Results	Results calculated from octave measurements
DIS 3744	94,0 dBA	—
Substitution	92,5 dBA	92,5 dBA
Juxtaposition	92,4 dBA	93,0 dBA

Table 1   780150

Fig.5.1.15. A weighted measured results

Selected Bibliography

ANGEVINE, O.L.:   *Improving the acoustic environment for in situ noise measurements,* J.A.S.A. Vol.61. No.2. Feb.1977

ANSI S1.21—1972:   *Methods for the Determination of Sound Power Levels of Small Sources in Reverberation Rooms*

ASHRAE 36-72:   *Methods of Testing for Sound Rating Heating, Refrigerating and Air-Conditioning Equipment*

ASHRAE 68-75:   *Method of testing sound power radiated into ducts from air moving devices*

BAADE, P.K.:   *Effects of Acoustic Loading on Axial Flow Fan Noise Operation,* Noise Control Engineering Vol.8. No.1. Jan/Feb. 1977

BIES, D.A.:   *Uses of Anechoic and Reverberant Rooms for the Investigation of Noise Sources.* Noise Control Engineering. Nov.-Dec.1976. pp.154-163

BODLUND, K.:   *A study of Diffusion in Reverberation Chambers provided with special devices.* Journal of Sound and Vibration (1977) 50(2), pp.253-283

149

DIEHL, G.M.   *Sound-Power measurements on large machinery installed indoors; Two-surface method. J.A.S.A. Vol.61. No.2. Feb.1977*

DIN 45635   *Geräuschmessung an Maschinen*

EBBING, C.E. &   *Reverberation-Room qualification for determination*
MALING, Jr. G.C.:   *of sound power of sources of discrete-frequency of sound J.A.S.A. Vol.54. No.4. 1973. pp.935-949*

EBBING, C.:   *Experimental Evaluation of Moving Sound Diffusers for Reverberation Rooms. J.A.S.A. Vol.45. pp.343(A), 1969*

FAHY, F.J.:   *Measurements with an Intensity Meter of the Acoustic Power of a Small Machine in a Room.* Journal of Sound and Vibration 1978 57(3). pp.311-322

FRANCOIS, P.:   *Characteristics and Calibration of Reference Sound Sources.* Noise Control Engineering. Vol.9. No.1. July/Aug.1977

HOLMER, C.I.:   *Investigation of procedures for estimation of sound power in the free field above a reflecting plane. J.A.S.A. Vol.61. No.2. Feb.1977*

HÜBNER, G.:   *Analysis of errors in measuring machine noise under free-field conditions. J.A.S.A. Vol.54. No.4. 1973. pp.967-977*

HÜBNER, G.:   *Qualification procedures for free-field conditions for sound power determination of sound sources and methods for the determination of the appropriate environmental correction. J.A.S.A. Vol.61. No.2. Feb.1977*

ISO 3740-3746:   *Acoustics-Determination of sound power levels of noise sources*

KODARAS, M.J. &   *Sound-power testing experiences of an independent*
BLANCK, M.W.:   *laboratory J.A.S.A. Vol.54. No.4. 1973. pp.956-959*

LANG, W.W.:   *Noise Measurement standards for machines in situ. J.A.S.A. Vol.54. No.4. 1973*

LARSEN, H.:   *An Easy and Accurate Method of Sound Power Measurements.* B & K Technical Review No.4—1976

LAWLER, E.D.:   *Rotating Diffusers for Reverberation Rooms. S/V* Sound and Vibration Vol.2. No.9. pp.16-20, 1968

LUBMAN, D.:   *Fluctuations of Sound with Position in a Reverberation Room. J.A.S.A. Vol.44. pp.1491-1502. 1968*

150

LUBMAN, D.:   *Spatial Averaging in Sound Power Measurements,* Journal of Sound and Vibration 1971. 16(1), pp.43-58

LUBMAN, D.,   *Effectiveness of continuous spatial averaging in a dif-* WATERHOUSE, R.V. & *fuse sound field.* J.A.S.A. Vol.53. No.2. 1973 CHI-SHING CHEN:

LYON, R.H.:   *Statistical Analysis of Power Injection and Response in Structures and Rooms,* J.A.S.A. Vol.45. 1969 pp.545-565

MALING, Jr. G.C.:   *Calculations of the Acoustic Power Radiated by a Monopole in a Reverberation Chamber,* J.A.S.A. Vol.42 1967. pp.859-865

MALING, Jr. G.C.:   *Guidelines for determination of the average sound power radiated by discrete-frequency sources in a reverberation room.* J.A.S.A. Vol.53. No.4. 1973

MARRACCINI L.C. &   *Predicting Sound Levels from Sound Power Data.* GIARDINO, D.A.:   S/V Sound and Vibration Nov.1974. pp.28-30

MOIR J. &   *Simple Sound Power Measurements.* Applied Acous- STEVENS, W.R.:   tics Vol.7, No.1. Jan.1974

MORELAND, J.B.:   *Measurement of sound absorption in rooms.* J.A.S.A. Vol.61. No.2. Feb. 1977

NOISE CONTROL   *Special Issue. Noise Measurement facilities and ANS* ENGINEERING: *S1.21-1972 qualification.* September-October 1976

PEDERSEN, O.J.:   *Simple Measurements of Sound Level of Noise Sources.* Proceedings of 9th International Congress on Acoustics, Madrid 1977

SCHULTZ, T.J.:   *Outlook for in-situ measurement of noise from machines.* J.A.S.A. Vol.54. No.4. 1973

SCHULTZ, T.J.:   *Persisting questions in steady-state measurements of noise power and sound absorption.* J.A.S.A. Vol.54. No.4. 1973 pp.978-981

TICHY, J.:   *The Effect of Rotating Wanes on the Sound Field in Reverberation Chambers at single frequencies.* J.A.S.A. 49, 89(A) 1971

WATERHOUSE, R.V.: *Interference Patterns in Reverberant Sound Fields.* J.A.S.A. Vol.27. No.2. March 1955

WATERHOUSE, R.V.: *Statistical Properties of reverberant sound fields.* J.A.S.A. Vol.43. 1968. p.1436

WATERHOUSE, R.V.: *Noise measurement in reverberant rooms.* J.A.S.A. Vol.54. No.4. 1973. pp.931-934

WATERHOUSE, R.V. & *Discrete versus Continuous Space Averaging in a Re-*
LUBMAN, D.: *verberant Sound Field.* J.A.S.A. Vol.48 pt.1. pp.1-5.
1970

ZAVERI, K. & *Comparison of Aerodynamic and Electroacoustic Cali-*
LARSEN,H.: *brated Sound Sources.* Noise Control and Vibration Isolation. Jan. 1978 pp.17-21

*Instruction Manual for Sound Power Source Type
4205.* B & K Publication

5.2. NOISE CONTROL IN WORKSHOPS, FACTORIES AND OFFICES

Noise is often a problem in the working environment, whether from production machinery in the factory or business machines in the office. Although
the level of noise, its characteristics, and the criteria used to assess it, differ
from one environment to another, the basic reasons for controlling the noise,
and the methods of doing so, are generally similar.

Noise may

(1) Damage hearing if consistently of a high level or of an impulsive nature.

(2) Impair Safety by making warnings difficult to hear.

(3) Hinder Communication between employees who work as a team and
where efforts are interactive, such as cargo handlers and foundry workers, or who carry out much of their work by telephone or direct discussion.

(4) Interfere with efficiency, either as a direct result of communication loss,
as above, or by causing fatigue and loss of concentration.

(5) Be annoying.

Whatever initially stimulates concern about a possible noise problem, the
first action should be to ascertain if a real problem exists, and especially
whether or not it is of a magnitude which could lead to hearing damage. The
only way to be sure of this is to measure it, and therefore have at hand objective information on which to base any subsequent decisions. The measured

152

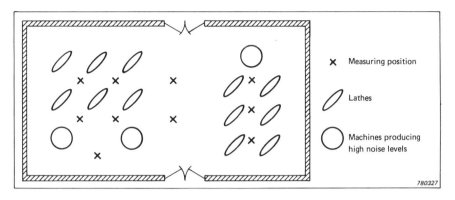

x	Measuring position
Lathes	
Machines producing high noise levels	

Fig.5.2.1. Distribution of measuring positions to determine noise levels in a factory

levels can then be compared with acceptable levels based on criteria given in Chapter 3.

In work-spaces with fairly uniform noise levels, the first step should be to determine the average level by making a number of A-weighted measurements with a portable sound level meter at points evenly distributed around

Fig.5.2.2. On-site noise measurement in a machine-shop

153

the room, as in Fig.5.2.1. If the result of these first simple measurements indicates a noise climate which is other than clearly acceptable, a further set of measurements should be made to investigate the noise spectrum in more detail, say in terms of octave bands. This can be done on the spot as shown in Fig.5.2.2 using an instrument like the Type 2215 Precision Sound Level Meter and Octave Analyzer, together with the Type 2306 Portable Level Recorder to provide a permanent record of the measurement results. This type of approach is suitable in most large reverberant workshops or rooms where a number of similarly noisy machines are installed. The room surfaces of workshops are often acoustically hard, with very little other absorption, and consequently problems arise from echoes and reflections as well as from the increased noise level caused by long reverberation times. A useful reduction of the overall level may be achieved in such circumstances by the introduction of large areas of absorbing material either applied to walls and ceilings or as free-standing or hanging panels. This is especially effective when absorbent surfaces are provided behind machines placed in corners so that much of the sound energy normally reflected back into the room is lost at those surfaces. Judiciously positioned these can also be made to eliminate the annoying reflections and flutter echoes caused by parallel surfaces.

If the original survey revealed that particular machines were the dominant noise sources in the room, these should be more intensively studied with a view to reducing their acoustic output at source. This may be simply accomplished by replacing the machine with a quieter type or by modifying it to radiate less sound, e.g. by fitting a quieter fan to air-moving equipment, a common source of noise especially in office buildings. Reduction of noise to an acceptable level may, however, demand careful redesign and alteration of the mechanical process and/or operating procedures.

Because of the growing awareness of the damage to hearing from impact noise, processes and machinery which generate this, such as bottling plant and punch-presses, have been the subject of extensive recent research noted in the bibliography at the end of this section. Air-moving and distribution equipment, because of its wide use in office buildings, is also an important area of interest for noise reduction engineers.

Vibration of machinery should be kept to a minimum as this is radiated into the room as noise, either directly from the machine by panels, worn bearings and moving parts, or via the supports and building's structure as structure-borne noise. Once established in the structure, it may travel to, and cause annoyance in the most distant rooms of a building, suffering only minimal attenuation during transmission. The importance of well-maintained, rigid, balanced, damped, and effectively isolated machinery cannot be overemphasized when discussing the reduction of radiated noise. A full discussion of vibration isolation and damping techniques is, however, outside the scope of this book, but much useful knowledge can be gained relatively simply from a vibration

154

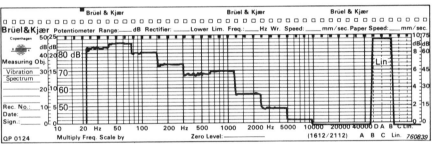

Fig.5.2.3. Measurement of vibration
a) accelerometer   b) octave spectrum

spectrum of the offending machine, its individual parts, and the local building structure. This can be obtained using an instrument such as the meter Type 2215 used in the preceding survey for octave band analysis of the noise with an accelerometer in place of the more usual microphone. Fig.5.2.3. shows a mounted accelerometer, together with an octave spectrum obtained from the machine.

When all possibilities for reducing source noise emission have been exhausted, modification of the transmission path between source and receiver may be the only feasible approach. Machines which have marked directivity patterns can be orientated so that operators are positioned in the quieter regions, and the high noise levels directed away from them into highly absorbent acoustic screens or partial enclosures. This is particularly effective when the noise is predominantly composed of high frequencies or can be easily reflected in a particular direction.

155

It may be possible to insulate the operator by controlling the machine remotely from an attenuating booth. Insulation treatments such as Acoustic screens and partial or complete enclosures may be preferable in certain circumstances. For example, temporary screens or partial enclosures can be erected around mobile compressors and generators and dismantled just as quickly when the job is finished. Permanent plant such as air movers, power plant, pumps and the like, which only require access for short periods and at infrequent intervals for inspection and maintenance may be totally enclosed. It must be remembered though, that much industrial plant needs air for operation or cooling which must be drawn in and exhausted through attenuated ducts.

The effectiveness of various commonly used attenuating structures is shown in Fig.5.2.4. It should be especially noted that the attenuation provided by light-weight structures and screens is particularly poor at low frequencies because of the effect of the mass law and diffraction respectively. A heavy enclosure with a lining of sound absorbing material is the best means of providing airborne sound insulation if high attenuation is required. A significant improvement in low-frequency attenuation can usually be obtained by isolating the source from the structure by means of anti-vibration mounts, thus reducing the amount of noise which is radiated back into the room by the "sounding-board" effect of the vibrating floor and walls. This is of major importance when methods are being contemplated to reduce the noise transmitted from one room to another in the same building, especially to one directly below. The airborne sound insulation of a structural floor is usually adequate for most purposes, but vibration transmitted into the floor from a machine can easily give rise to very high sound levels in the room below. This is because buildings of conventional construction have very low structural damping, which allows vibration generated at one place to be transmitted throughout the building with very low attenuation. Incidently, it is for this reason that many new city-centre buildings which have been constructed near or over railways, have been mounted on resilient supports to isolate them as far as is practicable from these extensive sources of structure-borne noise. The effectiveness of employing a combination of vibration isolators and a well-sealed heavy enclosure is well demonstrated in Fig.5.2.4.e. Further attenuation can be obtained in extreme circumstances, such as might arise with the continuous operation of noisy plant in residential areas or with concert halls and studios, by the use of multiple enclosures, sealed doors, and airlocks.

156

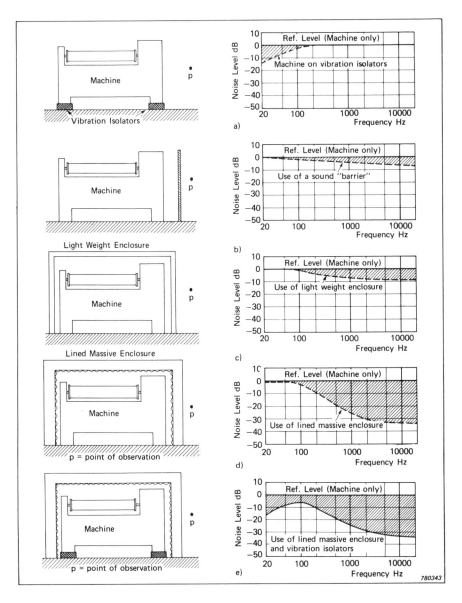

Fig.5.2.4. Various methods of noise attenuation
a) vibration isolators
b) sound barrier
c) lightweight enclosure
d) massive enclosure with absorbent lining
e) employing both a) and d)

157

Heavy duty compressors are a notorious source of high noise levels in factories, where they supply compressed air to a central system, in offices and shops where they form part of the airconditioning and refrigerating plant, and on construction sites where they provide the power for pneumatic tools. They are considered such a problem that a recent I.S.O. standard is dedicated to the method of measuring the noise output of compressors destined for outdoor use. The noise and vibration produced by a large reciprocating compressor, driven by an electric motor, and used for supplying compressed air throughout a factory complex, was investigated to demonstrate the approach to the problem. Measurements were made using a Precision Sound Level Meter and Octave Analyzer Type 2215 connected directly to a Portable Level Recorder Type 2306, to obtain immediate permanent documentation of the spectrum. A tape recording was also made so that a further analysis in third octaves, or perhaps even narrower bands, could be carried out in the laboratory at a later date if it was found that a closer definition of peaks in the spectrum was necessary.

Vibration was measured at several positions on the machine, and on the floor of the compressor room. This information often proves invaluable if some form of remedial treatment has to be designed to reduce the noise level in adjacent work areas. Where large machines are concerned, much of the received noise is the manifestation of vibration from the machine. Better mountings and balancing may alleviate this type of problem, whereas reduction of the actual sound output of the machine generally will not.

Three of the spectra obtained from these measurements are reproduced in Fig.5.2.5. The first is the usual unweighted octave spectrum of the noise in the room from which the noise rating value can be determined if required. The second is the A-weighted octave band spectrum, which can be measured directly using the special switch position on the 2215. This facility is especially useful when the noise criteria to be met are set in terms of dB(A), because it is possible to see immediately which octave bands are contributing most to the A-weighted noise level, and therefore where the noise control effort should be concentrated for maximum effect. In this example it is quite obvious that the best place to begin would be the relatively high levels in the 250 Hz and 1 kHz octave bands. The vibration spectrum of the compressor base, reproduced in the third figure, now demonstrates its usefulness because it also has a high level in the same frequency band as the measured noise, an indication that this particular noise is probably caused by mechanical vibration. The other maximum level was readily identified as being due to the air intake. Both these sources would require attention to achieve a worthwhile improvement in the overall noise level. In this way, methods of improvement can be tried in the order that they would be likely to yield the best results for the costs and effort involved.

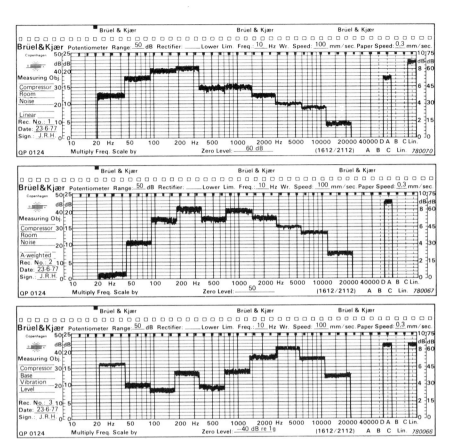

Fig.5.2.5. Octave spectra of compressor noise and vibration

Office Noise Measurement

The reduction required in a given situation depends primarily on the function of the area and the existing noise level within it. The overriding criterion, which must always be met, is that relating to hearing damage. In less noisy circumstances the allowable noise level may be defined by the requirements for adequate communication, employee comfort, or the avoidance of complaints from the community at large. In offices, however, one is unlikely to encounter noise levels high enough either to damage hearing or give rise to community annoyance, so the noise criterion is usually set by the need for easy face-to-face or telephone communication, or by the annoyance and distraction caused by intrusive noises. In this context it is as well to bear in mind that too low a general background noise level accentuates the intrusiveness of external noise, and also allows private conversations to be overheard

159

easily. This may occur both within the office and between offices if their sound insulation is poor. It is often possible to avoid this problem by controlled leakage of external noise so that the background noise level is high enough to prevent the understanding of distant conversations, but allows close conversation to be carried on normally and so is also acceptable to staff. Other passive noise control techniques include the careful positioning of acoustic screening, absorbent panels, and noise-producing office equipment. Active sound conditioning techniques have recently been developed which supply a continuous broad band noise with a special spectrum. The noise interferes with speech and renders it unintelligible beyond normal conversational distances, this providing an acoustically private local area, while at the same time masking potentially annoying noise. This method of background noise control is useful when normal insulation and absorption measures are difficult to install, or where extremely low existing background noise levels demand high insulation and therefore lead to high weight and cost. The more usual problem in office design is that of reducing noise from air-conditioning systems and office machines to an acceptable level according to the criteria discussed in Chapter 3. This is an area of much research and expertise, and interested readers are referred to the bibliography at the end of this section for a more extensive discussion of the problems of air-conditioning systems in particular, and the noise control techniques generally. The General Reference section also includes several books and periodicals dedicated to noise control engineering.

A survey of a typical office environment was made to determine the background levels before occupation, to check the noise emission of newly installed ventilation plant, and to measure the general noise levels after occupation. To do this required both a statistical and frequency analysis and the portable equipment used is shown in Fig.5.2.6. The Precision Sound Level Meter and Octave Analyzer Type 2215 was coupled directly to the Portable Level Recorder Type 2306 to record the time-varying noise level, as shown in Fig.5.2.7 and the levels obtained from the frequency analysis of the ventilation units. To obtain the statistical distribution, the Noise Level Analyzer was

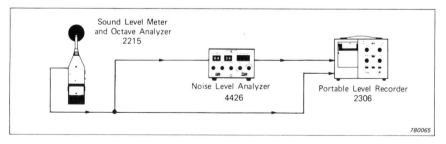

Fig.5.2.6. Instrumentation for statistical and frequency analysis of noise in an office

160

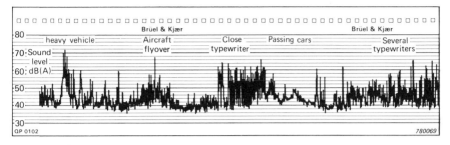

Fig.5.2.7. Typical time history of noise heard in an office

used to process the information and a permanent record of the analysis was made using the 2306.

The statistical analysis of the noise in the unoccupied office, in the absence of the new ventilation plant but with the old plant and services functioning normally, and with the other parts of the factory and other offices occupied, is reproduced in Fig.5.2.8. The noise level is concentrated around 40 dB(A), the level of continuous noise from the old ventilation plant. Intrusive events from outside the office, mainly from elsewhere in the factory and from road traffic but also from occasional aircraft, give rise internally to intermittent peaks up to nearly 70 dB(A). These facts should be compared with the time history of the noise level generated in the office during its normal operation. The typewriters clearly produce internal noise levels in excess of most of the noise originating from outside, and the background should therefore be acceptable to the office staff. The comparison between the ventilation noise before and after the installation of a new and more powerful system is a different story however. The noise spectra produced by the two systems are shown plotted on noise rating curves in Fig.5.2.9. The new system is demonstrably noisier than its predecessor, nearly 20 dB(A) in fact, the noise rating going up from an acceptable 33 to a quite unacceptable 55. The shape of the octave band spectrum, with a distinct maximum rising, in this case, almost 15 dB over the general level, is one of the problems most often encountered

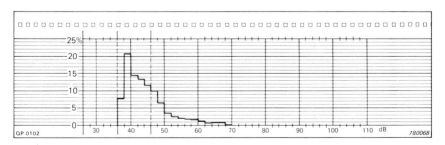

Fig.5.2.8. Statistical analysis of office noise

161

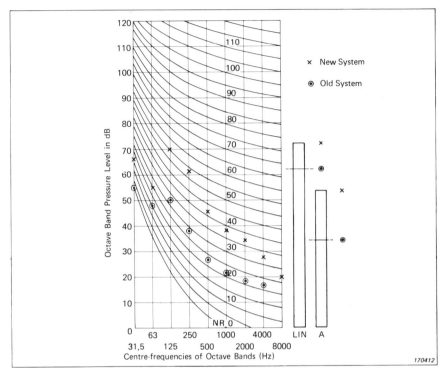

Fig.5.2.9. Octave analysis of two ventilation units plotted on Standard Noise Rating curves

with air moving systems. The spectral peak was annoyingly audible as a tone at approximately 125 Hz and was caused by a resonance in the delivery duct, the so-called organ-pipe effect.

Although a simple sound level meter can give a single number rating for this type of situation, this is not always satisfactory for all the problems associated with the provision of an adequate working environment. Particularly when levels are not steady, some sort of statistical analysis must be carried out to ensure that an adequate noise climate has been obtained, and wherever noise control measures are envisaged, an analysis into octave, or narrower, bands is usually required in order to select effective measures and to check later that the necessary improvement has been obtained.

Selected Bibliography

BAUER, E.:   *Kapselung von Maschinen, Lärmbekämpfung am Arbeitsplatz.* Jahrestagung 1965 des Deutschen Arbeitsringes für Lärmbekämpfung. S. 49.

BELL, A.:   *Lärm im Büro aus der Sicht des Angestellten.* Kampf dem Lärm Bd. 12, Heft 6, 1965, S. 150.

BERANEK, L. L.:   *Revised Criteria for Noise in Buildings.* Noise Control Vol. 3. January 19 57.

BOBRAN, H. W.:   *Schallschutztechnische Maßnahmen an Prüfständen.* Forderungen-Möglichkeiten und Grenzen. Lärmbekämpfung. Bd. 1, Heft 3/4, S.72.

BRUCKMAIER, F.:   *Bauakustische Anforderungen an Büroräume und Grundsätzliches zu ihrer Erfüllung.* Kampf dem Lärm. Bd. 12, Heft 2, 1965. S.39.

COX, H.:   *Linear Versus Logarithmic Averaging.* J.A.S.A. Vol. 39. April 1966. p. 688.

CUDWORTH, A. L.:   *Quietening Circular Saws.* Noise Control. Vol. 6. Jan-/Feb. 1960. p. 26.

DIN 45637:   *Aussengeräuschmessungen an Spurgebundenen Fahrzeugen 1977.*

DIRITA, R. A. and GEORGE, D. L.:   *How to Estimate Sound Levels in Industrial Environments,* Sound and Vibration. Sept. 1972.

FURDUEV, V. V.:   *Noise Reduction in the Acoustical Treatment of Noise Enclosures.* Akusticheskii Zuhrnal, Vol. 11. 1965.

GABLER, W.:   *Lärmbekämpfung im Städtebau und in der Raumordnung.* Kampf den Lärm. Jg. 13, Heft 4. 1966.

GERTH, D.:   *Über den Schallschutz bei der Rohrinstallation in Sanitär- und Heizungsanlagen.* Kampf dem Lärm Jg. 13, Heft 3. 1966.

GRAFE, K.:   *Bürolärm aus hygienischer Sicht.* Kampf dem Lärm. Bd. 12, Heft 1, 1965. S. 8.

GÖSELE, K.L: *Zum baulichen Schallschutz in Arbeitsräumen.* Lärmbekämpfung am Arbeitsplatz. Jahrestagung 1965 des Deutschen Arbeitsringes für Lärmbekämpfung. S. 75.

HUBERT, M.:   *Lärmentwicklung und Lärmminderung bei Lüftungsanlagen.* Lärmbekämpfung. Bd. 13. Heft 1. Februar 1969.

163

HÜFFMANN, G.:   *Wirkung von Maßnahmen zur Minderung des Geräuschpegels in und in der Umgebung von Schmieden.* Kamp dem Lärm Jg. 13. Heft. 1966.

JONES, D. I. G.:   *Damping Treatments for Noise and Vibration Control.* Sound and Vibration July 1972.

KEIGHLY, E. C.:   *The Determination of Acceptability Criteria for Office Noise.* J. Sound Vib. Vol. 4. No.1 1966. p. 73.

KNOFLACH, J.:   *Gewerbelärm — Messung und Abhilfe.* Lärmbekämpfung. Bd. 13. Heft 5. Oktober 1969.

KOSS, L. L. and   *Identification of Transient Sound Sources on a Punch*
ALFREDSON, R. J.:   *Press* J.S.V. Vol. 34. No.1. 1974. pp. 11—33.

KRAEGE, R.:   *Spezialprobleme des Baulichen Schallschutzer.* Kampf dem Lärm. Jg. 13, Heft 2. 1966.

KRAEGE, R.:   *Ergebnisse und Erfolge von Schallschutzprüfungen.* Kampf dem Lärm. 16 Jg. Heft 3. Juni 1969.

MELLING, T. H. and   *Noise Generation and Prediction in Automated Bott-*
WOOD, B. R.:   *ling Lines.* Noise Control. Engineering Sept./Oct. 1974.

MITCHELL, S. K.:   *Comment on "Linear Versus Logarithmic Averaging".* J.A.S.A. Vol. 41. April 1967. p. 863.

NEMECEK, J. and   *Der Bürolärm und seine Wirkungen.* Kampf dem
TURRIAN V.:   Lärm Vol.25, 1978, pp.50-57

PRIOR, R.:   *Does Sound Conditioning Work?* Noise Control and Vibration Reduction Sept. 1975. pp. 281—283.

RUB, F.:   *Lärmbekämpfung in den Werkstätten des Schlosser- und Masch. bauerz.* Bd. 3 — 1965. S. 158.

SABINE, H. J.:   *Acoustics of Open Plan Offices.* Sound and Vibration Sept. 1973. pp. 26—29.

SABINE, H. J. and   *Application of Sound Absorption to Factory Noise*
WILSON, R. A.:   *Problems.* J.A.S.A. Vol. 15. July 1943. p. 27.

SAHLIN, S.:   *Origins of Punch-Press Noise.* Internoise '74 proceedings. pp. 221—224.

SANDERS, G.J.:   *Noise Control in Air-Handling Systems.* Sound and Vibration. Vol. 1. No.2. Feb. 1967.

SCHULTZ, G.:   *Lärmminderung in Hütten und Walzwerken.* Lärmbekämpfung am Arbeitsplatz. Jahrestagung 1965 des Deutschen Arbeitsringes für Lärmbekämpfung. S. 133.

SCHWANDA, P.: *Industrielärmbekämpfung durch die Allgemeine Unfallversicherungsanstalt.* Lärmbekämpfung. Bd. 13. Heft 4. August 1969.

SEIFERT, E.: *Schalldämmende Fenster.* Kampf dem Lärm Jg. 13. Heft 1. 1966.

SHINAISHIN, O. A.: *Impact-Induced Industrial Noise.* Noise Control Engineering Vol. 2. No.1. 1974. pp. 30—36.

SMITH, J. J. B.: *Design Targets for Background Noise Levels in Buildings.* Noise Control, Vibration and Insulation. March 1977.

STEWART, N D., BAILEY, J. R. and DAGGERHART, J. A.: *Study of Parameters Influencing Punch Press Noise.* Noise Control Engineering. Sept.-Oct. 1974.

TREUSE, E.: *Lärmbekämpfung im Büro.* Kampf dem Lärm. Bd. 12, Heft 1, 1965. S. 4.

VDI 3720 *Lärmarm Konstruieren Beispielsammlung.* Blatt 2 July 1977.

VÖLKER, E-J.: *Privacy und Akustische Behaglichkeit im modernen Bürobau.* Kampf dem Lärm 25. Feb. 1978. pp.26—31.

WALLER, R. A.: *Office Acoustics—Effects of Background Noise.* Applied Acoustics. Vol. 2. No.2. April 1969. pp. 121-130

WILLMS, W.: *Theorie und Praxis der Beurteilung von Lärmimmissionen.* Lärmbekämpfung. Bd. 13. Heft 5. Oktober 1969.

WYN-ROBERTS, D.: *Acoustic Noise Control in a manned Space Vehicle — The Overall Approach for Spacelab.* ESA TN 137 Sept. 1977. ESTEC.

YUDIN, E. Ya. et.al.: *Noise Control.* (Russian) Moscow. 1964.

ZBORALSKI, D.: *Geräuschbekämpfung in Fahrzeugbau.* Arthur Tetzlaff. Frankfurt/main. 1960.

ZELLER, W.: *Einige Grundlagen für die Planung der Lärmfreiheit in der Industrie.* Lärmbekämpfung. Bd. 4, Heft 3 — 1960. S. 53.

ZELLER, W.: *Lärmabwehr bei Lüftungsanlagen.* Westdeutscher Verlag. Köln und Opladen. 1967.

ZÜRCHER, B.: *Die Lärmbekämpfung auf dem Lande.* Kampf dem Lärm Jg. 13, Heft 5. 1966.

5.3. PRODUCT NOISE ANALYSIS

A quiet product has distinct marketing advantages over its more noisy competitor, whether it is ultimately destined for the home, office, workplace, or transportation system. Legislation to reduce the more obvious excesses of noise pollution, e.g. from aircraft, road traffic, and factory, has led in turn to a more general appreciation of the benefits of quiet domestic and office equipment, and a demand for increased noise reduction and control effort. However, producing a worthwhile reduction in the noise output of a product can be an extremely costly, difficult, and time consuming process. Problems arise because of the ear's excellent sensitivity at extremely low sound pressures. A low-power domestic machine, say a hair-dryer, may consume 100 watts of electrical power. If only *one millionth* of this available power is converted into noise, the sound pressure level at a distance of 30 cm will be of the order of 80 dB. It is easy therefore to envisage the problems involved in reducing the noise from a normal small car engine which may typically generate about 50 kW., or a power station generator set which may handle 500 MW. It also explains why design Engineers never have to worry about the energy lost by conversion into acoustic radiation, although this tiny loss may emerge as an intolerable noise nuisance, and an intractable problem to the noise control Engineer.

Noise occurs as a by-product of mechanical or aerodynamic motion which may be necessary to, or produced by, the normal operation of the machine and can be readily associated with its various moving parts. Rubbing and rolling contact, impact of moving parts, panel resonances induced by imbalance, meshing of gears, turbulent flow, and fan tones, all have characteristic spectra from which the source of the noise can be identified.

Although a full description of the detailed techniques of noise reduction and control is outside the scope of this book, an explanation of how the problem can best be approached should be useful. When attempting to minimise the noise radiated by a product, both the noise producing and radiating mechanisms must be investigated if a noise control program is to be fully effective. Location of the vibrating components which often constitute the noise source, and the parts of the structure which are efficient radiators of sound, may necessitate a combination of both noise and vibration measurements.

As an example, let us look at a product where legislation is not only encouraging much research effort but which also involves a large number of noise producing mechanisms, many of which can be found in a variety of other products, namely the internal combustion engine. Sound sources include aerodynamic noise from the fan, impact noise from tappets and valves, explosive combustion of the charge, exhaust and induction pulses, gear and chain noise, and casing noise caused by out of balance vibration forces from rotating parts, primarily the crankshaft and camshaft. In a multi-source problem

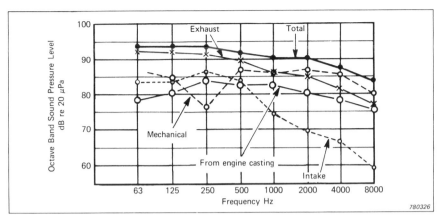

Fig.5.3.1. *Overall noise from an internal combustion engine and its constituent components*

such as this, the individual sources which contribute most towards the overall noise level or band spectrum levels should first be identified. The technical and economical feasibility of any noise control measures which might be taken can then be assessed in relation to their impact on the subjective noise level of the product. An example of this type of preliminary analysis is shown in Fig.5.3.1, demonstrating conclusively that the exhaust and mechanical noise contribute most to the total noise level. Any noise reduction effort should be concentrated on these sources, being the most likely to provide the greatest reduction in noise emission for the time and money expended on their investigation and redesign. A large scale noise investigation of this type will probably also employ vibration measurements in order to examine locally, in detail, noise producing mechanisms such as valve operation, combustion, and crankcase vibration, which are essentially mechanical in nature. Microphones would be used to measure overall noise spectra and directivity patterns, and those noise sources such as the exhaust, intake, and fan, which are directly concerned with the moving of air, the medium of both the engine cycle and sound transmission, and therefore obvious situations for acoustic measurement. The exact measurement and analysis techniques will depend on the complexity of the problem, and the difficulties encountered in providing the required reduction in noise.

Although a simple sound level measurement may show that a problem exists, a frequency analysis is usually required to identify its characteristics more accurately prior to redesign or remedial treatment. Whether a constant percentage bandwidth or constant bandwidth analysis should be used, and the bandwidth itself, depends upon the frequency resolution which is required for the particular application. If resolution is of greatest importance, then a narrow band, constant bandwidth analysis is required. This gives uni-

167

form resolution on a linear frequency scale and therefore gives equal separate of harmonically related components. Indeed, in the case of systems with very many closely-spaced peaks in the frequency spectrum, it may be necessary to further analyse the spectrum itself in order to identify side-bands and harmonics properly. This process is termed Cepstrum analysis and finds particular application to the condition analysis of complex gear trains.

Constant percentage bandwidth analysis in octave or third-octave bands is often used in the fields of noise reduction research and development and quality control, especially for products such as air conditioners, fans, ventilators and jet engines, for which the regulations define allowable noise levels in those terms. Quality control can then be carried out relatively quickly and a copy of the analysis included with each item to demonstrate that it conforms to the specifications. Narrow band analysis is more usually applied to monitoring the health of large machinery, where a more effective check may be kept on both the level and the frequency of identifiable peaks in the spectrum which are known to be related to the motion of key components. Changes in either of these parameters may, for example, indicate a loss of stiffness in a shaft, perhaps due to the beginning or growth of a fatigue crack which could ultimately lead to catastrophic failure.

Quality Control

Having reduced the noise radiated from the development prototype, the manufacturer must now ensure that production control is such that units leaving the factory meet his stated specifications. This will normally require the installation of a small test chamber or noise insulated region, together with the necessary instrumentation, in the inspection area. These often have a high background noise level which necessitates heavy construction for the chamber walls in order to provide sound insulation high enough to attain suitably quiet conditions for testing. In some cases this can be avoided by substituting an accelerometer for the microphone, and measuring at a point on the product where vibration is representative of the radiated noise level. Acoustic testing methods on the other hand have the advantage that they measure the actual radiated noise and do not involve contact with the test object.

An instrumentation arrangement suitable for this type of test is shown in Fig.5.3.2. The level recorder controls the switching of the filter set so that an octave or third octave analysis can be carried out automatically, and at the same time produces a permanent record of the test object's performance. This can be included with the product to assure the customer that specifications have been met, or may serve to assist the service engineer to diagnose the fault in the event of a failure. Fig.5.3.3 shows the results of a test on a small compressor compared with the target noise limits in both dB(A) and also in each of the octave bands. There may be only one limit spectrum sim-

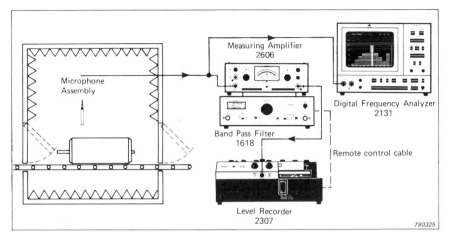

Fig.5.3.2. Quality control testing using a small anechoic chamber

ply to pass or fail a unit, or a family of spectra to divide the production units into a series of quality classes with regard to noise or vibration emission. Where detailed analysis at high speed is required a real-time analyzer, as also shown in Fig.5.3.2, can be used with advantage. The 1/3 octave spectrum of the test article can be displayed on the screen alternately one of a number of pre-prepared limit spectrum which may be read into the memory for comparison. Connection of a desk-top calculator makes the process fully automatic.

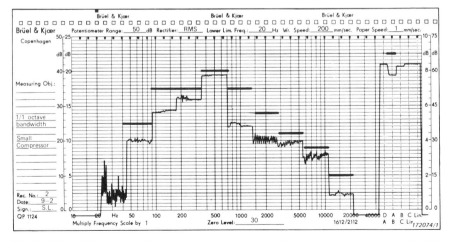

Fig.5.3.3. Octave band test results from a small compressor compared with limit levels

169

The acoustic and/or vibration inspection of a product not only ensures that it meets stated specifications, but also allows a diagnosis of any faulty components. This is particularly effective for mechanical equipment containing moving, and especially rotating, parts.

Machinery Condition Monitoring

As suggested in the previous section, a by-product of the noise and/or vibration measurements for quality control purposes will often be the spectrum of an item which has failed for some reason to meet stated specifications. This tells much about the product's mechanical state, and, because the sound emitted by machines changes in both level and character as wear takes place and faults develop, suggests that these diagnostic techniques may be extended beyond factory-based quality control procedures to monitoring of the machine's condition in service. Machines seldom break down or fail suddenly. Signs of impending failure often appear long before the occurrence of a catastrophic failure which interferes with production schedules or causes dangerous and expensive damage. However, the advantages of condition monitoring are wider than simply the prediction and avoidance of failures which might cause shutdowns. A planned maintenance system for example will often replace wear-prone parts, involving a shut-down of the system and subsequent loss of production, long before it is really justified as indicated by on-condition monitoring. Considerable savings can be made by increasing the mean time between shutdowns as well as by further reducing the possibility of an unpredicted catastrophic failure. This is done by frequent checks or continuous monitors connected directly to alarm systems, so that the elapsed

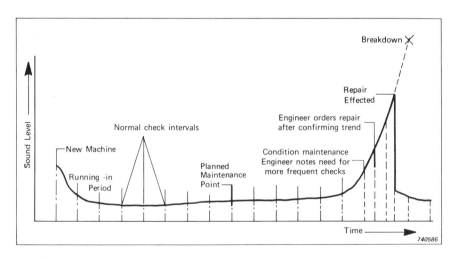

Fig.5.3.4. The operation of a machine condition monitoring procedure

170

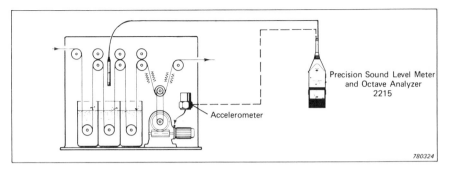

Fig.5.3.5. The application of both noise and vibration condition monitoring to continuous processing machinery

time between the development and the recognition of a fault is kept to a minimum. Suspicious increases in noise and/or vibration levels can be checked at more frequent intervals than normal, and the engineer can immediately order a repair if his suspicions are justified. Fig.5.3.4 shows how this procedure works in practice for a new machine, the levels decreasing during the initial running-in period, increasing very slowly as normal wear takes place, and finally increasing very rapidly towards a major failure, indicating the need for immediate replacement of vital parts.

The type of analysis system used to process the signal depends, as did the quality control procedure discussed earlier, on the complexity of both the machine itself and the technique being used for assessing its condition. A simple sound and/or vibration level measurement with perhaps octave or 1/3 octave filters may give sufficient information for the maintenance engineer to order repairs to the machine. In this case a sound level meter with a converter to allow the instrument to accept on accelerometer input may be used, as in the case of the process machinery in Fig.5.3.5.

At the other extreme, in the case of, for example, a complex gear train, a narrow band analysis is necessary to resolve the many different spectrum peaks from gear rotation, bearing rotation, and gear meshing. To reduce the time necessary to carry out such a detailed analysis, a system such as that shown in Fig.5.3.6 can be used. This incorporates a real-time digital narrow band analyzer to detect the pure tones and harmonics at shaft rotation and tooth meshing frequencies, as indicated. When dealing with complex structures and machines the problem of identifying noise sources becomes extremely involved. The advanced techniques needed to deal with these problems such as cepstrum, correlation, and coherence analysis, require a thorough knowledge of the subject, and there are many excellent specialist books and articles available, see references.

171

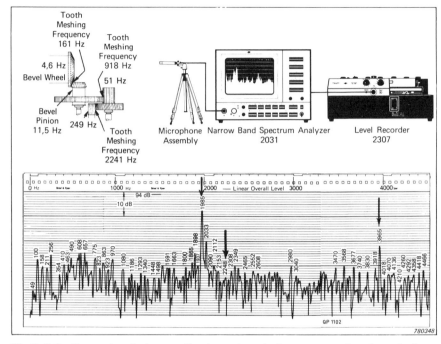

Fig.5.3.6. Example of the application of real time narrow band analysis to fault finding in a complex gear train

Selected Bibliography

BADGLEY, R. H. and
HARTMAN, R. M.:

Gearbox Noise Reduction: Prediction and Measure-ment of Mesh-Frequency Vibrations within an Operat-ing Helicopter Rotor-Drive Gerabox. Journal of Engineering for Industry. May 1974. pp. 567 — 577.

BENDAT, J. S. and
PIERSOL, A. G.:

Random Data: Analysis and Measurement proce-dures John Wiley inc. 1971.

COLLACOT, R. A.:

Machinery Fault Diagnosis by Sound Identification. Noise Control, Vibration and Insulation. Aug./Sept. 1976. pp. 246 — 252.

FIELDING, B. J. and
SKORECKI, J.:

Identification of Mechanical Sources of Noise in a Diesel Engine: Sound Emitted from the Valve Mechanism. Proceedings of the Inst. of Mech. Eng. 1966-67. Volume 181, Part 1.

GEISSLER, W.:

Untersuchungen über die Entstehung und Minderung starker Einzeltöne bei radialen Ventilator-Laufrädern grosser Laufradbreite. Kampf dem Lärm. Bd. 12. Heft 3. 1965. S. 59.

I.M.E.:

Acoustics as a Diagnostic Tool. Proceedings of a Conference held at the Institute of Mechanical Engineers on 20th October, 1970.

I.S.O.:

Recommendation 495-1966. General requirements for the preparation of test codes for measuring the noise emitted by machines.

I.S.O.:

Recommendation 1680-1970. Test code for the measurement of the airborne noise emitted by rotating electrical machinery.

I.S.O.:

Recommendation 2151-1972. Measurement of airborne noise emitted by compressor/primemover units intended for outdoor use.

I.S.O.:

Recommendation 3741-1975. Determination of sound power level of noise sources precision methods for broad-band sources in reverberation rooms.

I.S.O.:

Recommendation 3742-1975. Determination of sound power level of noise sources — Precision methods for discrete-frequency and narrow-band sources in reverberation rooms.

JAEKEL, K.:

Geräusch und Schwingungsmessungen an grossen Zahnradgetrieben. VDI-Zeitschrift (106) No.6, Feb. 1964. p. 215.

KURTZE, G. and
BROCH, J. T.:

Design and Use of a Small Noise Test Chamber. B & K Technical Review No.2 — 1964.

NESS, H. W.:

Pinpointing Vibration in Rotating Machinery. ASME Paper 65 GTP-24, January 1965.

NEWLAND, D. E.:

An Introduction to Random Vibrations and Spectral Analysis. Longman - 1975.

NOLL, A.M.:

Cepstrum pitch determination. J.A.S.A. Vol.41 No.2 1967

NOISEXPO 1973:

Proceedings of the Technical Programme. J.H. Botsford, Chairman. Held in Chicago Sept. 11-13, 1973.

PRIEDE, T.:

Origins of Automotive Vehicle Noise. J.S.V. Vol. 15. No.1. 1971. pp. 61 — 74.

RANDALL, R. B.:   *Cepstrum analysis and gearbox fault diagnosis,* B & K
                 Application Note No. 13—150

ROE, G. E.:   *The silencing of a high performance motorcycle.*
                 J.S.V. Vol. 33. No.1 1974. pp. 29 — 40.

ROFF, J. A. and   *A Review of Vehicle Noise Studies Carried out at*
PERRY, R. D. H.: *I.S.V.R.* J.S.V. Vol. 28. No.3. 1973. pp. 433 —
                 470.

SATO, T.,   *Real Time Bispectral Analysis of Gear Noise and its*
SASAKI, K. and   *Application to Contactless Diagnosis.* J.A.S.A. Vol.
NAKAMURA, Y.:   62. No.2. August 1977. pp. 383 — 387.

WEICHBRODT, B.:   *Mechanical Signature Analysis. A New Tool for Pro-*
                 duct Assurance and Early Fault Detection. G.E.C.
                 (U.S.A.) Report No. 68-C-197, 1968.

ZAVERI, K.:   *Acoustical Investigation of an Impact Drill.* B & K
                 Technical Review No.3 — 1974. pp. 3 — 25.

5.4. AUDIOMETRY

Audiometry is the process of determining the hearing threshold, i.e. the minimum sound pressure level which induces the sensation of hearing at a specified frequency. Industrial Health schemes often include audiometric tests as an integral part of hearing conservation programs. Such programs usually require that people working in particularly noisy environments are tested both before and at regular intervals during their employment in such areas. The purpose of the initial test is to define the pre-exposure hearing sensitivity and if possible identify any worker with hearing peculiarities or whose hearing is particularly susceptible to noise-induced damage. Those who need specialist treatment can be given it, and those with easily damaged hearing can be employed in quieter occupations. At the same time the industrial health team obtains pre-exposure thresholds with which to compare each employee's subsequent audiograms. This may be of crucial importance if, for instance, a claim for industrial injury is later made on the basis of a loss of hearing. A pre-employment screening is the only way to determine whether a claimed hearing loss was indeed caused by the current employment, or by some previous exposure, illness, or physical damage.

After the initial test, an audiogram should be taken at regular intervals to determine the effects of the noise exposure on the employee's hearing threshold. Any subsequent changes in hearing sensitivity can then be rapidly recognised and the affected worker either treated medically or transferred to work in less noisy areas.

The audiogram itself is determined by applying a slowly changing sound level to each ear in turn, usually by means of close fitting earphones, the subject indicating the level at which it can be heard. This procedure is normally carried out at several frequencies. In this way the subjects hearing threshold can be traced and compared with a standard curve representing the normal threshold derived from a series of tests on young adults with normal hearing. The basic requirement of an audiometer, then, are that it has a large dynamic range to cope with the wide variation of hearing sensitivities within the population, and can operate over the frequency range of interest. This is usually the mid and high frequency range above 500 Hz, but may vary somewhat depending on the use to which the results are put e.g. industrial screening or audiological research. The nominal normal threshold must be referred to some universally adopted standard so that valid comparisons between audiograms can be made.

This means that the instrument must be capable of calibration to ensure that this absolute threshold, defined in ISO 389 as the Standard Reference zero, is correct. In addition, tests in an industrial environment must be easy for the operator to administer, and simple for the subject to understand and perform. For these purposes a limited range pure tone instrument having 7 fixed frequencies at 500 Hz, 1, 2, 3, 4, 6, and 8 kHz is normally employed. The pure tone may be either continuous or pulsed, a technique which makes it much easier to distinguish from the background noise which exists to a greater or lesser extent in any industrial environment. In any case care should be taken to site audiometric test equipment in quiet areas, or failing this to provide some sort of sound reducing booth to lower the ambient noise to an acceptable level, typically as indicated below.

Octave band center Frequency	Maximum octave band levels (dB) re 20μPascals
500	40
1000	40
2000	47
4000	57
8000	67

There should also be no pure tones audible in the test area. Too high a background noise level leads to the definition of a false threshold in excess of the real one, indicating a hearing loss where in fact there may be none. For this reason it is prudent to include a small safety factor in the limits of the table of, say, 10 dB, to allow for possible future increases in the background and interruptions from intrusive noises.

175

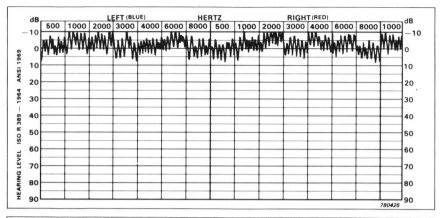

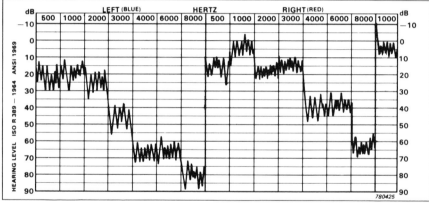

Fig.5.4.1. Typical Audiograms
a) Young person
b) Older person

The criteria for an instrument suitable for industrial use can be best met by an automatic recording audiometer such as the Type 1800, supplying a pulsed pure tone which is under the control of the subject via a handheld switch. The switch operates an automatic attenuator which controls the sound level emitted by the earphones worn by the subject. By pressing the switch when he first hears the tone and releasing it when he can no longer do so, his threshold is automatically plotted on a pre-printed chart suitable for documentation. This is done continuously without the intervention of the operator, although facilities are provided for the operator to overide the test manually if this proves necessary e.g. if the subject has not fully understood the instructions. The frequency of the test tone is changed automatically after a fixed time interval long enough to establish the hearing level at that frequency.

Both ears are tested in succession, and a 1 kHz retest is carried out automatically at the end of the procedure as a check.

Typical audiograms of a young person with good hearing and of an older person with substantial hearing loss, are reproduced in Fig.5.4.1. The hearing loss at high frequencies is apparent in the older person and can just be detected in the younger at 8 kHz. A 20 dB attenuator, ZA 0024 is available to alter the measuring range from the normal −10 dB to 90 dB Hearing Level to the range −30 dB to 70 dB Hearing Level. Valid measurements can be then made on people with exceptionally good hearing. Charts are available to correspond with either range.

The audiometer calibration should be checked at regular intervals of a week or less to ensure that the absolute threshold levels lie within acceptable tolerances. This can be done using a standard sound level meter coupled to the earphone via an artificial ear.

The sound level meter indicates the level which is present in the coupler of the artificial ear at the different frequencies for a test level of 90 dB Hearing Level (HL). The instruments necessary to carry out this procedure, which can be accomplished in only a few minutes, are shown set up in Fig.5.4.2.

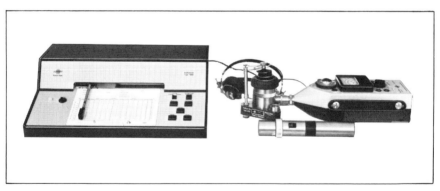

Fig.5.4.2. Automatic Recording Audiometer Type 1800 and calibration equipment

Selected Bibliography

BERRY, B.F.:   *Ambient noise limits for audiomtry,* NPL (England) Acoustics Report Ac 60, 1973

BRYAN, M. E. and   *Industrial Audiometry.* University of Salford Audiol-
TEMPEST, W.:   ogy Group.

177

BURNS, W.,　　　　　　　Hearing hazard from occupational noise: Observa-
ROBINSON, D.W.,　　　　tions on a population from heavy industry, NPL
SHIPTON, M.S. and　　　Acoustics Report Ac 80 Jan. 1977
SINCLAIR, A.:

HIRSCHORM, M. and　　　The effect of ambient noise on audiometric room se-
SINGER, S.:　　　　　　lection, Sound and Vibration, Vol.7, No.2 1973, pp
　　　　　　　　　　　　18-22

I.E.C.:　　　　　　　　177 (1965). Pure tone audiometers for general diag-
　　　　　　　　　　　　nostic purposes.

I.E.C.:　　　　　　　　178 (1965). Pure tone screening audiometers.

I.E.C.:　　　　　　　　200 (1966). Methods of measurement for loudspeak-
　　　　　　　　　　　　ers

I.E.C.:　　　　　　　　303 (1970). IEC provisional reference coupler for the
　　　　　　　　　　　　calibration of earphones used in audiometry.

I.E.C.:　　　　　　　　318 (1970). An IEC artificial ear, of the wide band
　　　　　　　　　　　　type, for the calibration of earphones used in audi-
　　　　　　　　　　　　ometry.

I.E.C.:　　　　　　　　389 (1975). Acoustics standard reference zero for
　　　　　　　　　　　　the calibration of pure-tone audiometers.

NILSSON, R.,　　　　　　Noise exposure and hearing impairment in the ship-
LIDEN, G., and　　　　　building industry. Scand. Audiol. Vol.6, No.2, 1977,
SONDEN, Å.:　　　　　　pp.59-69

ROBINSON, D.W. and　　A comparison of self-recording and manual audiom-
WHITTLE, L.S.:　　　　　try. J.S.V. Vol.26 No.1 1973. pp.41-62

ROBINSON, D.W.,　　　　Audiometry in Industrial Hearing Conservation —1,
SHIPTON, M.S., and　　　NPL (England) Acoustics Report Ac64, 1973
WHITTLE, L.S.:

SHIPTON, M. S. and　　　Ambient Noise Limits for Industrial Audiometry. NPL
ROBINSON, D. W.:　　　England. Acoustics Report AC 69 April 1975.

SPOOR, A, and　　　　　Spread in hearing-levels of non noise-exposed
PASSCHIER-VERMEER W.:　people at Various ages, Int. Audiol. Vol.8, pp.323

SPOOR, A.:　　　　　　Presbyacusis values in relation to noise-induced hear-
　　　　　　　　　　　　ing loss. Int. Audiol. 1967, Vol.6, pp.48

Journals
Scandinavian　　　　　Published by the Almqvist & Wiksell Periodical Com-
Audiology:　　　　　　pany, Stockholm, Sweden

Acta Oto-Laryngologia　Published by The Almqvist & Wiksell Periodical Com-
　　　　　　　　　　　　pany, Stockholm, Sweden

British Journal of
Audiology:

Published by The Royal National Institute for the
Deaf, 105 Gower Street, London WC1E 6AH, England

5.5. MEASUREMENT AND ANALYSIS OF TRANSIENT SOUNDS

Special techniques are required for the measurement and analysis of acoustic impulses and transient pressure changes, and also for evaluation of their perceived loudness, annoyance, or hearing damage risk. Gun shots, impacting bodies, explosions, and sonic booms all fall within this category. The difficulties encountered with these signals stem mainly from the fact that they often contain high spectrum levels at low frequencies, are usually non-repetitive events, and are of very short duration. The first of these characteristics necessitates use of systems which have a frequency response down to virtually DC. However, because the levels in the important hearing frequency range are often very much lower than those at low frequencies, a very large dynamic range is required if valid information is also to be obtained over the signal's entire frequency range. Usually this can only be achieved by splitting the signal into two, or perhaps more, frequency ranges, and recording each on separate channels of a multi-channel recorder.

The second characteristic, non-repetitive nature of the phenomena, places great importance on the ability of the system to capture the signal whenever it occurs. There will often be no advance warning, and the repetition of an event may be expensive, as in the case of say, a sonic boom experiment, or perhaps impossible, in the case of demolition by explosives. Thirdly, the short duration of the signal introduces problems into the subsequent analysis. The following discussion, using a gunshot and a clicking toy as examples, illustrates these points. Fig.5.5.1 shows a measurement and recording arrangement consisting of a special low frequency microphone and FM Carrier System Type 2631 connected via a measuring amplifier and high-pass filter to an FM Tape Recorder Type 7003. The purpose of the extra amplifier and high-pass filter is to split the frequency spectrum of the impulse into two regions, in order to obtain a greater dynamic range than would be possible on a single channel. The higher frequency components of these signals may be lost in the tape noise if the high spectrum levels at low frequencies are accommodated on the same channel. This refinement becomes extremely important when recording explosions and sonic booms (see Sec. 6.3). The choice of filter cut-off frequency depends on the duration of the transient, the shape of the frequency spectrum, and the purpose for which the data is required.

179

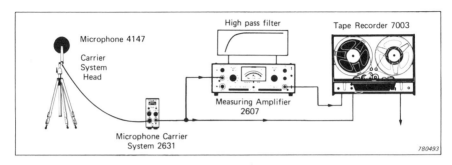

Fig.5.5.1. Instrumentation system suitable for recording acoustic impulses

The gun used here as a transient source was fired in an anechoic chamber to be sure of a well defined signal. If the time of occurrence of the signal is not under the control of the experimenter or is not well defined, the Digital Event Recorder Type 7502 described in section 4.7 can be incorporated in the system. The trigger facilities of this instrument can be used to capture the signal prior to tape recording it and the wide range of record/display rates improves the overall flexibility of the measuring system. Once recorded, the signal can be analysed sequentially using the instrumentation of Fig.5.5.2. A tape loop containing the transient is played through a Heterodyne Analyzer Type 2010, and the peak value of the filtered output is detected by the Measuring Amplifier Type 2607, which has a very fast peak detection circuit. The resulting spectrum is recorded on the Level Recorder. The Tape Signal Gate Type 2972 serves to gate out the tape splice noise, and also resets the peak detection circuit of the measuring amplifier.

An alternative and much faster method is to use the Narrow Band Spec-

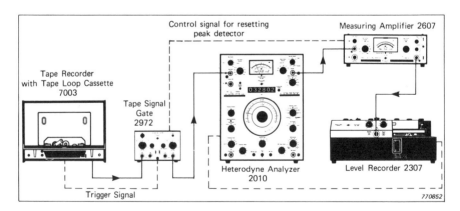

Fig.5.5.2. Instrumentation suitable for the frequency analysis of single impulses by sequential filtering

180

trum Analyzer Type 2031, which has extensive trigger facilities for capturing transient signals. Apart from automatically performing narrow band analysis in a number of ranges, the instrument also displays the captured transient and allows averaging of a number of events to produce a well-defined spectrum. In this case the instrumentation arrangement of Fig.5.5.3 was used to analyse the transient sound directly, although recordings from the set up of Fig.5.5.1 could have been used had that type of data collection been appropriate to the application. The trigger level of the 2031 was arranged a little below the expected maximum level of the gunshot, and the after trigger delay set to begin recording just before the trigger point. This ensures that the entire event, including the initial pressure rise and any pre-triggering signal, is retained.

The gunshot signature was thus captured, displayed directly on the screen, and a permanent trace of the waveform obtained from the Level Recorder. This time history, and the 0 to 20 kHz frequency analysis produced from it, are reproduced in Fig.5.5.4. The extremely short rise time, square pulse shape, and rapid decay of the signal in the anechoic conditions of the chamber, can be seen clearly in Fig.5.5.4(a). It should be noted that the amplitude scale of the signal signature is linear.

The scale of the time history on the visual display of the 2031 may be adjusted, so that either the entire length or approximately one-third of it fills the screen width. In the expanded mode the signal can also be moved across the screen to enable all parts of the record, not just the beginning, to be viewed in detail. This is especially useful when viewing transients which have very short duration or which contain high frequencies. As an example, a photograph of the screen display of the impulsive noise produced by a clicking toy is reproduced in Fig.5.5.5 in both normal and expanded modes. By measuring the wavelength of the chief components of the signal using the calibrated electronic curser, its dominant frequency was estimated to be between 4 and 6 kHz. A Level Recorder trace of the frequency spectrum of this

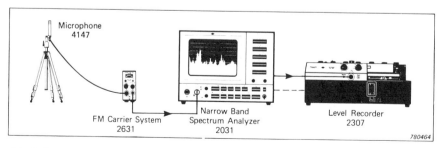

Fig.5.5.3. Instrumentation for the rapid automatic analysis of transient signals

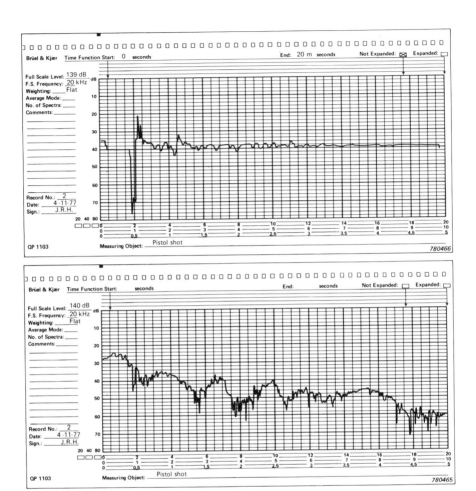

Fig.5.5.4. Analysis of a gunshot
a) Time History   *b) Frequency analysis*

pulse, reproduced in Fig.5.5.6, shows that the spectrum levels are indeed greatest in this frequency region. The important parameters describing the time-varying impulse itself e.g. rise time, shape, peak amplitude, etc., and its frequency analysis, could thus be obtained simultaneously.

A further facility of the 2031 which is invaluable when dealing with transients, is its ability to automatically capture and average a large number of similar events. This allows representative time histories and spectral values to be obtained for the many repeated processes in industry which generate impulsive noise likely to cause hearing damage, e.g. punch presses and bottling lines.

182

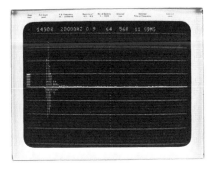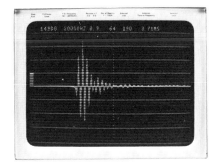

Fig.5.5.5. Photograph of 2031 visual display
a) normal mode   b) expanded mode

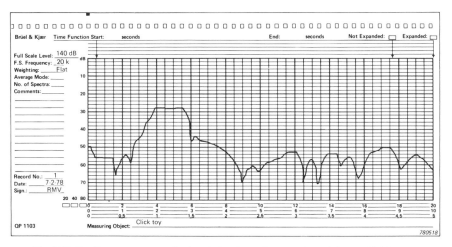

Fig.5.5.6. Frequency analysis of the impulse produced by a clicking toy

Selected Bibliography

BOONE, M. M.:   Loudness Measurements on Pure Tone and Broad
                     Band Impulsive Sounds. Acustica Vol. 29. 1973. pp.
                     198 — 204.

BRÜEL, P. V.:   Do we measure Damaging Noise Correctly? Brüel &
                     Kjær Technical Review No.1 — 1976. Also Noise
                     Control Engineering Vol. 8. No.2. March-April, 1977
                     pp. 52 — 60.

COLES, R. A. and   *Hazards from Impulsive Noise.* Annals of Occupa-
RICE, C. G.:   tional Hygiene Vol. 10. 1967. pp. 381 — 388.

DYM, C. L.:   *Sources of Industrial Impact/Impulsive Noise.* Noise
                    Control Engineering Vol. 8. No.2. March-April 1977.
                    pp. 81 — 87.

FIDDEL, S.,   *The Noisiness of Impulsive Sounds.* J.A.S.A. Vol.
PEARSONS, K. S.,   48. No.6. 1970. pp. 1304 — 1310.
GRIGNETTI, M. and
GREEN, D. M.:

McROBERT, H. and   *Damage-risk Criteria: The trading relation between in-*
WARD, W. D.:   *tensity and the number of non-reverberant impulses.*
                    J.A.S.A. Vol. 53. No.5. 1973. pp. 1297 — 1300.

SOLAINI, A. V.:   *Impulsive Noise — A brief review.* TRRL Supplemen-
                    tary Report 85 UC. Transport and Road Research La-
                    boratory 1974.

B.O.H.S.:   *Hygiene Standard for Impulsive Noise from the Com-*
                    mittee of Hygiene Standards of the British Occupa-
                    tional Hygiene Society. Annals of Occupational Hy-
                    giene Vol. 19. pp. 179 — 191.

6. NOISE IN THE COMMUNITY

6.1. MEASUREMENT AND CONTROL OF NOISE FROM ROAD TRAFFIC

Extensive surveys carried out in many of the developed countries have identified traffic as the most widespread and annoying source of noise. Annoyance has been shown to be dependent on such factors as previous noise exposure, class, and the general quality of the environment i.e. socioeconomic factors. Research carried out to identify the relative annoyance of different types of noise has shown that, for a given level, the noise produced by traffic is rated as more annoying than that from, for example, aircraft and trains. Because of the increasing number and usage of road vehicles, the indications are that, unless increasingly stringent measures are taken to control it, the intensity of traffic noise will continue to increase steadily well into the forseeable future. It is this widespread occurrence and the particularly annoying nature of traffic noise that has encouraged many industrialized countries to introduce legislation in an attempt to reduce it, or at the very least to keep its rate of increase under some sort of control.

These controls have taken many forms, such as limiting by law the amount of noise individual vehicles may produce under rigorous test conditions, zoning and road planning to separate traffic and noise-sensitive areas, and the introduction of one-way systems to improve traffic flow. Prediction methods for the noise from freely flowing traffic have been well established for some time and recently much attention has been concentrated on the difficult problem of developing similar methods to be applied to the congested traffic conditions more normally found in city centres. The intermittent nature of the noise emission, the relative importance of acceleration and braking, and the different effects of junctions, traffic controls and roundabouts have yet to be combined into a prectical everyday method of noise prediction. The effects of one-way systems, for example, may be to alter the traffic flow to such an extent that any improvement gained by reducing acceleration and braking noise may be more than offset by encouraging an increase in both traffic volume and average speed.

When considering traffic noise, a careful distinction should be drawn between the emission from individual vehicles and from the traffic stream as a whole. This is because the peaks in the long term noise level defined by the L_1 or L_{10} are due to the passage of individual vehicles in the stream acting

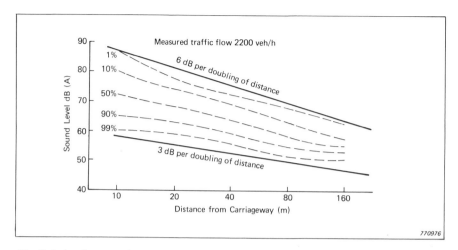

Fig.6.1.1. Attenuation of Traffic Noise with distance for various values of L_N (after Langdon and Scholes)

as point sources. The peak noise therefore decays in a rather similar manner i.e. by approximately 6 dB per doubling of distance, as one moves away from the road. However, the "background" level, defined as say L_{90}, contains significant contributions from a greater number of vehicles more distant in the traffic stream, and therefore acts more as a line source, attenuating by only about 3 dB per doubling of distance. See Fig.6.1.1.

Whereas the entire traffic stream, and therefore its noise, is to some extent under the control of planning authorities in terms of position, gradient, shielding, composition and volume, the individual vehicles are not. Their noise output depends on less controllable factors, such as driving style, vehicle condition, and their original design noise level. A long-term educational program appears to be the only way that attitudes towards noise can be changed and the first two factors eliminated. Only the design noise levels can be significantly effected by regulations and most countries are now encouraging manufacturers to produce quieter vehicles by imposing design limits which become more stringent as time proceeds. Currently allowable noise levels within the EEC for a wide range of vehicles are shown in Fig.6.1.2.

The intention is to lower the limits progressively as decreases in acoustic emissions are made possible by improvements in design and technology. One noise-conscious city in the U.S.A., Chicago, has set out the schedule shown in Fig.6.1.3 for vehicular drive-by noise emission up to 1980; measured at 15 m (Twice the distance adopted by the International Standards Organisation and in Europe. Approximately 6 dB should be added to these figures to compare them with the ISO or European criteria.)

186

Vehicle category	Value expressed in dB(A)
Vehicles intended for the carriage of passengers and comprising not more than nine seats including the driver's seat.	82
Vehicles intended for the carriage of passengers comprising more than nine seats including the driver's seat, and having a permissible maximum weight not exceeding 3,5 metric tons.	84
Vehicles intended for the carriage of goods and having a permissible maximum weight not exceeding 3,5 metric tons.	84
Vehicles intended for the carriage of passengers, comprising more than nine seats including the driver's seat, and having a permissible maximum weight exceeding 3,5 metric tons.	89
Vehicles intended for the carriage of goods and having a permissible maximum weight not exceeding 3,5 metric tons.	89
Vehicles intended for the carriage of passengers, comprising more than nine seats including the driver's seat, and having an engine power equal to or exceeding 200 HP DIN.	91
Vehicles intended for the carriage of goods or materials, having an engine power equal to or exceeding 200 HP DIN and a permissible maximum weight exceeding 12 metric tons.	91 780146

Fig.6.1.2. European communities directive concerning maximum permissible noise limits for new vehicles

Both the American and International recommendations for the assessment of noise from individual moving vehicles have been based on the maximum drive-by noise level in dB(A). Good correlation between this and subjective response has been demonstrated except for some classes of vehicles, especially motorcycles, which are rated as particularly disturbing for a given maximum noise level. Much of this work was carried out ten years or more ago and this difference may no longer be as significant as it was. Although no recent extensive measurements are available, multiple cylinders, better silencing and higher engine speeds have led to a lessening of the impulsive nature of noise from earlier motorcycles which was thought to be an important factor in producing increased annoyance.

The ISO procedure is to accelerate in a standard way past a microphone set up at a height of 1.2 m and at a defined distance from the path of the vehicle. The test region should be on flat ground of at least 50 m radius, the

Vehicle category	Date of construction	Maximum limit (dBA)
Motorcycles	Before 1 January, 1970	92
	After 1 January, 1970	88
	After 1 January, 1973	86
	After 1 January, 1975	84
	After 1 January, 1980	75
Vehicles heavier than 8 000 pounds	After 1 January, 1968	88
	After 1 January, 1973	86
	After 1 January, 1975	84
	After 1 January, 1980	75
Private cars and other motor vehicles	Before 1 January, 1973	86
	After 1 January, 1973	84
	After 1 January, 1975	80
	After 1 January, 1980	75

780147

Fig.6.1.3. Chicago's gradually tightening standards for noise emission

centre 20 metres of which should be a hard surface such as asphalt or concrete. It should be free of reflecting obstructions, have a noise-free surface, a low ambient noise level, and wind and bystanders must not be allowed to influence the measurements. The test site should be as in Fig.6.1.4 and the vehicle should follow the path CC. It should be driven in second gear (or third gear if it has more than 4 gears) at a speed corresponding to 3/4 of the maximum engine speed or 50 km/h, whichever is the lowest. On reaching the

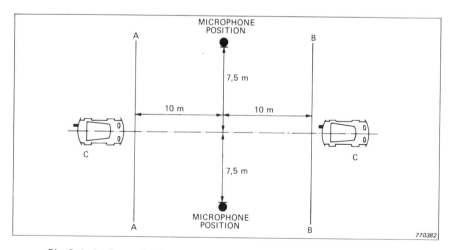

Fig.6.1.4. Test site for moving vehicle test recommended by I.S.O.

line AA, the throttle should be opened fully and maintained in this position until the rear of the vehicle has reached the line BB. At least two measurements should be carried out on each side of the vehicle and the report should contain all relevant details of the vehicle such as loading, power rating, capacity and engine speeds.

The measurement of noise from traffic streams is a rather more complicated affair, expressed in a variety of units in use in different countries, and often involves statistical analysis and integration procedures. To demonstrate the general methods and techniques, and to illustrate typical results from different types of road, traffic noise measurements were carried out in a heavily trafficked main thoroughfare in central Copenhagen and a motorway on the outskirts of the city.

Short term traffic noise measurements

A totally portable Measurement system was used, consisting of a Microphone Type 4165 and Preamplifier Type 2619 connected directly to a Noise Level Analyzer Type 4426 which also supplied the microphone's power. The microphone was protected from wind-generated noise by a windshield which is especially important in traffic noise measurements where significant air currents can be generated by large, fast-moving vehicles. Two output devices were used in order to provide results in both numerical and graphic form. These were the Alphanumeric Printer Type 2312 and Portable Level Recorder Type 2306 respectively. A diagram of the equipment used is shown in Fig.6.1.5. The procedure for both measuring positions was the same, the microphone was mounted on the tripod at a distance of 1.2 meters above the ground and a suitable distance from the carriageway. In the case of the motorway this was 15 meters, but in the restrictions of the city centre this had to be reduced to only 5 meters, a problem typical of practical urban noise measurements where ideal measuring conditions are rarely obtained. The

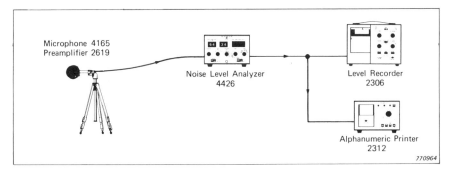

Fig.6.1.5. Portable instrumentation for traffic noise measurement

189

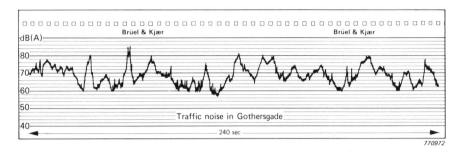

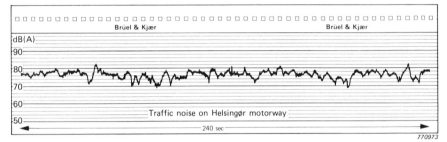

Fig.6.1.6. Typical Traffic Noise time histories
a) Gothersgade, City Centre
b) The Helsingør Motorway

4426 was then calibrated by a Sound Level Calibrator Type 4230 which supplies a 94 dB pure tone at 1000 Hz.

A representative period of noise was first recorded directly onto the portable level recorder at each measurement position and tape recordings were
made in parallel in order to carry out further detailed analysis in the laboratory. The noise level time histories of Fig.6.1.6 clearly show the different nature of congested and freely-flowing traffic. The former varies far more in level and contains the occasional high peak caused by an accelerating vehicle.
The latter is less peaky, both because each individual vehicle is travelling at a
steady cruising speed, and because the time interval between successive vehicles in the traffic stream is relatively short. These two factors combine to
produce the almost steady noise typical of motorways, which is heard as a
rushing sound close to the carriageway but which becomes a deep rumble far
from it as the selective absorption of the atmosphere takes its toll of the high
frequencies in the spectrum.

At each site a series of 10 minute samples was analyzed by the 4426, and
both the probability and cumulative distributions were recorded directly
onto the 2306. Some of these plots are reproduced in Fig.6.1.7. In addition
the 2312 could be activated to print out, in numeric form, pre-programmed
information from the 4426.

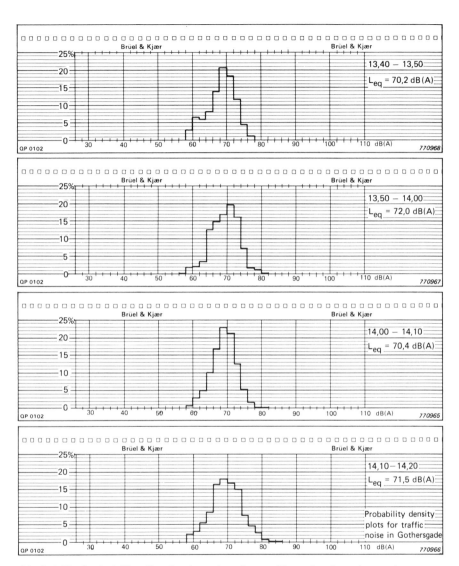

Fig.6.1.7. Probability distribution plots for traffic noise in a busy city street, taken at 10 minute intervals over a 40 minute period

The distribution histograms of Figs.6.1.7 and 6.1.8, from the 10 minute sample measurements of congested and freely-flowing traffic respectively, clearly demonstrate another difference between them. The motorway noise distribution is symmetrical in a narrow range of noise levels, but the city centre distribution is skew over a wider range and also varies significantly from sample to sample.

191

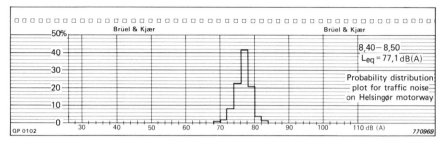

Fig.6.1.8. Probability distribution plot for motorway noise

The cumulative distribution of a set of noise samples may also be output, either via the printer by suitably programming the 4426 or graphically via the portable level recorder as in Fig.6.1.9 allowing any value of L_N to be quickly obtained. The programming facilities of the 4426 allow a wide range of parameters to be output at time intervals which may be set on the printer's front panel. The day and time may also be preset on the internal clock and subsequently printed at the head of the data at the requested time intervals. The sound level, number of accumulated samples, L_{eq}, any value of L_N from 1 to 99, and the distribution and cumulative distribution can all be obtained by suitable programming of the Noise Level Analyzer. An example of a typical output from the traffic noise measurements can be seen in Fig.6.1.10, giving a complete analysis of the noise environment, including several important units and the distribution of the samples, at 10 minute intervals throughout the day. The instrument may be interrogated via the front panel controls to check on the progress of the measurement at any time during the aquisition of data without interfering with the stored values.

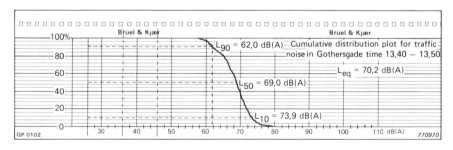

Fig.6.1.9. Cumulative distribution plot for traffic noise in a busy city street (compare with Fig.6.1.7 for the same time interval)

192

```
01:13:40  S=05715
     L0001=077.3DB
     L0005=074.8DB
     L0010=073.8DB
     L0050=069.0DB
     L0090=062.0DB
     L0095=060.5DB
       LEQ=070.2DB
 D026.0DB=000.0%
 D028.0DB=000.0%
 D030.0DB=000.0%
 D032.0DB=000.0%
 D034.0DB=000.0%
 D036.0DB=000.0%
 D038.0DB=000.0%
 D040.0DB=000.0%
 D042.0DB=000.0%
 D044.0DB=000.0%
 D046.0DB=000.0%
 D048.0DB=000.0%
```

```
 D050.0DB=000.0%
 D052.0DB=000.0%
 D054.0DB=000.0%
 D056.0DB=000.3%
 D058.0DB=003.3%
 D060.0DB=006.6%
 D062.0DB=006.8%
 D064.0DB=008.9%
 D066.0DB=013.5%
 D068.0DB=020.8%
 D070.0DB=018.6%
 D072.0DB=012.8%
 D074.0DB=005.7%
 D076.0DB=001.5%
 D078.0DB=000.6%
 D080.0DB=000.0%
 D082.0DB=000.0%
 D084.0DB=000.0%
 D086.0DB=000.0%
 D088.0DB=000.0%
```

Fig.6.1.10. Example of Noise Level Analyser data printed out using the Alphanumeric printer

A full frequency analysis, either of a single vehicle drive-by or the traffic stream as a whole, can provide much useful information about the chief sources of noise, as well as its potential to annoy. Sequential analysis of representative periods of data in octave or third octave bands is, unfortunately, an extremely long and tedious process involving perhaps 30 or more passes of the selected sample through the filters necessary to cover the frequency range of interest. As a period of even ten minutes may be considered small in statistical terms when considering traffic noise, we are talking in terms of many hours of analysis time. Sequential filtering techniques are therefore more suitable for application to short events or steady noises.

The advent of the real-time or parallel analyzer has made practicable the analysis of non-steady noises into octave, third octave and narrow bands in the time it takes to collect the data, either directly or from a tape-recorded signal. The data in this case came from recorded measurements made at the same places and times as the analyses discussed above, using a Direct Recorder Type 7004. A calibration signal was recorded in the normal way and the

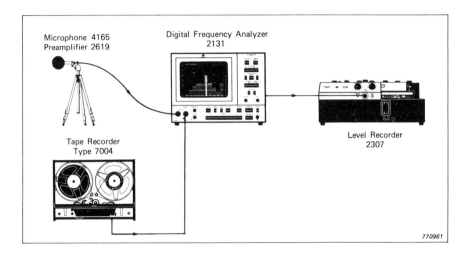

Fig.6.1.11. Instrumentation for the real-time 1/3 octave analysis of road traffic noise

input controls of the Digital Frequency Analyzer Type 2131 adjusted to calibrate from this signal. Permanent records of the spectra displayed on the screen were obtained via a level recorder, directly connected to, and calibrated with, the analyzer. The instrumentation is shown in Fig.6.1.11 and level recorder charts of the short term average spectra of both congested and freely flowing traffic streams are reproduced in Fig.6.1.12. These clearly show the different characteristics of the two types of noise. The motorway noise example has a well-defined maximum in the 63 and 80 Hz third octave bands, which represents the firing frequency of the majority of vehicles at cruising speed, and a general high level around 1 kHz which is due in the main to tyre and wind noise. The congested traffic spectrum also has a maximum caused by the engine firing rate but it is at a lower frequency, as one would expect from the generally slower traffic speeds, and is wider because the range of engine speeds of a sample of vehicles during acceleration and braking is greater than at cruising speed. Of particular note is the total absence of the other peak of energy distributed around 1 kHz. At the relatively low speeds typical of town traffic the contribution to the spectrum from tyre and wind noise is very small, although tyre noise becomes more prominent if the road surface is wet.

194

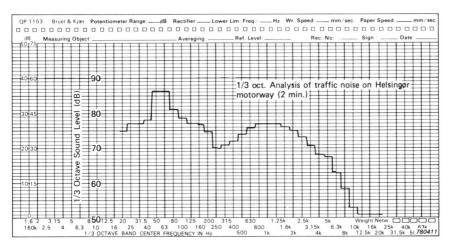

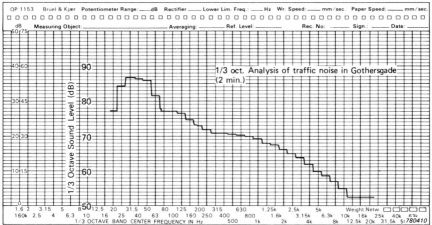

Fig.6.1.12. 1/3 octave analysis of traffic noise
a) Freely flowing motorway traffic
b) Congested City traffic

Measurement of single events

One of the advantages of the L_{eq} measurements used in many countries is that it provides a method of rating the overall noise environment by the addition of the constituent events. A convenient way of characterising these individual events is to express them as L_{AX}, the level which if maintained for a duration of one second would cause the same A-weighted sound energy to be received as the event itself. L_{eq} and L_{AX} are dealt with in greater detail in Chapter 3.

To illustrate the use of the units, vehicle drive-bys were measured using the Integrating Sound Level Meter Type 2218, which allows both L_{eq} and L_{AX} to be read directly, and the corresponding time histories were recorded on a level recorder. Fig.6.1.13 shows noise level time histories of a Bus and a motorcycle drive-by. The L_{eq} values are noted, and the L_{AX} is represented by the level lasting for one second which contains the same energy as the entire event which follows it. An important feature of L_{AX} is that whereas the L_{eq}, as an *averaged-energy* value, depends on the duration of the integration used to obtain it, the L_{AX}, as a *total energy* value will be independent of the time over which it is measured, *as long as it contains the entire event.*

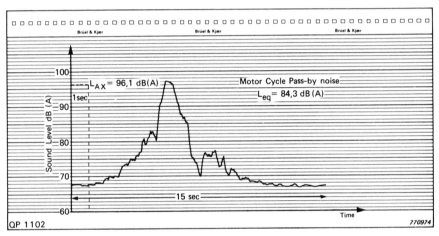

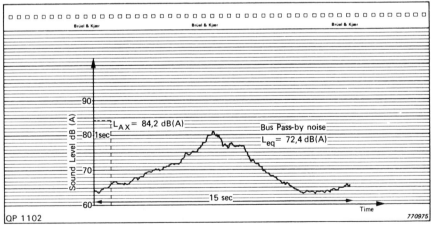

Fig.6.1.13. Noise Level history of vehicle drive-bys
a) Motor Cycle
b) Public Bus

196

Selected Bibliography

ALEXANDRE, A. and BARDE, J-Ph.:   *Le Temps du Bruit.* Flammarion, Paris 1973.

BENEDETTO, G. and SPAGNOLO, R.:   *Traffic Noise Survey of Turin, Italy.* Applied Acoustics. Vol. 10. No. 3 July 1977. pp. 201 — 222

BRASCH, J. K.:   *Vehicular Traffic Noise Near High Speed Highways.* Sound and Vibration. Vol 1. No.12. Dec. 1967.

B.R.E.:   *Prediction of Traffic Noise, Parts 1 and 2.* Building Research Establishment Digests Nos. 185-186, January, February 1976. H.M.S.O. London.

BRUCKMAYER, F.:   *Zusammenhang zwischen städtischen Zonung und Strassenverkehrslärm.* Lärmbekämpfung. Bd. 13. Heft 1. Februar 1969 und Heft 2, April 1969.

BRUCHMAYER, F. and LANG, J.:   *Disturbance of the Population due to Traffic Noise.* Öst. Ing. Zeitshr. No.8. pp. 302 — 306. No.9. pp. 338 — 344. No.10. pp. 376 — 385 1967.

BRUGES, M. A.:   *Noise Prediction for Urban Traffic Conditions Related to Measurements in the Sydney Metropolitan Area.* Applied Acoustics January 1977. pp. 1 — 7.

CITY OF CHICAGO: *New Noise Regulations.* Department of Environmental Control. Chicago 1971.

CLOSE, W. H.:   *Should there be Truck Tyre Noise Regulations?* Sound and Vibration. Feb. 1975. pp. 24 — 27.

DELANEY, M. E., HARLAND, D. G., HOOD, R. A. and SCHOLES, W. E.:   *The Prediction of Noise Levels L_{10} due to Road Traffic.* J.S.V. 1976. Vol. 48. No.3. pp. 305 — 325.

FORD, R. D. and SAUNDERS, D. J.:   *The Measurement of Noise Inside Cars.* Applied Acoustics. Vol. 3. No.1. Jan. 1970.

GAUSS, F. and JAKEL, S.:   *Special Noises of Commercial Vehicles.* Automobile technische Zeitschrift. December 1976. pp. 519 — 521.

GILBERT, D.:   *Noise from Road Traffic (Interrupted Flow).* J.S.V. 1977. Vol. 51. No.2. pp. 171 — 181.

GUTHOF, D. und GABLESKE, R.:   *Verkehrslärmmessungen in Köln.* Kampf dem Lärm. Jg. 15, Heft 6, Dezember 1968. S. 150.

HÄRTLING, F.:   *Zum Schutz von Verkehrslärm bei Krankenhäusern.* Kampf dem Lärm. Bd. 12, Heft 1. 1965, S. 11.

HEWLING, M.:   *Town Planning and Traffic Noise.* Applied Acoustics. Vol. 2. No.4. Oct. 1969.

H.M.S.O.:   *Noise*. Final report of the Committee on the Problem of Noise. Sir Allan Wilson, Chairman, Command 2056. H.M.S.O. London, July 1963.

I.S.O. R.362 1964.:   *Measurement of noise emitted by vehicles*

I.S.O. D.I.S. 5130   *Acoustics — Measurement of noise emitted by sta-*
1978:   *tionary road vehicles — Survey method*

JONSSON, E.,   *Annoyance reactions to traffic noise in Italy and*
KAJLAND, A.,   *Sweden*. Arch. Environ. Health. No. 19. 1969. pp.
PACAGNELLA, B. and   692 — 699.
SöRENSEN, S.:

KIHLMAN, T.:   *Traffic Noise Control in Sweden*. Noise Control Engineering. Nov.-Dec. 1975. pp. 24 — 30.

LANGDON, F. J.:   *Noise Nuisance Caused by Road Traffic in Residential Areas*. Parts I and II, J.S.V. 1976 Vol. 47 pp. 243 — 282. Part III, J.S.V. 1976 vol. 49 No.2 pp. 241 — 256.

LANGDON, F. J. and   *The Traffic Noise Index; a method of controlling*
SCHOLES, W. E.:   *Noise Nuisance*. Arch. J. No.147. April 1968 and B.R.S. report 38/68.

MILLS, C. H. G. and   *Subjective Rating of Motor Vehicle Noise*. Engineer.
ROBINSON, D. W.:   Vol. 211. No.5501. p.1070. (Also enclosed in the Wilson Committee Report)'

MANTEL, J.:   *Lärmpegel-, Lautstärke-, Lärmbelästigung im Bereich des Strassenverkehreslärmes*. Kampf dem Lärm (1977) No. 24. pp. 110—119.

PARKIN, P. H.,   *The London Noise Survey*. H.M.S.O. London 1968.
PURKIS, H. J.,
STEPHENSON, R. J. and
SCHLAFFENBERG, B.:

REIHER, H.:   *Lärmminderung auf Baustellen*. Kampf dem Lärm. 16. Jg. Heft 5. Oktober 1969.

REVILL, D.:   *Traffic Noise Measurement and Prediction Techniques*. Noise Control, Vibration and Insulation. Jan. 1976. pp. 26 — 32.

ROBERTS, J. E. and   *Florida's Approach to Motor Vehicle Noise Control*.
BORTHWICK, J. O.:   Sound and Vibration. Dec. 1975. pp. 18 — 22.

ROBINSON, D. W.,   *Motor Vehicle Noise Measurement*. Engineer. Vol.
COPELAND, W. C. and   211, No.5488. 1961. p. 493.
RENNIE, A. J.:

ROBINSON, D.W.: *An Outline Guide to Criteria for the Limitation of Urban Noise.* Aeronautical Research Council Current Papers, CP 1112. March 1969.

ROE, G. E.: *The Silencing of a High Performance Motorcycle.* J.S.V. Vol. 33, No.1. 1974. pp. 29 — 40.

ROWLEY, D. W.: *Control of Farm Tractor Intake and Exhaust Noise.* Sound and Vibration. Vol. 1. No.3. March 1967.

SANDERS, G. J.: *Silencers: Their Design and Application.* Sound and Vibration. Vol. 2. No.2. Febr. 1968.

SCHENKER-SPRÜNGLI: *Fortschritte der Lärmbekämpfung in der Schweiz.* Lärmbekämpfung. Bd. 13. Heft 3. Juni 1069.

SCOLES, W. E.: *Traffic Noise Criteria.* Applied Acoustics. Vol. 3. No.1 Jan. 1970.

SCHOLES, W. E. and SARGENT, J. W.: *Designing against noise from road traffic.* Applied Acoustics. Vol. 4. pp. 203 — 234. 1971.

SCOLES, W. E. and VULKAN, G. H.: *A Note of the Objective Measurement of Road Traffic Noise.* Applied Acoustics. Vol. 2. No.3. July 1969

SPANNER, P.: *Das Geräusch von Verbrennungsmotoren.* Kampf dem Lärm. Bd. 12. Heft 5. 1965. S. 116.

STÜBER, C.: *Möglichkeiten zur Minderung des Innen- und Aussengeräusches von Schienenfahrzeugen.* Kampf dem Lärm. 16. Jg. Heft 1, Februar 1969 und Heft 2, April 1969.

THIESSEN, G. J. and OLSON, N.: *Community Noise — Surface Transportation.* Sound and Vibration. Vol. 2. No.4. April 1968.

THOMAS, R. J.: *Traffic-Noise — The Performance and Economics of Noise Reducing Materials.* Applied Acoustics. Vol. 2. No.3. July 1969.

TOMASZEWSKI, L.: *Untersuchungen über Lärmabschirmung von Gebäuden an Verkehrsstrassen.* Kampf dem Lärm 16. Jg. Heft 3. Juni 1969.

U.S. Dept. Trans.: *Noise Prediction Method.* U.S. Department of Transportation 1972.

WIENER, F. M.: *Experimental Study of the Airborne Noise Generated by Passenger Automobile Tires.* Noise Control. Vol. 6. No.4. July/August 1960. p.13 (161).

WIETHAUP, H.: *Lärmbekämpfung in der Bundesrepublik Deutschland.* Carl Heymanns Verlag K.G. Köln. 1967.

6.2. AIRCRAFT NOISE MEASUREMENT

The determination of noisiness and annoyance caused by exposure to aircraft noise has been the subject of a considerable period of extensive research, which has generally fallen into one of the following two main areas.

Firstly, measurement units which accurately describe the noisiness or annoyance caused by an individual noisy event have been determined both in the laboratory and in the field following judgement tests using panels of listeners. These experiments were usually in the form of paired-comparison tests carried out by judging the noise to be rated against a reference sound. Both noises were usually presented by loudspeakers in laboratory experiments, but a second aircraft was used as a reference source for the judgement of actual aircraft flyovers. Good agreement between the actual and laboratory tests was observed, and one of the interesting subsidiary facts which came out of the work was that people appeared to be consistently less tolerant of aircraft noise heard indoors than they were of the same noise heard outdoors by approximately 20 dB, the attenuation typically provided by the structure of a house.

Secondly, measurements have been made of the long-term noise exposure of overflown populations, carried out in the surrounding area. The reaction of the population was related to their measured noise exposure via a wide selection of derived units of various complexities, some of which have been briefly described earlier in section 3.7. This work resulted in the definition of community noise limits for residential areas near airports, take-off noise limits for individual aircraft operations and also led to the introduction of type certification tests for new aircraft. This latter procedure effectively attempts to reduce the source noise of new aircraft types by stimulating improvements in engine design and encouraging the use of noise-reduction measures.

Only conventional fixed-wing aircraft were originally included in the International Standard for these measurements, but recent changes have been made to include other flight vehicles, including helicopters, although it is specifically stated that the impulsive noise which is a feature of some rotorcraft cannot be adequately rated by the normal methods.

Other recent developments in the aircraft noise field include a new rating unit which has been proposed as a planning tool for the purpose of comparing the noise from both existing and new airports, although it could be equally applicable to the sites of other noisy activities. The procedure attempts to relate the noise nuisance caused to the residents in the vicinity of an airport to its benefits to the community as a whole. Effectively then, this is a measure of the efficiency of the airport operations in terms of the noise nuisance which it generates, expressed in man-days of serious noise nuisance per airport passenger, and called the Noise Burden Factor (NBF). The

Noise Burden, of course, can manifest itself in a variety of easily measured ways such as decreased property values, the cost of insulating against the noise, and interference with work, which can be assigned actual monetary values.

The Air transport industry has expanded rapidly during the last few decades in terms of both the total number of aircraft movements and the geographical regions which are served. In order to carry the increased number of passengers economically, larger and faster aircraft have been developed with increased engine power. All these factors, increased movements, more airports, bigger, more powerful aircraft, have combined to produce high noise levels and spread the effects even further from the airport boundary. It is only in recent years that the advent of the high-by-pass-ratio fan jet engines now installed in the new generation of wide-bodied aircraft has began to reverse this trend, following a period of only mild success with the noise-abatement operating procedures and retrospective engine/nacelle modifications.

The aircraft noise problem falls naturally into 3 main areas, the sound power of the aircraft as source, the operating procedures which restrain that source, and the planning of new, or the extension of existing, airports. The first two areas are under the control of national or international regulations to which every new, or significantly modified aircraft type must be tested, the type certification test. This very closely defines the operations to be carried out, the condition of the aircraft, the positioning and specification of the measuring equipment, the atmospheric conditions and a wide variety of other parameters known to affect noise generation and propagation. A large volume of subsidiary information is required to normalize noise measurements to standard operating and atmospheric conditions, a procedure necessitated by the vast differences between international airports in such parameters as temperature, pressure and humidity. These have important effects on engine performance and sound propagation through the atmosphere and therefore on the intensity of noise received at the ground measuring station. A brief description of the procedure is given later in this section, but it is imperative that before any work of this type is carried out, a detailed study of all the relevant documents is made to ensure that the most recent methods of calculation and measurement are fully understood and utilised.

An internationally accepted standard for aircraft noise certification is, because of the world-wide nature of aircraft operations, of great importance in controlling aircraft noise at source and providing standardised information to planning authorities at other airports and in other countries. This data can then easily be used locally after applying the appropriate corrections for the airport concerned. At existing airports, the effects on noise exposure of airport extensions, the introduction of new aircraft, and changes to operating procedures, can be determined. Alternative sites for new airports can be assessed for their comparative environmental impact and for the planning of land usage in their vicinities. In this way the conflict between aircraft operations and acceptable living conditions, which has grown up with many of the long established airports, can hopefully be avoided at the planning stage in future.

The second noise control area arises directly from this consideration: noise monitoring around an existing airport to determine the actual exposure, on the ground, from normal airport operations. A suitable system may consist of many microphones measuring simultaneously at locations around the airport, feeding information back to a central processing system, or individual events recorded at specific points and analysed later in the laboratory. Either of these methods can be used to compute a noise contour map in any of the many ratings currently used to express aircraft noise exposure.

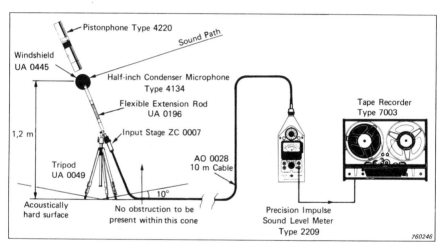

Fig.6.2.1. Portable Instrumentation for aircraft noise measurement and recording

A typical aircraft noise measuring arrangement is shown in Fig.6.2.1. The diaphragm of the pressure-response microphone should be mounted at grazing incidence to the aircraft flight path at a height of 1,2 metres above an acoustically hard surface, and no obstruction should be present within the 80° cone shown in the figure. Personnel carrying out the measurements may themselves constitute such obstructions, necessitating the use of a remotely placed microphone if simultaneous meter readings are also to be taken. There must be no precipitation, or winds in excess of 5 m/s at a height of 10 m above the ground. Measurements are made with a precision sound level meter, the system being calibrated with a pistonphone and the microphone protected against wind noise by a suitable shield. Approximate values of peak perceived noise level can be obtained from simple A or D-weighted sound level meter readings by applying the relevant correction factors. However, an unweighted recorded signal can be analysed later in the laboratory to yield very much more information about the flyover, such as the continuous variation of level and or spectral content with time. These are required for full Perceived Noise calculations to Type Certification standards.

Analysis of the recorded signal may be made in several ways, the method chosen depending on the quantity of data, the application of the final results, and the complexity of procedure which can either be accepted or undertaken. If a simple approach is practicable, the signal may be either frequency weighted or sequentially filtered and the output fed to a graphic level recorder as shown in Fig.6.2.2. This method quickly provides time histories of the frequency-weighted noise levels from which derived units such as L_{eq} and approximations to L_{EPN} can be calculated. Sequential analysis in terms of 1/3 octave bands, also recorded as functions of time, is necessary if actual calculations of Perceived Noise Level complete with tone and duration corrections are to be carried out.

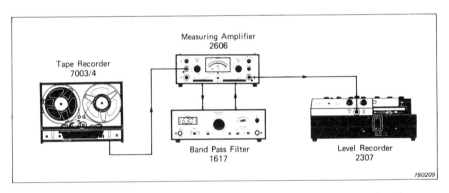

Fig.6.2.2. Instrumentation for the analysis of recorded aircraft noise

A more advanced measurement technique has considerable advantages over the sequential filtering and graphical recording method if large quantities of data have to be handled and/or complicated calculations have to be made. This is essential for example, when calculating effective perceived noise levels, L_{EPN} , for certification purposes, the procedure for which requires the spectrum to be available at intervals of not more than half a second during the flyover period. The quantity L_{EPN} , which has been adopted as the best descriptor of aircraft noise nuisance, is obtained by taking into account both the spectrum and the time history of the noise at each time interval. This can only be achieved within realistic bounds of time and effort, by

203

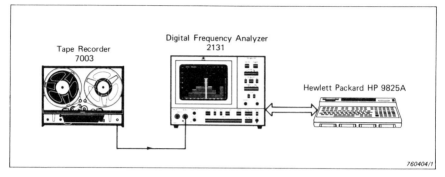

Fig.6.2.3. Instrumentation for high speed automatic analysis of recorded aircraft noise

parallel filtering of the signal and digital processing of the outputs with a system similar to that suggested in Fig.6.2.3. A typical analysis from this system is shown in Fig.6.2.4 together with a level recorder trace of the flyover noise level.

For each spectrum, the sound pressure level in each 1/3 octave band from 50 to 10000 Hz is converted to perceived noisiness values (in noys) by means of either a table or contours such as those shown in Fig.6.2.5. For each spectrum the noy values for all the 1/3 octave bands are then combined according to the formula

$$N = n_{max} + 0.15 \left(\sum n - n_{max} \right)$$

where n_{max} is the greatest value of n
and $\sum n$ is the sum of the noisiness values in all the bands.

N is now converted to the perceived noise level, L_{PN}, either by means of a table of numerical values or a scale such as that shown to the right of Fig.6.2.5. Both are derived from the following defining equation

$$L_{PN} = 40 + \frac{10 \, log_{10} \, N}{log_{10} \, 2}$$

If the spectrum is not "smooth", i.e. a pure tone or other irregularity is present, and if this is not due to spurious ground reflection effects, a correction is made to account for its increased annoyance. The identification of the irregularity and the level-difference between it and the notionally "smooth" spectrum is an extremely complex procedure using a two-pass averaging tech-

```
***** LTPN *****

A OR B STORAGE
 BUFFER ?
B
TIME/SEC LTPN/DB
-------------------
   5.05   115.2
   5.56   117.6
   6.06   118.3
   6.57   121.1
   7.07   124.9
   7.58   125.8
   8.08   125.8
   8.59   126.1
```

```
    9.60   128.5
   10.10   131.2
*  10.61  *131.8
   11.11   131.4
   11.62   129.4
   12.12   128.8
   12.63   128.5
   13.13   123.3
   13.64   124.1
   14.14   120.6
   14.65   117.0
   15.15   116.7

*  INDICATES
   MAX. LTPN
```

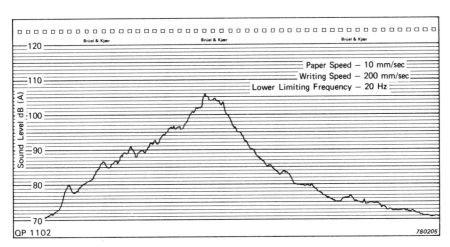

Fig.6.2.4. Typical aircraft noise analysis from the arrangement of Fig.6.2.3 and a flyover time history

nique, usually computerised. The relevant standard should be consulted if the detailed method is required. The tone-correction (C) can be found from this level-difference, using the relevant curve of Fig.6.2.6, which takes the tone's frequency into account, and is added to L_{PN} to form the tone-corrected perceived noise level, L_{TPN} .

205

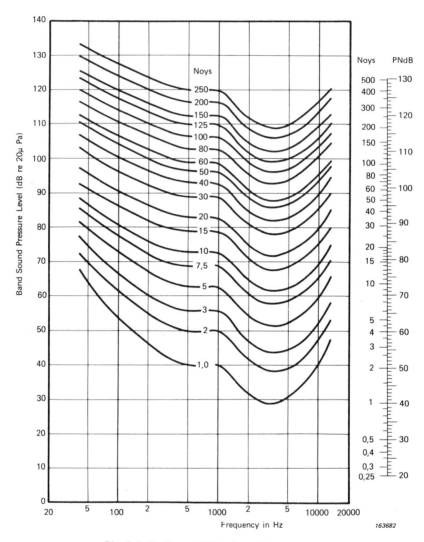

Fig.6.2.5. Equal "Noisiness" contours

A typical curve of the variation of the tone-corrected perceived noise level with time is illustrated in Fig.6.2.7, demonstrating the "double-peak" effect which often occurs and which is caused by the directional nature of the aircraft as a noise source. The highest sound intensities are radiated both from the intake and exhaust of jet engines as separate sources moving past the observer at different times depending on the aircraft speed, altitude, direction and orientation.

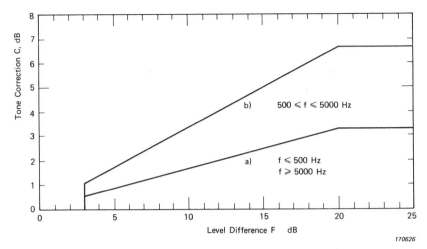

Fig.6.2.6. Tone correction graph for aircraft noise

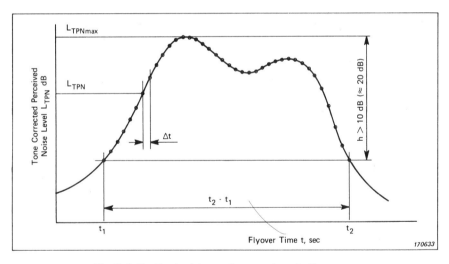

Fig.6.2.7. Typical L_{TPN} for an aircraft flyover

The overall subjective effect of an aircraft flyover depends, however, not only on the maximum tone-corrected noise level but also on the duration of the event. To account for influence of time, the effective perceived noise level L_{EPN} has been defined by the expression

$$L_{EPN} = 10 \, log_{10} \frac{1}{10} \int_{-\infty}^{\infty} 10^{\frac{L \cdot TPN}{10}} \cdot dt$$

207

The integration is more usually made over a time interval t_2-t_1, where $t1_1$ is the instant when the noise level first exceeds a specific value, usually taken as 10 dB below the maximum, and t_2 is the instant when it last decreases to below that value.

In practice L_{EPN} is often expressed as the algebraic sum of L_{TPNmax} and a duration allowance, ΔPN, which is defined

$$\Delta PN = 10 \, log_{10} \frac{\tau}{\tau_{ref}}$$

where $\tau_{ref} = 10$

and $\tau = \dfrac{\displaystyle\int_{t_1}^{t_2} 10^{\left(\frac{L_{TPN}}{10}\right)} \cdot dt}{10^{\left(\frac{L_{TPNmax}}{10}\right)}}$

The continuous integral in this expression can be replaced by a discrete summation if the values of L_{TPN} are known at sufficiently small intervals, say less than 1/2 second.

To normalize the above measurements to standard conditions, the following information about atmospheric and aircraft conditions is required, and should be recorded concurrently with the acoustic data

Atmospheric Conditions

Air temperature (°Celcius)
Relative humidity (per cent)
Wind speed (in m/s)
} Measured at a height of 10 metres above the measurement position

Atmospheric pressure at sea level
Wind direction

Aircraft Conditions

Type of aircraft and engine serial numbers
Aircraft weight (in kg)
Aircraft configuration (flap, landing gear positions)
True Airspeed (m/s)
Aircraft height (m)
Engine parameters (rotational speeds, intake configuration, power settings reheat, etc.)
Flight path, distance and angle.

Two main operations are of importance when considering noise around an airport; the take-off and the approach, and both are usually extensively measured in order to be able to produce noise contours. For the take-off case measurements should, if possible, be made under the following conditions,

aircraft at maximum take-off weight
maximum take-off power
climb speed of V_2 + 10 Knots (1 knot = 0,5144 m/s) (V_2 is the initial climb-out safety speed)
Operational take-off configuration

For an approach the aircraft should:

be stabilised on a 3° glide slope
have maximum allowable flap setting
be at maximum landing weight
have a stabilized airspeed of $1,3 V_s$ + 10 knots. (V_s is the stalling speed)

Sideline noise must also be measured during take-off to determine the contour while the aircraft is still producing maximum power on the ground. In addition, measurements of engine ground running are often made to assess the effect on local communities which may be distant from the normal flight paths although near to maintenance areas.

Apart from the above procedure for determining L_{EPN}, which has been continuously refined over a long period of time until it is now generally accepted as the most suitable unit for describing single event aircraft noise, the I.S.O. draft standard also defines methods of a somewhat simpler nature, requiring only frequency weighted measurements. Because of this fact they are often used for community noise assessment and for airport monitoring systems which are discussed more fully later.

An approximate value of L_{EPN} can also be obtained by adding 7 dB to the maximum D-weighted sound level and by the further addition of a duration correction defined as follows

$$\Delta_{PN} = 10 \ log_{10}\left(\frac{t_2 - t_1}{2\tau_{ref}}\right)$$

where t_2-t_1, is the time interval between the first and last instant when the D-weighted sound level is within 10 dB of its maximum, and τ_{ref} = 10 seconds.

In a similar fashion an A-weighted single-event exposure level L_{AX} can be obtained from the maximum A-weighted value by the addition of a duration correction defined as

$$\Delta_A = 10 \log_{10}\left(\frac{t_2 - t_1}{2\tau_{ref}}\right)$$

where t_2-t_1 takes the same meaning as above except that the A-weighted time history is used, but $\tau_{ref} = 1$ second, to be compatible with other related physical quantities such as L_{eq}.

The units may be extended to the measurement of exposure from any number of events by introducing the concept of equivalent perceived noise level, L_{PNeq}, or L_{eq} for which the integrated energy over the measurement period is the same as the succession of actual events.

We have $$L_{PNeq} = 10 \log_{10}\left(\frac{10}{T}\sum_i 10^{\left(\frac{L_{EPN_i}}{10}\right)}\right)$$

and $$L_{eq} = 10 \log_{10}\left(\frac{1}{T}\sum_i 10^{\left(\frac{L_{AX_i}}{10}\right)}\right)$$

where L_{EPNi} is the effective perceived noise level for the ith event.
L_{AXi} is the A-weighted single event noise exposure level for the ith event.
T   is the measurement period in seconds.

These units of noise exposure are in addition to those described earlier in Chapter 3, such as Noise and Number Index, (N.N.I.), Community Noise Rating, (C.N.R.), and Noise Exposure Forecast, (N.E.F.). There is therefore no shortage of available rating units and techniques from which to choose, the decision often being made either locally by the authority responsible for noise at a particular airport, or by the complexity which a specific situation demands.

The State of California, for instance, prescribes the use of the A-weighted sound exposure level for Single Events (SENEL), Community Noise Exposure, (CNEL), and Noise Impact (NI). These regulations also define noise limits for residential areas around existing major airports which become increasingly stringent as time proceeds. Proposed new airports, however, must meet the most stringent limit immediately, and land use recommendations are made for the unacceptably noisy areas. This would be a situation in which complex methods could be effectively employed, but for smaller private airfields simpler measurement and analysis methods would be more appropriate.

Whichever units and methods are finally selected they can provide useful contours which can be used for assessment of community response or the effectiveness of a variety of noise abatement plans. A typical noise contour map of this type, showing a Noise Exposure Forecast for a large International

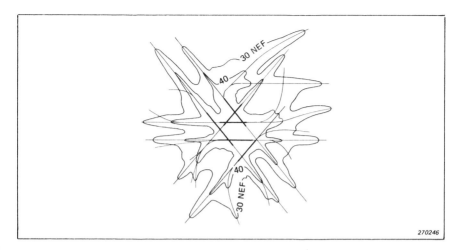

Fig.6.2.8. Typical airport noise exposure contours (Noise Exposure Forecast (NEF), after Bishop and Horonjeff)

airport is reproduced in Fig.6.2.8. Although useful initially for planning purposes, these predictions are usually backed up by a system which continuously monitors the noise at several locations around the airport. This has two main functions. Firstly, a check can be kept on aircraft which infringe airport noise limits, and secondly, data can be recorded over a long time period to obtain continuously updated measured noise contours and thus ascertain the actual long term effects of any noise control measures which may have been instituded. The publics increasing awareness of its right to a quiet environment, and the sensitivity of the controlling authorities to public opinion in relation to aircraft noise, is likely to lead to an increase in the numbers of such monitoring systems in the future.

Because of the extensive complex calculations required to determine the L_{EPN} , it is not well suited to monitoring systems except for special one-off occasions such as a type certification test or for basic research. It is usual in the case of airport monitoring systems to measure the A or D-weighted sound levels and apply the relevant corrections to obtain an approximate value for L_{EPN} . A typical basic system consists of a number of outdoor microphone units with weighting networks transmitting back to a central processing station where nonacoustic data is added. This information will usually consist of the date, time of day, temperature, atmospheric pressure, wind velocity, microphone location, flight number, the aircraft operation and any other relevant Air Traffic Control Data. Facilities may be included to record actual time histories in order to be able to carry out a full $1/3$ octave L_{EPN} analysis on demand. The airport authority can thus identify an aircraft causing an infringement of airport noise regulations, and at the same time amass data for long term statistical analysis of trends in noise level for the purpose of community noise assessment and planning.

For continuous outdoor operation the microphone unit of such a system must be weatherproof, reliable over long periods of time in the polluted air normally found around airports, and because it is normally inaccessible after installation, it must also be capable of remote calibration. The Type 4921 outdoor microphone system is specially designed to fulfil these requirements. The number and distribution of microphone locations around an airport can only be decided after careful consideration of the problems associated with that particular airport. Take-off and approach routes obviously require monitoring but it must also be remembered that residential areas close beside runways or maintenance areas are likely to receive high noise levels even though they may be remote from any of the flight paths. Any large commercial or industrial undertaking such as an airport is also bound to generate workshops, construction sites, and other noisy activity, as well as a traffic noise problem in transporting passengers, services, and cargo to and from the aircraft. Good public relations demands that especially vulnerable residential areas under the take-off and approach paths should be given special attention to ensure that noise abatement procedures are being adhered to.

Selected Bibliography

ARNESEN, G.:	*Aircraft Noise Measurement, Evaluation and Control.* B & K Techn. Rev. No.4 — 1965.
B.B.N.:	*Land Use Planning Relating to Aircraft Noise.* Clearinghouse for Federal Scientific and Technical Information. October 1964.
BERANEK, L. L. and RUDMOSE, H. W.:	*Sound Control in Airplanes.* J.A.S.A. Vol. 19. 1947.
BERANEK, L. L., KRYTER, K. D. and MILLER, L.N.:	*Reaction of People to Exterior Aircraft Noise.* Noise Control. Vol. 5. No.5. Sept. 1959. p. 23 (287)
BISHOP, D. E.:	*Cruise Flight Noise Levels in a Turbojet Transport Airplane.* Noise Control. Vol. 7, No.2, 1961, p. 37.
BISHOP,D. E.:	*Judgements of the relative and absolute acceptability of aircraft Noise.* J.A.S.A. Vol. 40. pp. 108 — 122 1966.
BISHOP, D. E. and HORONJEFF, R. D.:	*Noise Exposure Forecast Contours for Aircraft Noise Tradeoff Studies at Three Major Airports.* FAA. No.70. 7 July 1970.
BOLT, R. H.:	*The Aircraft Noise Problem.* J.A.S.A. Vol. 25. 1953.

BROADBENT, D. E. and *Subjective Measurement of the relative annoyance of*
ROBINSON, D. W.: *simulated sonic bangs and aircraft noise.* J-S.V. Vol.
1, 1964. pp. 162 — 174.

CALIF.: *California Airport Noise Standards.* Dept. of Aeronau-
tics Subchapter 6 Noise Standards.

CHESTNUTT, D.: *Jet Engine Inlet Noise Control.* Sound and Vibration.
Vol. 2. No.12. Dec. 1968.

F.A.A.: *Noise Standards: Aircraft Type Certification.* Federal
Aviation Regulation. Part 36. Rules Service Co.
Washington D.C. 1969.

GALLOWAY, W. J.: *Analysis of the Public Health and Welfare Effects of
E.P.A. Proposed Aircraft Noise Regulations.* Bolt, Beranek and Newman Report No. BBN-3171 March
1976.

GALLOWAY, W. J. and *Technical Review of Federal Aviation Regulations*
BISHOP, D. E.: *Part 36. Noise Standards: Aircraft Certification.* Bolt,
Beranek and Newman, Report No. BBN-2943 March
1976.

GREATREX, F. B.: *Take-off and Landing Noise of the Supersonic Transport Aircraft.* Engineering. Aug. 1963.

HAZARD, W. R.: *Prediction of Noise Disturbance near Large Airports.*
J.S.V. Vol. 15. No.4. 1971. pp. 425 — 446.

HAZARD, W. R.: *Community Reactions to Aircraft Noise — Public
Reactions.* Conference on NASA Research relating to
Noise Alleviation of large Subsonic Jet Aircraft.
NASA Langley Research Centre. Virginia. 1968.

HUBBARD, H. H. and *Noise Considerations in the Design and Operation of
MAGLIERI, D. J.: the Supersonic Transport.* Noise Control. Vol. 7.
No.4. 1961. p.4.

HUWILER, A.: *Ärtzliche Boebachtungen über den Gesundheitszu-
ztand bei Anwohnern des Flughafens Kloten.* Kampf
dem Lärm. Bd. 12. Heft 2. April 1965. S. 35.

ICAO: *Aircraft Noise.* Annex 16 to the Convention on International Civil Aviation. International Civil Aviation Organisation.

INGERSLEV, F. and *Preliminary Studies of Sound Propagation in the
SVANE, C.: lower Layers of the Atmosphere.* 6th I.C.A. Congress. Tokyo. August 1968.

I.S.O. 3891: *Acoustics — Procedure for describing aircraft noise
1978: heard on the ground — 1978.* (Revision of ISO/R
507/1966 and ISO/R 1761/1970).

KOPPE, E. W., MATSCHAT, K. R. and MÜLLER, E. A.: *Abstract of a Procedure for the Description and Assessment of Aircraft Noise in the Vicinity of an Airport* Acustica. Vol. 16. No.4. 1965/66. p.251.

KRYTER, K. D. and PEARSONS, K. S.: *Judgement Tests of the sound from piston, turbojet and turbofan aircraft.* Sound 1. No.2. 1962. pp. 24 — 31.

KRYTER, K. D. and PEARSONS, K. S.: *Some effects of spectral content and duration on perceived noise level.* J.A.S.A. 35. 1963. pp. 866 — 883.

KRYTER, K. D., JOHNSON, P. J. and YOUNG, J. R.: *Judgement Tests of Flyover Noise from Various Aircraft.* N.A.S.A. Report No. CR-1635. Stanford Research Institute 1969.

LITTLE, J. W. and MABRY, J. E.: *Empirical Comparisons of Calculation Procedures for Estimating Annoyance of Aircraft Flyovers.* J. Sound Vibr. Vol. 10. No.1. 1969.

McKENNELL, A. C.: *Aircraft Annoyance around London Heathrow Airport.* U.K. Government Social Survey for the Wilson Committee on the Problem of Noise. Command 2056 H.M.S.O. London, 1963.

MELINIKOV, B. N.: *Noise Generated on the Ground During Takeoff and Landing of the Tu-124 Passenger Aircraft.* Akusticheskii Zuhrnal. Vol. 11. 1965.

MILLER, L. N. and BERANEK, L. L.: *Airports and Jet Noise.* Noise Control. Vol. 5. No.1. Jan. 1959. p.24.

ORAN, F. and SINGLETON, V.: *Technology of Ground Run-up Suppressors.* Sound and Vibration. Vol. 2. No.1. Jan. 1968.

RICHARDS, E. J.: *The Constraining Order of Airport Noise.* I.S.A.V. Report No. 148. University of Southampton, July 1966.

RICHARDS, E. J.: *A Historical Review of Aircraft Noise Suppression.* I.S.A.V. Report No. 151. University of Southampton, August 1966.

RICHARDS, E. J.: *Putting a value on noise — The Development of an Index which is fair to both Airport Operators and the Public.* The Aeronautical Journal of the Royal Aeronautical Society, May 1976. pp. 193 — 204. Republished in J.S.V. Vol. 49. No.1. 1976. pp. 53 — 73.

ROBINSON, D. W., BOWSHER, J. M. and COPELAND, W. C.: *On Judging the Noise from Aircraft in Flight.* Acustica. Vol. 13. 1963. p. 324.

214

ROEWER, H.:   *Schutz vor Fluglärm durch Neuordnung der Flugplatz-bereiche.* Kampf dem Lärm. 16. Jg. Heft 5. Oktober 1969.

SCHAUDINISCHKY, L.H. *Acoustical Aspects of the Jet-Engine-Test-Cell Con-* and SCHWARTZ, A.:   *struction.* Applied Acoustics. Vol. 2. No.1. January 1969.

SCHOLTEN, R. und   *Lärmprobleme der VTOL-Technik in Gegenwart und* FLEMMING, M.:   *Zukunft.* Kampf dem Lärm. 16. Jg. Heft 6. Dezember 1969.

SMITH, M. J. T.:   *How Quickly will the Aircraft Noise Problem Subside?* Intervia October 1976. pp. 889 — 991.

TOBIAS, J. V.:   *Noise in Light Twin-Engine Aircraft.* Sound and Vibration. Vol. 3. No.9. Sept. 1969.

TRACOR LTD.:   *Community Reaction to Airport Noise.* Final Report NASA Contract NASWA 1549 1970.

U.S. Dept.   *Noise Standards: Aircraft Type Certification.* U.S. De-Trans.:   partment of Transportation Federal Aviation Administration Part 36.

WIT, G. A. M. de: *On the Noise in the Vicinity of the Brussels National Airport.* Lärmbekämpfung. Bd. 13. Heft 2. April 1969.

YOUNG, R. W. and   *On Estimating Noisiness of Aircraft Sounds.* J.A.S.A. PETERSON, A.:   Vol. 45. No.4. 1969.

6.3. THE SONIC BOOM

The advent of regular supersonic commercial passenger traffic has introduced a new type of noise into the environment in the form of the Sonic Boom. Although of very short duration (approx 300 ms) it has a high sound pressure level (approx 130 dB) and occurs over a large area below the overflying supersonic aircraft. Aircraft noise is thus introduced into large areas, remote from airports, where normal subsonic aircraft are usually at cruising altitude and therefore no longer a noise problem. The extent of the boom's "carpet", the distance that it can be heard on each side of the aircraft's ground track, and its intensity, vary with the aircraft's height, speed, weight, flight condition, and with the prevailing atmospheric conditions. Typical maximum figures for current SST (Super Sonic Transport) aircraft are 80 km (Ca. 50 miles) and positive peak overpressures between 50 & 100 Pa. (ca. 1 lbf/ft^2).

Two separate effects of sonic booms, namely noise annoyance and the response of buildings, became the subjects of extensive research in the late 1960's and early 1970's when the introduction of the SST into commercial service appeared inevitable. Military aircraft and prototype SSTs were available which were similar to the production aircraft in terms of speed, weight and cruising height, and their measured booms could be related to both theoretical work and to data obtained from earlier experiments which had used lighter aircraft, such as fighters, to generate the boom.

A sonic boom is produced by any body which is moving at a velocity greater than the local speed of sound and is independent of any noise produced by that body. The acoustic emission of the aircraft is therefore no longer of importance once it is travelling supersonically and the boom produced has essentially the same characteristic as an otherwise equivalent, unpowered projectile.

To explain the production, propagation, and perception of a sonic boom, let us first consider sound radiation from a point source. Fig.6.3.1a represents the sound radiation pattern from such a stationary source. Each wave front propagated at one of a set of equal time intervals travels at the speed of sound (c) radially away from the source, and therefore a set of concentric wave-fronts (spheres in the true three-dimensional case) centred on the stationary source, are formed. If we now give the source a velocity of half the speed of sound in direction x, then the position of the wave fronts emitted at equal consecutive time intervals is as shown in diagram 6.3.1b. The wave fronts directly in front of the body become more closely spaced as the velocity of the source is increased, until the speed of sound they coalesce to form a weak local shock front, the Mach Line, perpendicular to the direction of travel as shown in Fig.6.3.1c. At this speed no information can be communicated in front of the body by means of an acoustic disturbance. The air cannot therefore accommodate itself to the approaching body in advance as it would

216

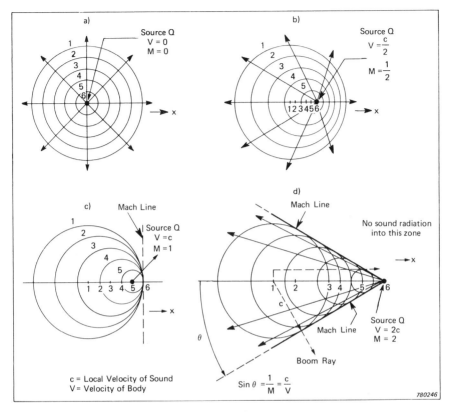

Fig.6.3.1. Sound propagation from a point source
a) Stationary source
b) Source moving at half the local speed of sound (v = c/2)
c) Source moving at the local speed of sound (v = c)
d) Source moving at twice the local speed of sound (v = 2c)

in the case of subsonic flow, and pressure changes take place rapidly across the shock front producing a sonic boom.

If the speed of the source is further increased, say to twice the speed of sound, approximately that of present supersonic transports, the Mach Lines, the tangents to wave fronts from consecutive disturbances, bend further back and extend the region into which no sound is propagated. The Mach Lines form, in three-dimensions, a cone the apex of which travels along with the supersonic source and which subtends an angle of $\theta = \text{Sin}^{-1}\ 1/M = \text{Sin}^{-1}c/V$ to the direction of travel, see Fig.6.3.1d, extending to the ground. The boom is heard by an observer as the line formed by the intercept of this cone

217

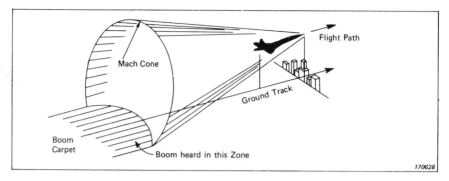

Fig.6.3.2. *Boom propagation from an aircraft flying at supersonic speed*

and the ground surface passes him. The region in which the boom can be heard, called the boom "carpet", is indicated in Fig.6.3.2, the intensity being greatest directly below the flight path and reducing as one moves to either side of it.

As mentioned previously the boom is independent of the noise produced by the source, the shock "wave" being produced by the coalescence of all pressure disturbances along the Mach Line. For a body moving with a velocity greater than that of the local speed of sound, it can be shown that a rapid rise in pressure occurs at the leading edge, as indicated in Fig.6.3.3.

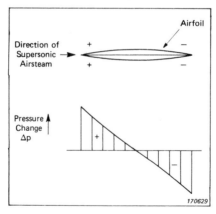

Fig.6.3.3. *Pressure distribution around an airfoil in a supersonic airstream*

The pressure gradually decreases, regaining ambient at the mid-point, and becoming negative towards the trailing edge of the aerofoil where it increases rapidly to regain ambient. The shape of the pressure distribution re-

218

sembles the letter N and the shock wave signature thus generated is often called an N-wave for this reason. A real aircraft, however, is composed of many shock-producing surfaces, which generate a complex shock pattern composed of many superimposed N-waves in the near field of the aircraft. Further from the aircraft the individual shocks merge together, eventually forming a more recognisable N-wave, as indicated in Fig.6.3.4. At distances far from the aircraft the N-wave becomes rounded as the high-frequency components, which contribute to the sharp corners of the N, are attenuated by the atmosphere to produce the practical shape of Fig.6.3.4d. The rounded profile and a finite rise time give rise to the dull boom typical of large high-flying supersonic aircraft.

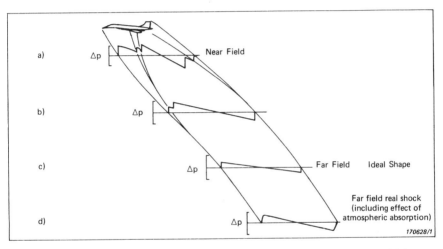

Fig.6.3.4. Development of the N-wave from the near to the far field

For an aircraft flying supersonically at a constant speed on a straight and level flight path, the boom is most intense along the ground track, falling off in intensity and changing in shape as one moves away to either side, see Fig.6.3.5. If, having constrained the aircraft to straight and level flight we also stipulate a perfect atmosphere and assume that the speed of sound varies only with temperature, i.e., altitude, then the increase in the speed of sound as the boom ray descends into the warmer lower atmosphere tends to refract it away from the ground (see Chapter 2). Therefore, along a line to each side of the ground track the initial boom ray angle is such that this refraction prevents the boom from ever reaching the ground, as also shown in Fig.6.3.5, and areas beyond this line will experience no booms.

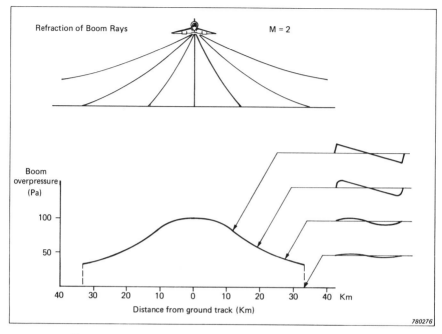

Fig.6.3.5. Boom variation at the side of the ground track

Measuring the Sonic Boom

When an N-wave reaches the ground it is reflected by the ground and other local surfaces. Any measured N-wave will thus be composed of the sum of the incident and reflected waves, see Fig.6.3.6. For this reason, the International Standard for measuring sonic booms requires that the microphone be mounted flush with the ground surface in an acoustically hard baffle at least 1,5 m in diameter, and that no obstructions which may cause reflections exist which, in total subtend a solid angle of more than 0,004 steradian. As shown in Fig.6.3.7a, a microphone mounted in this way will measure the superimposed incident and reflected waves, producing a pressure signature similar in shape but with twice the real amplitude of the incident wave. Any deviation from this mounting method will measure a wave which is of a more complex shape, formed by superimposed incident and reflected waves separated by a time interval which depends on microphone height as indicated in Figures 6.3.7.b, c and d.

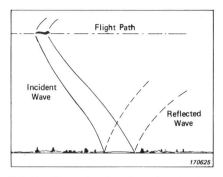

Fig.6.3.6. Ground reflection of a shock wave

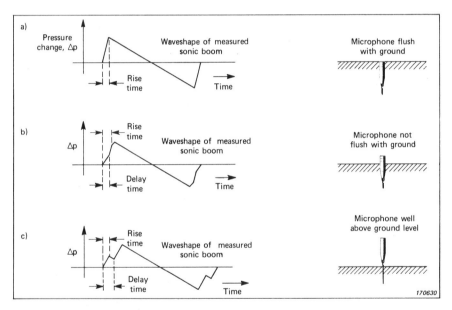

Fig.6.3.7. Variation of measured waveshape with microphone position

Subjective Effects of the Sonic Boom

Extensive research has been carried out to determine the boom's loudness, the annoyance it generates, and building response which it causes. Loudness has been found to vary with parameters such as the peak overpressure, rise time, delay time, but not significantly with N-wave duration, at least within the range 100 — 500 ms., embracing booms produced by existing and foreseeable supersonic aircraft. For a given positive peak pressure the loudness of a sonic boom, calculated from the energy spectral density of its signature

221

averaged over the auditory response time, has been shown to vary by up to 25 phons with rise and delay times from 0 to 16 ms.

Human response, however, depends on factors other than this calculated loudness, and in order to compare the subjective effects of booms and noise from conventional aircraft, several comparison tests have been made and show two interesting trends. Firstly, the noise from a conventional aircraft at about 110 PNdB was about equally as acceptable as a boom of 85 Pa nominal overpressure. Both these values are typical of present subsonic and supersonic aircraft. Secondly, annoyance was found to increase far more rapidly for an increase in nominal boom intensity than for a similar increase in the intensity of conventional aircraft noise. A given intensity indoors was rated as much more annoying than the same intensity out-doors, again demonstrating, as was mentioned earlier with regard to conventional aircraft noise, that people expect a higher degree of acoustic privacy indoors than out. However, it must be remembered that the spectrum of a boom attains its highest levels at frequencies below 100 Hz (a fact well illustrated by the theoretical spectrum of Fig.6.3.8). This efficiently excites building structures and elements, the vibration of which gives rise to rattle-type noises from neutrally stable or "loose" objects around the home. These secondary noise sources appear to be extremely annoying to residents, representing an "intrusion" into what is considered the privacy of their own home, and also giving rise to fears, however groundless, of actual damage to their property. The importance of this

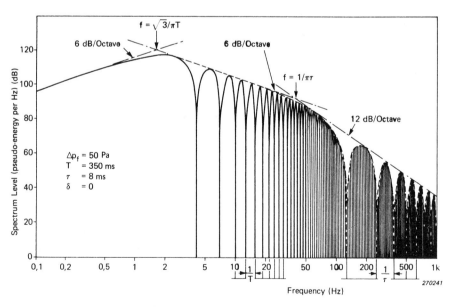

Fig.6.3.8. Theoretical sonic boom spectrum (After Johnson and Robinson)

222

aspect of boom response was well illustrated by the Oklahoma City Sonic Boom study of 1964, rattles caused by house shaking heading by a wide margin the list of annoyance factors listed below.

Type of Interference	% annoyed
House shaking-rattles	54
Startle	28
Sleep interruption	14
Rest interruption	14
Conversation interruption	10
Radio-TV interruption	6

Percent of Respondents Annoyed by Various Sonic Boom Interferences. From Borsky.

Most building elements and rooms have their fundamental and low harmonic frequencies where sonic boom energy is concentrated, below 100 Hz. It is natural therefore to think that some damage might occur by setting certain building elements into resonance and thereby to cause failure. Although there is well documented evidence that this can certainly be the case for "architectural" items such as glass, tiles and plaster, especially if old or in poor condition, it has been demonstrated that the stress levels produced in major structural elements of buildings can be considered negligible at the peak overpressures normally produced by supersonic aircraft. Greater vibration, and indeed higher noise levels, are likely to be caused by normal activities such as the slamming of doors.

Sonic Boom Measurement Systems

As with any other impulsive noise, the measurement of a sonic boom places very severe constraints on the measurement equipment in terms of both frequency response and dynamic range. Although it is possible to employ a single channel direct recorder if interest is restricted to the range of hearing, for most purposes an F.M. multichannel recorder will be required so that the signal can be filtered and split into two distinct frequency ranges. From Fig.6.3.8 it can be seen that most of the energy in a typical boom of duration 350 ms lies below 100 Hz, being concentrated round the "fundamental frequency" of the boom, in this case at approximately $1/T$ or 3 Hz. At 100 Hz the spectrum level has fallen by 40 dB or so, already dangerously near the dynamic range of the recorder. The important frequencies as far as hearing is concerned are those above 100 Hz, and these will be lost in the

223

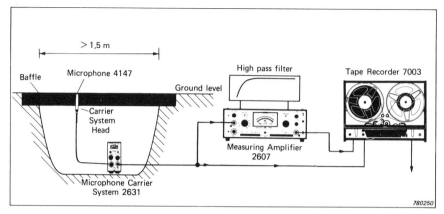

Fig.6.3.9. Instrumentation for the recording of sonic booms

tape noise if the very high levels at low frequencies are to be accommodated at the same time.

To overcome these problems the signal is split into two parts, one part being fed directly to one channel of an F.M. recorder, and the other passed through a high pass filter with a suitable cut-off frequency, the relevant I.S.O. standard in fact recommends 100 Hz, and thence to a second channel on the recorder, the gains being optimally adjusted for the signal amplitude within each frequency range. A diagram of the measuring arrangement is shown in Fig.6.3.9. The special 1/2" microphone and carrier system allows the response to be extended below 0,01 Hz and above 10 kHz and it may also be advisable to utilise the remaining 2 channels, with different input attenuations, in order to achieve the maximum possible dynamic range. In this way boom characteristics which give rise to effects which depend on low frequency energy content, mainly concerned with structural response, and those which depend on the high frequency content, concerning human response, can be determined simultaneously for an event which may be difficult to repeat.

A second method, employing a Digital Event Recorder Type 7502, is often useful for recording a short event such as sonic boom, whose exact time of occurrence is usually difficult to determine. A built-in trigger on the instrument can be pre-set to capture the event when it subsequently exceeds the trigger level. Apart from automatically capturing the event, the Digital Event Recorder improves the flexibility of the recording system in a second way. Having automatically recorded the boom at one of a large number of sample rates, the playback rate can also be adjusted over a wide range. This enables the user to replay the event slowly enough to obtain a trace of the boom signature, record the captured signal conveniently onto magnetic or punched tape, or analyze the event immediately. See Fig.6.3.10.

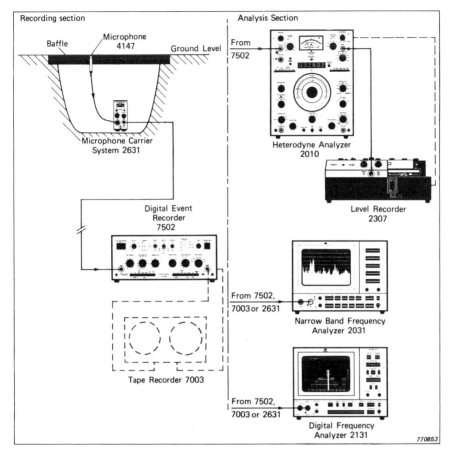

Recording section | Analysis Section

Baffle | Microphone 4147 | Ground Level | From 7502

Microphone Carrier System 2631

Heterodyne Analyzer 2010

Digital Event Recorder 7502

Level Recorder 2307

From 7502, 7003 or 2631

Narrow Band Frequency Analyzer 2031

Tape Recorder 7003

From 7502, 7003 or 2631

Digital Frequency Analyzer 2131

770853

Fig.6.3.10. Instrumentation for the capture, recording and analysis of Sonic Booms

If the boom is recorded for later laboratory analysis, it may be replayed into the event recorder to give the same flexibility in the analysis process. Frequency transformation may then be used, either to speed up the analysis or to shift low frequency components into the normal analysis range of acoustic instrumentation.

Analysis of the signal in narrow bands of constant bandwidth can be carried out by the Heterodyne Analyzer Type 2010, which sweeps continuously through the frequency range, the output being recorded on a Level Recorder. A faster analysis may be made by the Narrow Band Spectrum Analyzer Type 2031, which performs the task in real time and displays the continuously updated spectrum on the screen. This instrument also has extensive trigger facilities (discussed in greater detail in Section 5.5) for the direct capture of

225

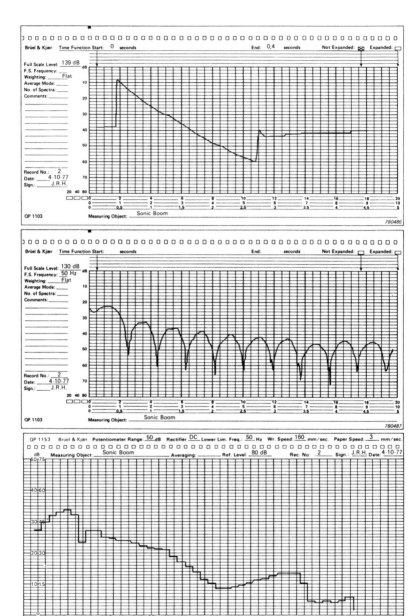

Fig.6.3.11. A Sonic Boom and its frequency analysis
   a) Typical pressure signature
   b) Narrow band analysis in the range 0—50 Hz (from 2031)
   c) 1/3 octave analysis from 1,6 Hz to 20 kHz (from 2131)

transients, which enable it to be used as a completely independent system for the capture, analysis, and display of sonic booms.

For some applications, e.g. loudness evaluation, it is necessary to analyze in 1/3 octave bands, using an instrument such as the Type 2131 Digital Frequency Analyzer. Its frequency range, from 1,6 Hz to 20 kHz, covers the range of interest associated with the sonic booms from current and foreseeable supersonic aircraft types.

A measured sonic boom signature, exhibiting the typical N-wave form, and two examples from an extensive analysis using the two real-time analyses, are shown in Fig.6.3.11. These measured spectra should be compared with the theoretical spectrum of Fig.6.3.8.

Selected Bibliography

BROADBENT, D. E. and ROBINSON, D. W.: *Subjective Measurements of the Relative Annoyance of Simulated Sonic Bangs and Aircraft Noise.* J. Sound Vibr. Vol. 1. No.2. April 1964. p. 162.

BROSKY, P. N.: *Community Reactions to Sonic Booms in the Oklahoma City Area (Parts I and II).* Wright Paterson A.F.B. AMRL-TR-65-37, AD 613 620 (1965)

BROCH, J. T. and OLESEN, H. P.: *On the Frequency Analysis of Mechanical Shocks and Single Impulses.* B & K Technical Review 1970. No.3I

CARLSON, H. W., MACK, R. J. and MORRIS, O. A.: *Sonic Boom Pressure-Field Estimation Techniques.* J.A.S.A. Vol. 39. No.5 (Part 2). May 1966

CLARKSON, B. L. and MAYES, W. H.: *Sonic-Boom-Induced Building Structure Responses Including Damage.* J.A.S.A. Vol. 51. 1972. pp. 742.

CRANDALL, S. H. and KURZWEIL, L.: *On the Rattling of Windows by Sonic Booms.* J.A.S.A. Vol. 44. No.2. August 1968

CROCKER, M. J. and HUDSON, R. R.: *Structural Response to Sonic Booms.* J. Sound Vib. Vol. 9. No.3. 1969

DEMPSEY, D. F.: *Focusing Conditions for Sonic Booms.* J.A.S.A. Vol. 61. No.3. March 1977. pp. 655 — 658

GIERKE, H. E. von and NIXON, C. W.: *Human Response to Sonic Booms.* In "Aircraft Engine Noise and Sonic Boom". AGARD, Nov. 1969.

GIERKE, H. E. von: *Effects of Sonic Boom on People: Review and Outlook.* J.A.S.A. Vol. 39. No.5 (Part 2). May 1966.

HILTON, D. A. and NEWMAN, J. W. Jr.: *Sonic Boom Signatures.* J.A.S.A. Vol. 39. No.5 (Part 2). May 1966.

HUBBARD, H. H.:   *Nature of the Sonic Boom Problem.* J.A.S.A. Vol. 39.
                           No.5 (Part 2). May 1966.

ISO 2249-1973:   *I.S.O. Standard 2249, Acoustics — Description and
                           Measurement of Physical Properties of Sonic Booms*

J.A.S.A.:   *Sonic Boom Symposium.* The 70th Meeting of the
                           Acoustical Society of America, St. Louis, U.S.A. 3rd
                           Nov. 1965. Published as J.A.S.A. Vol. 39. No.5
                           (Part 2). May 1966.

JOHNSON, D. R. and   *The Subjective Evaluation of Sonic Bangs.* Acustica
ROBINSON, D. W.:   Vol. 18. No.5. 1967.

JOHNSON, D. R. and   *Procedure for Calculating the Loudness of Sonic
ROBINSON, D. W.:   Bangs.* Acustica. Vol. 21. No.6. 1969.

KRYTER, K. D.:   *Sonic Boom — Results of Laboratory and Field Stud-
                           ies.* Conference — Noise as a Public Health Hazard,
                           Held in Washington DC, June 13—14, 1968. Report
                           4 of the American Speech and Hearing Association
                           Feb. 1969.

KRYTER, K. D.:   *Laboratory Tests of Physiological-Psychological Reac-
                           tions to Sonic Booms.* J.A.S.A. Vol. 39. No.5 (Part
                           2). May 1966.

KRYTER, K. D.:   *Evaluation of Exposures to Impulse Noise.* Archives
                           of Environmental Health. May 1970.

LIENARD, P. and   *Qu'est-ce que le "Bang Sonique".* Annales des Téléc-
LAMBOURIAN, J.:   ommunications. Vol. 22. No.3-4. April 1967. pp.
                           107 ÷ 119.

LILLEY, G. M.:   *The Sonic Boom.* Flight International. 11 June
                           1970. pp. 969 — 971.

MAGLIERI, D. J. and   *Sonic Booms from Aircraft Maneuvers.* Sound. Vol.
LANSING, D. L.:   2. No.2. 1963. p. 39.

MAGLIERI, D. J. and   *Atmospheric Effects on Sonic Boom Pressure Signa-
PARROTT, T. L.:   tures.* Sound. Vol. 2. No.2. 1963. p. 11.

MAGLIERI, D. J.:   *Some Effects of Airplane Operation and the Atmos-
                           phere on Sonic-Boom Signatures.* J.A.S.A. Vol. 39.
                           No.5 (Part 2). May 1966.

MAGLIERI, D. J.,   *Variability in Sonic Boom Signatures Measured
HUCKEL, V.,   Along an 8000-foot Linear Array.* NASA TN D-5040.
HENDERSON, H. . and
McLEOD, N. J.:

MAY, D. N.:   *Sonic Boom Startle.* A Field Study in Meppen, West
                           Germany. J.S.V. Vol. 24. No.3. 1972. pp. 337 —
                           347.

228

NIXON, C. W. and
BORSKY, P. N.:
Effects of Sonic Boom on People: St. Louis, Missouri, 1961—1962. J.A.S.A. Vol. 39. No.5 (Part 2). May 1966.

OLESEN, H. P.:
Frequency Analysis of Single Pulses. B & K Technical Review 1969. No.3.

PEASE, C.B.:
A note on the Spectrum Analysis of Transients and Loudness of Sonic Bangs. J.S.V. Vol.6. No.3 pp.310-314

POWERS, J. O. and
MAGLIERI, D. J.:
A Survey of Sonic Boom Experiments. A paper given at the Aviation and Space Conference of the ASME. June 16 — 19, 1968, Beverly Hills, California.

PRETLOVE, A. J. and
BOWLER, J. F.:
An Estimate of Sonic Boom Damage to Large Windows. J.S.V. Vol. 22. No.1. 1972. pp. 107 — 112.

RYLANDER, R. (Ed.):
Sonic Boom Exposure Effects: A report from a workshop on methods and criteria, Stockholm, 1971. J.S.V. Vol. 20. No.4. 1972. pp. 477 — 544.

RYLANDER, R.,
SØRENSEN, S. and
BERGLUND, K.:
Sonic Boom Effects on Sleep — A Field Experiment of Military and Civilian Populations. J.S.V. Vol. 24. No.1. 1972. pp. 41 — 50.

SHEPHERD, L. J. and
SUTHERLAND, W. W.:
Relative Annoyance and Loudness Judgements of Various Simulated Sonic Boom Waveforms. NASA CR 1112. September 1968.

SKØDE, F.:
Low Frequency Measurements Using Capacitive Transducers. B & K Technical Review No.1 1969.

TANIGUCHI, H. T.:
Instrumentation for Measurement of Sonic Boom. Noise Control. Vol. 7. Mar-Apr. 1966.

THACKRAY, R. I.,
TOUCHSTONE, R. M.
and BAILEY, J. P.:
A Comparison of the Startle Effects Resulting from Exposure to Two Levels of Simulated Sonic Booms. J.S.V. Vol. 33. No.4. pp. 379 — 390.

WARREN, C. H. E.:
Experience in the United Kingdom on the Effects of Sonic Bangs. J.A.S.A. Vol. 39. No.5 (Part 2). May 1966.

WEBB, D. R. B. and
WARREN, C. H. E.:
An Investigation of the Effects of Bangs on the Selective Reaction of a Community. R.A.E. Technical Report No. 66072 (March 1966).

WEBER, G.:
Probability of Aircraft Noise and Sonic Boom Induced Building Damages. In "Aircraft Engine Noise and Sonic Boom". AGARD. Nov. 1969.

WEBER, G.:
Wirkung von Flugzeugknallen auf Gebäude und Bauteile. VDI-Berichte Nr. 135. 1969.

ZEPLER, E.E. and   *The Loudness of sonic booms and other impulsive*
HAREL, J.R.P.   *sounds. J.S.V. Vol.2. No.3 1965*

6.4. CONSTRUCTION NOISE

Noise caused by construction and demolition operations is beginning to be treated as a subject in its own right, and this interest is reflected in the many new standards being considered at both international and national levels. This move has been brought about by the recognition of a number of important characteristics of construction noise which accentuate both community annoyance and noise reduction problems. Some of the more important of these factors are:

1) The site is often in a long-established commercial or residential area, whose inhabitants have had long experience of the existing background noise level. The construction work therefore appears particularly intrusive, and brings with it other undesirable features, such as dust, heavy vehicles, and restriction of access, as well as the noise problem which concerns us here.

2) Work takes place predominantly in the open air. The building itself therefore provides very little sound insulation of the activities except in the very latest stages, and even then most of the noisy plant remains outside.

3) Planning and zoning to separate noisy from noise-sensitive areas can obviously not work, because of the limited duration of the work.

4. The noise emissions vary greatly during the day, with very high levels for short periods of time. In addition, impulsive noise, which is particularly annoying, forms a high proportion of noise emissions from construction sites.

5) Noise arises from a large number of different processes which vary greatly in intensity and character as the site activities change during the construction period.

6) The whole construction process is transitory by nature. Virtually everything to do with it is therefore in a continual state of change, making any attempt at noise control extremely difficult.

Much of the noise is emitted by the heavy plant which is used to supply compressed air or electrical power to the site, to drive cranes and conveyors, or to cut materials such as stone, concrete, and wood. Woodworking machinery is a particularly serious offender, producing dangerously high levels of high frequency noise. This should be housed in closed work-shops wherever possible, special care being taken to protect the hearing of those employed. Vehicles, both those restricted to the site, and those moving materials to and from the site, are a significant source of annoyance, especially on road construction sites, where fill is often moved almost continuously through the day and night by extremely large, powerful, and usually noisy, off-road vehicles.

One of the most important characteristics of construction noise is the high proportion of impulsive noise which is present. This occurs from processes as different as hammering, materials handling, impact chipping and drilling, fixing by percussive guns, and piling. All of these give rise to high levels of impulsive noise, which is a potential cause of public annoyance as well as damage to employees' hearing. Conventional piling techniques involving the impact of a heavy mass on the driven pile are capable of causing hearing damage at up to 100 metres, and have been known to draw complaints from residential areas as far as 2 kilometres away. In such cases, annoyance can often be lessened by circulating the likely areas of complaint beforehand with a letter explaining what is about to happen, why it is being done, and when and for how long the disturbance will last. This procedure not only forewarns people, so that the activity does not come as an unwelcome surprise, but also assures them that the construction company is aware of the disturbance being caused.

Solutions to many of the noise problems associated with construction are bedeviled by the open-air nature of the operations and their continual movement around the site. Reduction at source is therefore of utmost importance in obtaining reasonable levels of noise emission. This applies equally to permanently operating installations such as compressors and generators, and to producers of short term high intensity noise. Some processes, for example piling and compaction, also generate high levels of ground borne vibration which may manifest itself as considerable noise in buildings far from the site. The airborne noise itself may be acceptable, but often gives rise to fears that the *vibration* may be damaging to the property, although this is rarely the case.

Source noise can often be reduced by replacing a machine or a process by a less noisy one, for example using hydraulic concrete breakers instead of pneumatic drills, or high tensile bolts in place of rivets. Of particular interest is the new generation of pile driving techniques, which attempt to get away from impact methods by using hydraulic rams to force down the piles, sometimes vibrating them to assist the process. In comparison with traditional methods these are remarkably quiet.

Where reduction at source is not possible for any reason, or is found to be inadequate, temporary enclosures which can be quickly erected around the work area may reduce noise to an acceptable level, at least for the occupants of the surrounding buildings. For the operator, this may cause a greater problem as the enclosure will now tend to increase the level of the noise received by him by reflection from its walls. The effect of this can be reduced by lining the enclosure with absorbent material. Screens and partial enclosures may also be useful, although care should be taken not to reflect sound into other sensitive regions. Site vehicles can often be fitted with more efficient silencers which may reduce emissions by up to 20 dB in some cases, and partial engine enclosures could account for a further improvement of 5 dB or so.

The wide variation of noise levels and characteristics at any measuring position near a construction site leads to some problems in finding units to describe the climate adequately and in setting limits. The recent tendency is towards adopting L_{eq} or L_{dn}. A relatively new British Standard recommends that measurements are made to determine the A-weighted L_{eq}, and suggests an L_{eq} limit of 75 dB(A), measured over a 12 hour daytime period from 07.00 to 19.00 hrs. In addition, absolute peak and impulsive noise limits may be set by agreement to suit local conditions. No really universal techniques have been agreed to cope with the difficult problems associated with impulsive noise, and it is still the subject of some controversy in this field as in others. At all times though, the limits must be set to maintain the exposure of employees below that required by the law to protect them from hearing damage. This is the case even where higher levels of noise are acceptable from the point of view of community annoyance.

Monitoring of construction site noise is complicated by several factors which have to be taken into account when organising a survey.

1) The levels fluctuate widely during the day, with very intense noise present for short periods, so the measurement time must be long enough to be representative. This may necessitate long term monitoring because many processes only occur infrequently.

2) Impulsive noise, which can be dominant on some types of site, may have to be assessed separately.

3) Levels may vary significantly at different points around the site at different times depending on the nature of operations. A good starting point for measurements is often the nearest inhabited building, unless inspection of the site reveals an obvious problem area.

4) If the site is near to a road, railway, or other noisy source, ambient noise may be high enough to interfere with the measurements.

To illustrate some of these points, a survey was undertaken at a site in a suburb of Copenhagen where many of the problems mentioned above were in evidence. Two different sets of fully portable instrumentation were used to carry out these measurements. Fig.6.4.1 shows one arrangement consiting of an Integrating Sound Level Meter Type 2218 to calculate the L_{eq} directly, and a Level Recorder Type 2306 to provide a permanent time history of the measured sound levels. In this case the noise source was a continuous road breaking, loading, and compacting operation employing several different machines. This generated a high continuous noise level and irregular peaks. Fig.6.4.2 shows a typical sound level trace and clearly demonstrates how the short-term, high-level peaks in the signal, influence the process of L_{eq} calculation. The L_{eq} is 89.1 dB although the sound level only exceeds this value for a very small percentage of the measurement period. Because of the impulsive nature of the noise, it is imperative that a sound level meter with a large dynamic range, such as the Type 2218 with an 80 dB range, is used.

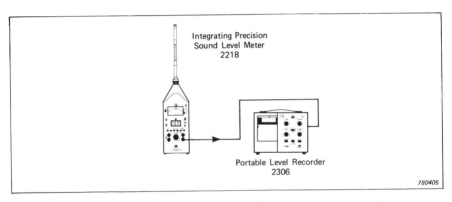

Fig.6.4.1. Portable instrumentation for measurement and recording of construction noise

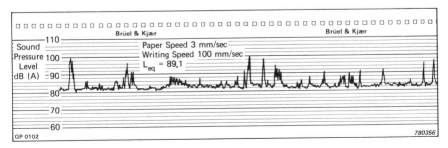

Fig.6.4.2. Time history of a road breaking, loading, and compacting operation

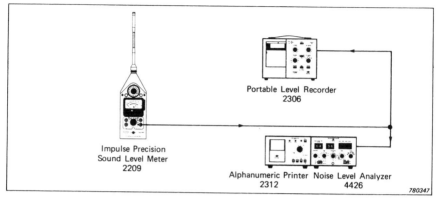

Fig.6.4.3. *Portable instrumentation for the measurement and statistical analysis of construction noise*

A complete statistical analysis of fluctuating noise may be made using the arrangement of Fig.6.4.3, which enables the measured sound level to be plotted on the level recorder, and the statistical parameters calculated by the 4426 and printed on the Alphanumeric Printer Type 2312. Thus the signal and its analysis are documented automatically, and the results are available on site at the time of the measurements. The 4426 can be pre-programmed to output a wide range of parameters of which the most important in this case are the L_{eq}, L_N, and the probability distribution. Fig.6.4.4 is a reproduction of a short period of level recorder trace of noise recorded at the boundary of the site. The fluctuating level, caused by many different noise sources, is typical of construction work. Again the L_{eq} is dominated by the higher levels which exist for relatively short periods, but the statistical parameters reproduced in Fig.6.4.5 now allow the signal variation to be studied in far more detail. An additional advantage of this type of analysis is that the L_N value, for any integer value of N from 1 to 99, may be read out at regular pre-determined intervals during an extended monitoring period. The extent of short-term variations can then be assessed.

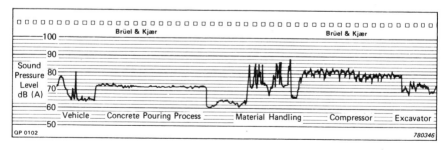

Fig.6.4.4. *Noise time history typical of construction sites*

234

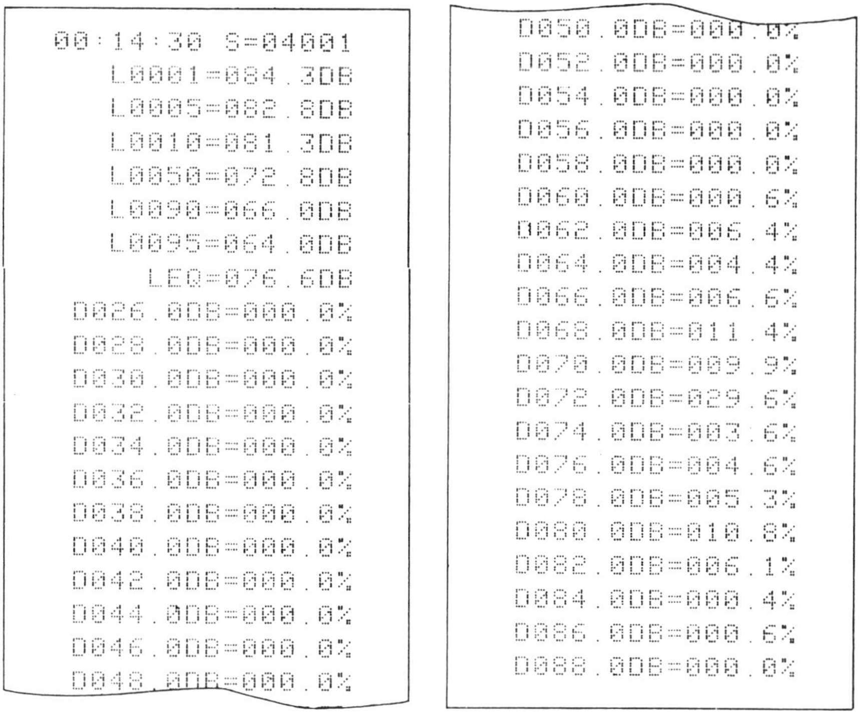

```
00:14:30 S=04001
  L0001=084.3DB
  L0005=082.8DB
  L0010=081.3DB
  L0050=072.8DB
  L0090=066.0DB
  L0095=064.0DB
    LEQ=076.6DB
D026.0DB=000.0%
D028.0DB=000.0%
D030.0DB=000.0%
D032.0DB=000.0%
D034.0DB=000.0%
D036.0DB=000.0%
D038.0DB=000.0%
D040.0DB=000.0%
D042.0DB=000.0%
D044.0DB=000.0%
D046.0DB=000.0%
D048.0DB=000.0%
```

```
D050.0DB=000.0%
D052.0DB=000.0%
D054.0DB=000.0%
D056.0DB=000.0%
D058.0DB=000.0%
D060.0DB=000.6%
D062.0DB=006.4%
D064.0DB=004.4%
D066.0DB=006.6%
D068.0DB=011.4%
D070.0DB=009.9%
D072.0DB=029.6%
D074.0DB=003.6%
D076.0DB=004.6%
D078.0DB=005.3%
D080.0DB=010.8%
D082.0DB=006.1%
D084.0DB=000.4%
D086.0DB=000.6%
D088.0DB=000.0%
```

Fig.6.4.5. Example of 4426 analysis printed out using the Alphanumeric Printer Type 2312

Selected Bibliography

B.S. 5228: Code of Practice for Noise Control on Construction and Demolition Sites. British Standards Institution, London 1975.

I.S.O.: 2151 1972. Measurement of airborne noise emitted by compressor/primemover-units intended for outdoor use.

LARGE, J. B. and LUDLOW, J. E.: Community Reaction to Noise from a Construction Site. Noise Control Engineering March/April 1976. pp. 59 — 65.

SEMPLE, W.: Quieter Pile Driving. Noise Control and Vibration Reduction. Sept. 1974. pp. 289 — 295.

7. STANDARDS AND RECOMMENDATIONS

The following pages contain a list of the standards and recommendations which are related to the instrumentation and procedures for measuring acoustic noise. The list contains a large number of international and national standards, and has been produced after recent contact with the standards authorities in many countries. It is of course not possible to guarantee that the survey is complete and many of the Recommendations or Proposals may have been adopted as full Standards at the time of reading. Similarly, others may be replaced or revised in the light of research and development in noise and acoustics, and in instrumentation for its measurement. Before undertaking measurements, it is advisable to check the institutions of your own country to ensure that measurements are being made in accordance with the latest Standards where these are applicable.

The Author accepts that there will be omissions and changes, and would appreciate any relevant corrections or comments to maintain an up-to-date list. Thanks are especially extended to those who supplied the information from which the list was compiled.

In order to make the list as easy to use as possible, the various standards have been grouped in alphabetical order of country (with I.S.O. and IEC standards last) under the following headings.

A. General
B. Noise Rating Recommendations
C. Noise Measuring Equipment
D. Measurements of Noise Emitted by Machines
E. Measurement of Sound Transmission loss and Building Acoustics
F. Measurement of Vehicle and Traffic Noise
G. Special Acoustic Equipment
H. Measurement of Aircraft Noise

I. Acoustic Noise Measurements

A. General

Argentina

F 40-36	Acoustical terminology
4061	Preferred frequencies
4065	Expression of the physical and subjective magnitudes of sound or noise
4066	Normal loudness contours
4067	Loudness and loudness level

Australia
Standards House, 80 Arthur Street, North Sydney

Z33-1967	Preferred frequencies and band centres for acoustical measurements
AS.Z44-1969	Expression of the power & intensity levels of sound or noise
AS.1047-1971	Expression of the physical and subjective magnitudes of sound or noise
AS.1633-1974	Glossary of acoustic terms
C.S.I.R.O.	National measurement laboratory "Tests and Measurements" (Commonwealth Scientific & Industrial Research Organisation)

Austria
Österreichisches Normungsinstitut 1020 Wien Leopoldsg. 4

S 5001 Entwurf	Grundbegriffe der Akustik
S 5002	Normfrequenzen für akustische Messungen
S 5003	Teil 1; Grundlagen der Schallmessung, Physikalische und subjektive Größen von Schall
S 5003 Entwurf	Teil 2; Grundlagen der Schallmessung, Normalkurven gleicher Lautstärkepegel
S 5030	Bestimmung der Schalleistung von Schallquellen; Anwendung grundlegender Normen und Erstellung typenbezogener Prüfbestimmungen
S 5031	Bestimmung der Schalleistung von Schallquellen; Verfahren im Hallraum
S 5033	Bestimmung der Schalleistung von Schallquellen; Verfahren in besonderen Hallräumen
S 5034	Bestimmung der Schalleistung von Schallquellen; Verfahren im Freifeld über einem reflektierenden Boden
S 5035	Bestimmung der Schalleistung von Schallquellen; Verfahren in reflexionsarmen Räumen
S 5037	Bestimmung der Schalleistung von Schallquellen; Verfahren mit Bezugsschallquelle
	Österreichischer Arbeitsring für Lärmbekämpfung, Regierungsgebäude, 1012 Wien
ÖAL-Richtlinie Nr.3 (4. Ausg.)	Schalltechnische Grundlagen für die Beurteilung von Lärm
ÖAL-Richtlinie Nr.11 (4.Augs.)	Rechtliche Grundlagen für die Lärmbekämpfung
ÖAL-Richtlinie Nr.13	Gehörschutzmittel
ÖAL-Richtlinie Nr.20	Lärmschutztechnische Begriffe und Messungen

Belgium
Institut Belge de Normalisation, 29 av. de la Brabançonne, 1040 Bruxelles

NBN576.02- 1961 2.édition	Niveaux Physiques et subjectif d'un son ou d'un bruit et échelle de sonie
NBN576.03- 1961 2.édition: NBN S01.003	Les lignes isosoniques normales pour sons pour écoutes en champ libre et le seuil d'audition binauriculaire en champ libre
NBN576.04- 1961	Fréquences normales pour mesures acoustiques
Addendum to NBN576.04	

Bulgaria
Institut de Normalisation, 8, rue Sveta Sofia, Sofia

BDS 4610-69	Standard tuning frequencies
BDS 4792-62	Acoustical quantities, symbols, definitions and units

Canada
CSA 178 Rexdale Boulevard Rexdale Ontario

Z 107.2	Same as ANSI S1.13-1971
Z 107.3	Same as ANSI S1.21-1972

C.S.S.R.
Office for Standards and Measurements, 11 347 Praha 1, Václavské Náměsti 19

ČSN 01 1304	Quantities, units and symbols of acoustics
ČSN 01 1600	Terminology of acoustics
ČSN 01 1601	Preferred frequencies in acoustics
ČSN 01 1602	Procedure for the calculation of the loudness and loudness level of noise
ČSN 01 1603	Methods for noise measurements
ČSN 01 1610	Fundamental tuning tones
ČSN 34 0870	Series of nominal electro-acoustical power of the supersonic equipment

Denmark
Dansk Standardiseringsråd, Aurehøjvej 12, 2900 Hellerup

DS/ISO R.131	Udtryk for lyds og støjs fysiske og subjektive styrke
DS/ISO R.226	Normalkurver for rene toner med samme hørestyrke og normal høretærskel ved aflytning i frit felt
DS/ISO R.266	Normalfrekvenser for akustiske målinger
DS/ISO R.357	Udtryk for lyds og støjs effekt- og intensitetsniveau

DS/ISO R.454	Forholdet mellem de lydtryksniveauer af smalle støjbånd, der i et diffust felt og i et frontalt indfaldende, frit felt giver samme lydindtryk
DS/ISO R.532	Fremgangsmåde til beregning af hørestyrke
DS/ISO R.2204	Akustik. Retningslinier for måling af luftbåren akustisk støj og vurdering af dennes virkning på mennesket
DS/ISO R.2249	Akustik. Beskrivelse og måling af fysiske størrelser ved overlydsbrag
	Miljøstyrelsen, Kampmannsgade 1, 1604 København V
Publikation 27	Støj. Forslag til bekæmpelse (Noise abatement)
Publikation 28	Støjproblemer i forbindelse med fjernelse af affald. (Noise problems connected with garbage disposal)
Vejledning 3/1974	Extern støj fra virksomheder
	Arbejderbeskyttelsesfondet Vesterbrogade 69, 1620 København V
Direktoratet for Arbejdstilsynet Publ.No. 38	Støj på arbejdspladsen
	Statens Byggeforskningsinstitut
	Støj i byen del. I
	Den nordiske komite for bygningsbestemmelser. Boligministeriet
NKB nr.17-1971	Støj og byplan. Praktiske anvisninger (Noise Abatement in Town Planning)

Finland

Suomen Standardisoimisliitto
PL 205, 00121 Helsinki 12

SFS 3084	Same as ISO R.131-1959
SFS 3085	Same as ISO R.226-1961
SFS 3086	Same as ISO R.266-1962
SFS 3087	Same as ISO R.357-1963
SFS 3088	Same as ISO R.454-1965
SFS 3089	Same as ISO R.532-1966

France

L'Association Française de Normalisation (AFNOR), Tour Europe, 92 Courbevoie

NF S 30-002 1972	Fréquences normales pour les mesures acoustiques
NF S 30-003 1965	Lignes isosoniques normales pour sons purs écoutes en champ libre et seuil d'audition binauriculaire en champ libre
NF S 30-004 1966	Expression des caractériques physiques et des caractéristiques psychophysiologiques d'un son ou d'un bruit
NF S 30-005 1966	Méthode de calcul du niveau d'isosonie
NF S 30-007 1967	Zéro normal de référence pour l'étalonnage des audiomètres à sons purs
NF S 30-008 1970	Guide pour la mesure du bruit et l'évaluation de ses effets sur l'homme

NF S 30-009 1972	Atténuation du son dans l'air
NF S 30-010 1974	Acoustique — courbes nr d'évaluation du bruit
NF S 30-101 1973	Vocabulaire de l'acoustique — définitions générales
NF S 30-102 1973	Vocabulaire de l'acoustique — systèmes de transmission et de propagation du son et des vibrations
NF S 30-103 1973	Vocabulaire de l'acoustique — appareillage acoustique
NF S 30-104 1974	Vocabulaire de l'acoustique — enregistrement et lecture
NF S 30-105 1975	Vocabulaire de l'acoustique — acoustique physiologique de psychoacoustique (avec NF S 30-101 à NF S 30-103, septembre 1973, NF S 30-104, octobre 1974, NF S 30-106, septembre 1975 et NF S 30-107, décembre 1972, remplace NF S 30-001, septembre 1973)
NF S 30-106 1975	Vocabulaire de l'acoustique — acoustique architecturale (avec NF S 30-101 à NF S 30-103, septembre 1973, NF S 30-104, octobre 1974, NF S 30-105, septembre 1975 et NF S 30-107, décembre 1972, remplace NF S 30-001, septembre 1973)
NF S 30-107 1972	Vocabulaire de l'acoustique musicale
NF C 97-030 1970	Echelles des graphiques pour le tracé des courbes de réponse en fréquence des appareils électroacoustiques (Enr.) (1 page)

Germany (B.R.D.)

Beuth Vertrieb GmbH.
1000 Berlin 30, Bruggrafenstr. 4 — 7 und 5000 Köln, Kamekestr. 2 — 8

DIN 1318	Lautstärkepegel; Begriffe, Meßverfahren
DIN 1320	Akustik, Grundbegriffe
DIN 1332	Akustik, Formelzeichen
DIN 45401	Normfrequenzen für akustische Messungen
DIN 45402	Effektivwertmessung in der Elektroakustik
DIN 45403 Bl. 1 — 4	Messung von nichtlinearen Verzerrungen in der Elektroakustik ...
DIN 45611	Messung der Schalldämmung von Gehörschützern. (Hörschwellenmethode)
DIN 45630	Grundlagen der Schallmessung. Bl.1: Physikalische und subjektive Größen von Schall Bl.2: Normalkurven gleicher Lautstärke
DIN 45631	Berechnung des Lautstärke-Pegels aus dem Geräusch-Spektrum. (Verfahren nach Zwicker)

Germany (D.D.R.)

Amt für Standardisierung der Deutschen Demokratischen Republik Mohrenstrasse 37a 108 Berlin

TGL 10688/1 1970	Meßverfahren der Akustik: Luftschallmessungen am Aufenthaltsort von Menschen
TGL 10688/2	Luftschallmessungen an Maschinen

TGL 10688/3 1970 1	Messverfahren der Akustik: Bestimmung der Luftschall- und Trittschalldämmung (Ersatz für TGL 10687/3 und 4, Ausg. 10.63)
TGL 10688/4 1970	Messverfahren der Akustik: Bestimmung der dynamischen Steifigkeit von Dämmschichten (Ersatz für TGL 10687/4, Ausg. 10.63
TGL 10688/5 1970	Messverfahren der Akustik: Bestimmung des Schallabsorptionsgrades im Hallraum
TGL 10688/6 1970	Messverfahren der Akustik: Bestimmung des Schallabsorptionsgrades und der Schallimpedanz im Messrohr
TGL 10688/7 1970	Messverfahren der Akustik: Bestimmung der Strömungsresistanz
TGL 10688/8 1970	Messverfahren der Akustik: Bestimmung der Nachhallzeit von Räumen
TGL 10688/9 1970	Messverfahren der Akustik: Bestimmung der valenten Schallabsorptionsfläche (Ersatz für TGL 10687/4, Ausg. 10.63)
Great Britain	British Standards Institution, 2 Park Street, London W. 1
BS.3045: 1958	The relation between the sone scale of loudness and the phon scale of loundness level
BS.3383: 1961	Normal equal-loudness contours for pure tones and normal threshold of hearing under free-field listening conditions
BS.3593: 1963	Recommendation on preferred frequencies for acoustical measurements
BS.4198: 1967	Method for calculating loudness
BS. 661: 1969	Glossary of acoustical terms
BS.2497:	Reference zero for the calibration of pure-tone audiometers
BS.5108: 1974	Method of measurement of attenuation of hearing protectors at threshold
Hungary	Magyar Szabványügyi Hivatal, Budapest IX, Üllöi út. 25
M.Sz.3391-60 1960	Acoustical terminology and formulae
M.Sz.3392-54 1954	Acoustical measurements
M.Sz.11121-53 1953	Sound technics. General terminology and demands
India	Indian Standards Institution, Manak Bhavan, 9 Bahadur Shah, Zafar Marg, New Delhi 1
IS: 1885 Part III	Electrotechnical vocabulary: Acoustics: Section 1. Physical Acoustics Section 2. Acoustical Systems Section 4. Sonics, ultrasonics and underwater acoustics Section 6. Acoustical instruments Section 8. Architectural acoustics
IS: 2264-1963	Preferred frequencies for acoustical measurements

Japan	Japanese standards association, 1-24, Akasaka 4 chome, Minato-ku, Tokyo
JIS Z 8106 (1961)	Glossary of acoustical terms (General)
JIS Z 8107 (1963)	Glossary of acoustical terms (Transducers and instruments)
JIS Z 8731 (1966)	Method of sound level measurements
JIS Z 8108 (1965)	Glossary of acoustical terms (Sound recording and sound reproducing)
JIS Z 8109 (1967)	Glossary of acoustical terms (Speech and hearing, music)
Netherlands	Nederlands Normalisatie-Instituut, Polakweg 5, Rijswijk (Z-H)
NEN 10050	Same as IEC 50
NEN 20131	Same as ISO R.131
NEN 20226	Same as ISO R.226
NEN 20266	Same as ISO R.266
NEN 20357	Same as ISO R.357
NEN 20532	Same as ISO R.532
NEN 22204	Same as ISO R.2204
NEN 30454	Same as ISO R.454
New Zealand	
1009:1951	Musical pitch. Gr 4. Amendment No. 1, 1967
2066:1965	The relation between the sone scale of loudness and the phon scale of loudness level. Gr 2
2067:1965	Recommendation on preferred frequencies for acoustical measurements. Gr 2
Norway	Norges Standardiseringsforbund, Håkon 7. gt. 2, Oslo 1
NS 1020.07	Del 7. Størrelser og SI-enheter. Akustikk
NS 4800	Kammertonen (Standard tonehøyde)
NS 4801	Fysiske og subjektive størrelser for beskrivelse av lyd og støy
NS 4802	Normale likelydskurver for rene toner og normal høreterskel under fritt-felt-forhold
NS 4803	Prefererte frekvenser ved akustiske målinger
NS 4805	Effekt- og intensitetsnivåer for lyd og støy
NS 4807	Forskjellen mellom lydtrykknivåer av smalbåndstøy målt i diffust felt og i et frontalt innfallende fritt felt har samme hørestyrke
NS 4810	Metode for beregning av hørestyrkenivå. (Inkl. ISO R.532)
	Nordisk Komite for bygningsbestemmelser. Kommunal og Arbejdsdepartementet
NKB Nr. 17-1971	Støj og Byplan (Noise Abatement in Town Planning)

239

Poland	Polski Komitet Normalizacji i Miar ul. Elektoralna 2, 00-139 - Warszawa
PN-61 B-02153	Building acoustics Terminology and definitions
PN-71 M-01300	Noise of machines and equipment. Methods for determination of acoustic parameters
PN N-01301	Acoustics. Measuring frequencies (Polish Draft Standards for experimental application)
PN N-01303	Acoustics. Method of determination of audibility and audibility levels (Polish Draft Standard for experimental application)
PN M-01305	Acoustics. Plotting curves of equal sound levels and threshold of audibility of normal tones (Polish Draft Standard for experimental application)
PN T-01009	Electroacoustics. Terms and definitions (Polish Draft Standard for experimental application)
Portugal	Inspecção Geral dos Produtos Agricolas e Industriais (Repartição de Normalização) Avenida de Berna—1 Lisboa—1
I-855 1975	Acustica. Terminologia (terminology)
Roumania	Oficiul de stat pentru Standarde, Str. Edgar Quinet 6, Bucarest 1
STAS 1957-66	Acoustics. Quantities, units and symbols
STAS 6342-61	Frequencies of tones
STAS 6451-61	Physical and physiological expressions of sound and noise
STAS 6533-62	Electroacoustics, terminology
STAS 6702-63	Electroacoustics. Conventional symbols
STAS 6901-64	Normal equal loudness contours
STAS 7024-64	Supersonic acoustics. Terminology
Spain	Instituto Nacional de Racionalizacion y Normalizacion Serrano Nr. 150 Madrid 6
50 (08) 1960	Vocabulario Electrotécnico Internacional Electroacústica
117-12 1968	Doceava parte: Diagramas de espectros de frecuencias
268-1 1968	Primera parte: Generalidades
268-2 1971	Segunda parte: Definición de los términos generales
Sweden	Sveriges standardiseringskommission, Box 3295, 10366 Stockholm
SEN 590100	Akustik, översikt över normer
SEN 011501	Akustisk ordlista
SIS 016170	Storheter och Enheter, Akustik

Switzerland	Eidgenössische Drucksachen und Materialzentrale, Bern 3,
—	Lärmbekämpfung in der Schweiz
U.S.A.	American National Standards Institute, 1430 Broadway, New York, NY 10018
S1.1-1960	Acoustical terminology
S1.2-1962	Method for physical measurement of sound
S1.6-1967	Preferred frequencies and band numbers for acoustical measurements
S1.8-1969	Preferred ref. quantities for acoustical levels
S1.13-1971	Method for the measurement of sound pressure levels
S3.4-1968	Procedure for the computation of the loudness of noise
S3.20-1973	Psychoacoustical terminology
S6.1-1973	Qualifying a sound data acquisition system
Y10.11-1953	Standard letter symbols for acoustics
U.S.S.R.	Komitet Standardtov, Leninsky Prospekt 9 b, 117049, Moskva M-49
Gost 8849-58	Acoustical units
Gost 12090-66	Preferred frequencies for acoustical measurements
Gost 9865-68	Supersonic equipment. Series of nominal electrical power
Gost 14761-69	Grammophone test records. Technical conditions. Testing
Yugoslavia	
1/NN 4010	Physiological and subjective magnitude of sound or noise
2/NN 4011	Preferred frequencies for acoustical measurements
International (I.E.C.)	International Organization for Standardization, 1, Rue de Varembé, Geneva, Switzerland
50 (08) (1960)	International electrotechnical vocabulary, electro-acoustics
IEC Draft Proposal	Definition of dynamic ranges at the input of digital signal processing equipment for acoustical measurements
International (I.S.O.)	International Organization for Standardization, 1, Rue de Varembé, Geneva, Switzerland
R.31 Part VII 1965	Quantities and units of acoustics
R.131-1959	Expression of the physical and subjective magnitudes of sound or noise
R.226-1961	Normal equal-loudness contours for pure tones and normal threshold of hearing under free field listening conditions
R.266-1975	Preferred frequencies for acoustical measurements

R.357-1963 Supplementary to R.131	Expression of the power and intensity levels of sound or noise
R.454-1965	Relation between sound pressure levels or narrow bands of noise in a diffuse field and in a frontally-incident free field for equal loudness
R.532-1975	Method for calculating loudness level
R.2204-1973	Guide to the measurement of acoustical noise and evaluation of its effect on man
R.2249-1973	Description and measurement of physical properties of sonic booms
R.3352-1974	Assessment of noise with respect to its effect on the intelligibility of speech
ISO Draft Proposals	A guide to the evaluation or assessment of noise
	Digital processing of acoustical signals
	Reference acoustical quantities
	Recommended methods for measuring the intelligibility of speech

B. Noise Rating Recommendations

Argentina

4079	Noise evaluation for hearing conservation
Australia	Standards House, 80 Arthur Street, North Sydney
AS.1055-1973	Noise assessment in residential areas
AS.1469-1973	Criteria curves for rating noise and establishing acoustic environment
DR.72084	Australian standard code of practice for hearing conservation
	Council of the City of Sydney
	Draft code for the control and regulation of noise on building sites
Austria	Staatsdruckerei, Wien
Bundesgesetz-blatt 15. Stück 1974 Nr. 39	Gesundheitliche Eignung von Arbeit-nehmern für bestimmte Tätigkeiten
Bundesgesetz-blatt 288	Kraftfahrverordnung 1955
Bundesgesetz-blatt 103	Seenverkehrsordnung 1961
	Österreichisches Normungsinstitut Leopoldsg. 4 1020 Wien
S 5010 Entwurf	Schallabstrahlung von Industriebau-ten, Nachbarschaftsschutz
S 5021 Entwurf	Teil 1; Schalltechnische Grundlagen für die örtliche und überörtliche Raum-planung und Raumordnung
S 5021 Entwurf	Teil 2; Darstellung von Lärmkategorien in Plänen

	Österreichischer Arbeitsring für Lärmbekämpfung, Regierungsgebäude, 1012 Wien
ÖAL-Richtlinie Nr.6 (2. Ausg.)	Gesundheitsschäden durch Lärm
ÖAL-Richtlinie Nr.15	Sicherung der Nachtruhe
ÖAL-Richtlinie Nr.18	Die ärztliche Begutachtung von Störun-gen durch Lärm
ÖAL-Richtlinie Nr.19	Schalltechnische Grundlagen für die Beurteilung von Baulärm
ÖAL-Richtlinie Nr.21	Schalltechnische Grundlagen für örtli-che und überörtliche Raumplanung
Belgium	Institut Belge de Normalisation, 29 av. de la Brabançonne, 1040 Bruxelles
NBN576.11-1961	Courbes d'évaluation du niveau de bruit
Brasil	Associação Brasileira de Normas Técnicas — ABNT Av. Almirante Barroso 54 Rio de Janeiro — RJ
NB 95 1966	Níveis de Ruido Aceitáveis
Decreto 11.467 30.10.1974	Diário Oficial do Município de São Paulo regulamenta a Lei 8106 de 30.08.1974. Dispõe sobre Sons Urbanos
C.S.S.R.	Ministry of Health, Praha
Hygienical Requirements No. 32	Requirements for protection against noise
Denmark	Dansk Standardiseringsråd, Aurehøjvej 12, 2900 Hellerup
DS/ISO R.1996	Akustik. Bedømmelse af støj med hensyn til omgivelsernes reaktion
DS/ISO R.1999	Akustik. Bedømmelse af støjeksponering på arbejdspladsen med henblik på hørebeskyttelse
Finland	Lääkintöhallitus Siltasaarenk. 18 A 00530 Helsinki 53
1551	Yleiskirje: Terveydenhoitolain (469/65) ja-asetuksen (55/67) nojalla annetut melua koskevat terveydelliset suositukset
	Valtion Painatuskeskus PL 516, 00101 Helsinki 10
VNP 730/1974	VNP työssä vallitsevan melun torjunnasta
France	L'Association Française de Normalisation (AFNOR), Tour Europe, 92 Courbevoie
NF S 31-010 1974	Mesure du bruit dans une zone habitée vue de l'évaluation de la gêne de la population
NF S 31-013 1975	Evaluation de l'exposition au bruit au cours du travail en vue de la protection de l'ouïe (remplace S 31-013, avril 1969)
NF S 31-047 1975	Evaluation des distances d'intelligibilité de la parole dans une ambiance bruyante

241

Germany (B.R.D.)	Beuth Vertrieb GmbH. 1000 Berlin 30, Burggrafenstr. 4 — 7 und 5000 Köln, Kamekestr. 2 — 8
DIN 18005 Vornorm + Neuentwurf	Schallschutz im Städtebau Hinweise für die Planung Berechnungs- und Bewertungsgrundlagen
DIN 45641	Mittelungspegel und Beurteilungspegel zeitlich schwankender Schallvorgänge
DIN 45645 Entwurf	Einheitliche Ermittlung des Beurteilungspegels für Geräuschimmissionen
VDI 2058	Beurteilung und Abwehr von Arbeitslärm; Bl. 1: In der Nachbarschaft Bl. 2: Am Arbeitsplatz hinsichtlich Gehörschäden
VDI 2565 Entwurf	Beurteilung von Lärm in Wohnungen
VDI 2574 Entwurf	Beurteilung der Innengeräusche von Kraftfahrzeugen
	Bundesanzeiger u.a.
	Bundes-Immissionsschutzgesetz, Folge-Verordnungen
	Allgemeine Verwaltungsvorschrift zum Schutz gegen Baulärm; Geräuschimmissionen
	Allgemeine Verwaltungsvorschrift zum Schutz gegen Baulärm; Emissionsmeßverfahren
	Technische Anleitung zum Schutz gegen Lärm (TA Lärm)
	Arbeitsstättenverordnung
	Unfallverhütungsvorschrift Lärm

Great Britain	British Standards Institution, 2 Park Street, London W. 1
Dept. of Env.	Code of practice for reducing the exposure of employed persons to noise
Statutory Instrument 1974 No. 903	Woodworking machines regulations (44)
BS.4142:1967	Method of rating industrial noise affecting mixed residential and industrial areas. With amendment AMD 1661. January 1975
Statutory Instrument 1973 No. 1363	Building & Buildings — Noise control regulations 1973
BS.5228:1975	Code of practice for noise control on construction and demolition sites
Dept. of Env. (1975)	Calculation of road traffic noise
H.M. Govt.	Control of pollution act 1974, chapter 40
Statutory Instrument 1976 No. 37	The control of noise/measurement — Registers Regulations 1976
Dept. of Env. Circular 2/76	Control of pollution act — Implementation of part III — Noise

Hungary	Magyar Szabvanyügyi Hivatal, Budapest IX, Üllöl ut. 25
SZOT 6/1965 (IV)	Verordnungen des Landesrates der Geverkschaften
M.SZ. 11143 T 1970	Max. permitted noise levels by medical instruments and equipment

India	Indian Standards Institution, Manak Bhavan, 9 Bahadur Shah Zafar Marg, New Delhi 1
IS: 4954-1968	Recommendations for noise abatement in town planning
IS: 7194-1973	Specifications for assessment of noise-exposure during work for hearing conservation purposes

Netherlands	Nederlands Normalisatie-Instituut, Polakweg 5, Rijswijk (Z-H)
NEN 20532	Same as ISO R.532

Norway	Statens Forurenings Tilsyn
1975	Retningslinjer for begrensning av støy fra industri m.v.
	Oslo Helseråd, St. Olavs Plass 5, Oslo 1
1975	Forskrifter om begrensning av støy

Poland	Polski Komitet Normalizacji i Miar ul. Elektoralna 2, 00-139 - Warszawa
PN-70 B-02151	Building acoustics. Sound proof protection for rooms in buildings
PN-72 E-06019	Electrical rotating machinery. Admissible sound level
PN-75 E-06260	Appliances for domestic and similar purposes. Noise level. Examinations and principles of fixing of admissible level
PN-75 M-35200	Admissible sound levels in rooms with energetic objects
PN-75 M-47015	Earth moving machinery. Operator's stand. Admissible noise level and methods of tests
PN M-55725	Machine tools for metals. Test methods and admissible noise levels (Polish Draft Standard for experimental application)
PN-75 M-78030	Drived carriageway cars. Admissible noise level and methods of tests
PN N-01302	Acoustics. Method of determination on the risk of weakened hearing (Polish Draft Standard for experimental application)

Portugal	Inspecção Geral dos Produtos Agricolas e Industriais (Repartição de Normalizacão) Avenida de Berna—1 Lisboa—1
NP 302 1964	Ruidos industriais (industrial noise). 2 provisory standards a. Reaction to noise in residential areas b. Estimation of risk for hearing damage

242

South Africa	South African Bureau of Standards, Private Bag X191 Pretoria 0001
SABS 083-1970	Code of practice for the rating of noise for hearing conservation
SABS 0103-1970	Code of practice for the rating of noise for speech communication with respect to annoyance
Sweden	Sveriges Standardiserings-kommission, Box 3295, 10366 Stockholm
SEN 590111	Bedömning av risk för hörselskada vid bullerexponering, (Risk for hearing damage)
	Liber Förlag, Fack, 10320 Stockholm
Arbetarskydds-styrelsens anvis-ningar nr 110,	Buller i arbetslivet
Sjöfartsverkets meddelanden nr 27-1973,	Bestämmelser och rekommendationer om skydd mot buller på fartyg
Statens Natur-vårdsverks pub-likation 1973:5,	Riktvärden för externt industribuller
Switzerland	Eidgenössische Drucksachen und Materialzentrale, Bern 3
—	Lärmbekämpfung in der Schweiz
13 März 1964	Bundesgesetz über die Arbeit in Indu-strie, Gewerbe und Handel (Arbeitsge-setz)
26 März 1969	Verordnung IV zum Arbeitsgesetz
	Schweiz, Unfallversicherungsanstalt, Luzern
März 1965 NR 66 und 67	Schweizerische Blätter für Arbeitssi-cherheit
U.S.A.	Air-Conditioning and Refrigeration Institute 1815 North Fort Myer Drive Arlington, VA 22209
ARI Standard 270 (1967)	Standard for sound rating of outdoor unitary equipment
ARI Standard 275 (1969)	Standard for application of sound rated outdoor unitary equipment
ARI Standard 443 (1970)	Standard for sound rating of room fan-coil air-conditioners
ARI Standard 446 (1968)	Standards for sound rating of room air-induction units
	Air Moving and Conditioning Association 30 West University Drive Arlington Heights, IL 60004
AMCA Bulletin 301 (1965)	Standard method of publishing sound ratings for air moving devices
AMCA Bulletin 302 (1965)	Application of sone loudness ratings for nonducted air moving devices
AMCA Publica-tion 303 (1965)	Application of sound power ratings for ducted air moving devices
AMCA Publica-tion 311(1967)	Certified sound ratings program for air moving devices
	American National Standards Institute 1430 Broadway New York, NY 10018

S3.1-1960	Criteria for background noise in audiometer rooms
	Association of Home Appliance Manufacturers 20 North Wacker Drive Chicago, IL 60606
AHAM RAC-2SR (1971)	Room air conditioner sound rating
	U.S. Department of Labor Washington D.C.
OSHA	Walsh-Healey Code (administered under Occupational Safety and Health Act of 1969)
U.S.S.R.	Komitet Standardtov, Leninsky Prospekt 9 b, 117049 Moskva M-49
Gost 12.1.003 1976	Noise. General safety requirements
Gost 15762-1970	Individual noise-protection devices hyg. requirements
Yugoslavia	Official Gazette
8 July 1971	General precautionary measures and standards for protection at work against noise at working places
International (I.S.O.)	International Organization for Standardization, 1, Rue de Varembé, Geneva, Switzerland
R.1996-1971	Assessment of noise with respect to community response
R.1999-1975	Assessment of occupational noise exposure for hearing conservation purposes
ISO Draft Proposal	Code of noise classification of pneumatic equipment for construction sites

C. Noise Measuring Equipment

Argentina

F 40-74	General purpose sound level meter
Australia	Standards House, 80 Arthur Street, North Sydney
AS.1259-1976 Part 1	Sound level meters, type 1, general purpose
AS.1259-1976 Part 2	Sound level meters, type 2, precision
AS.Z41-1969	Octave, half octave, and one third octave band pass filters intended for the analysis of sound and vibrations
DR 72070	Specifications for precision sound level meters for the measurement of impulsive sounds
Belgium	Institut Belge de Normalisation, 29 av. de la Brabançonne, Bruxelles 4
NBN576.80-1962	Sonomètre de précision

Canada	Canadian Standards Association 178 Rexdale Boulevard Rexdale, Ontario		**Great Britain**	British Standards Institution, 2 Park Street, London W. 1
Z 107.4	Pure tone audiometers for limited measurement of hearing and for screening		BS. 3489:1962	Sound level meters (industrial grade)
Z 107.1	Same as ANSI S1.4-1971		BS.3539:1962	Sound level meters for the measurement of noise emitted by motor vehicles
Z 107.5	Same as ANSI S1.11-1966			
C.S.S.R.	Office for Standards and Measurements, 11347 Praha 1, Václavské Naměsti 19		BS.2475:1964	Octave and one third octave band pass filters with amendment PD 5536 May 1965
ČSN 35 6870	Sound level meter and band pass filter		BS.4197:1967	A precision sound level meter, amendment slip No. 1
ČSN 36 8210 1970	Microphones		**Hungary**	Magyar Szabványügyi Hivatal, Budapest IX, Üllöl út. 25
Denmark	Dansk Standardiseringsråd Aurehøjvej 12 2900 Hellerup		M.SZ.11144 1969	Sound measuring instruments basic requirements
DS/IEC 179	Præcisionslydtrykmålere		**India**	Indian Standards Institution, Manak Bhavan, 9 Bahadur Shah, Zafar Marg, New Delhi 1
DS/IEC 179 A	Præcisionslydtrykmålere. 1. tillæg: Tillægskrav til lydimpulsmålere			
DS/IEC 327	Præcisionsmetode til trykkalibrering af one inch standard kondensatormikrofoner ved reciprocitetsmetoden		IS:3931-1966	Specification for sound level meters for the measurement of noise emitted by motor vehicles
DS/IEC 402	Forenklet metode til trykkalibrering af one inch kondensatormikrofoner ved reciprocitetsmetoden		IS:3932-1966	Specification for sound level meters for general purpose use
Finland	Suomen Standardisoimisliitto PL 205, 00121 Helsinki 12		IS:6964-1973	Specification for octave, half-octave and third-octave band filters for analysis of sound and vibrations
SFS 2877	Same as IEC 123 (1961)		**Italy**	AEI, Via S. Paolo, 10, Milano
SFS 2881	Same as IEC 179			
SFS 2885	Same as IEC 225 (1966)		19-1 1958	Misucatori di livello sonoro
France	L'Association Française de Normalisation (AFNOR), Tour Europe, 92 Courbevoie		29-4 1968	Filtri de banda di ottava, di mezza ottava e di terzi ottava per analisi acustiche
NF C 97-010 1974	Filtres de bandes d'octave, de demi- octave et de tiers d'octave destinés à l'analyse des bruits et des vibrations (Enr.) (10 pages)		**Japan**	Japanese Standards Association 1-24, Akasaka 4 chome, Minato-ku Tokyo
NF S 31-009 1974	Sonomètres de précision		JIS C 1502 (1970)	Sound level meters
Germany **(B.R.D.)**	Beuth Vertrieb GmbH. 1000 Berlin 30, Burggrafenstr. 4 — 7 und 5000 Köln, Kamekestr. 2 — 8		JIS C 1503 (1969)	Sound level meters
DIN 45633	Präzisionsschallpegelmesser. Bl.1: Allgemeine Anforderungen Bl. 2: Sonderanforderungen für Impuls- messungen		**Netherlands**	Nederlands Normalisatie-Instituut, Polakweg 5, Rijswijk (Z-H)
DIN 45634	Schallpegelmesser und Impulsschallpe- gelmesser. Anforderung, Prüfung		NEN 10123	Same as IEC 123
DIN 45651	Oktavfilter für elektroakustische Mes- sungen		NEN 10179	Same as IEC 179 & 179 A - 1973
DIN 45652	Terzfilter für elektroakustische Messun- gen		NEN 10-268-2	Same as IEC 268-2-1971
Germany **(D.D.R.)**	Amt für Standardisierung, Mohrenstrasse 37a 108 Berlin		**New Zealand**	
TGL 200-7755 1971	Geräte zur Messung des Schalldruckpegels		1499:1965	Octave and one-third octave band-pass filters. Gr 3. Amendment No. 1, 1974
Bl. 1	Schallpegelmesser		**Poland**	Polski Komitet Normalizacji i Miar, ul. Elektoralna 2, 00-139 - Warszawa
Bl. 2	Terz- und Oktavfilter			
Bl. 3	Registrier- und Auswerteinrichtungen		PN-64 T-06460	Sound level meter. General requirements and technical tests

Spain	Instituto Nacional de Racionalization y Normalizacion Serrano Nr. 150, Madrid 6
123 1961	Recomendaciones para los aparatos de medida del nivel del sonido (sonómetros)
179 1973	Sonòmetros de precisiòn
225 1966	Filtros de banda de octava, semioctava y tercio de octava, destinados al análisis de ruidos y vibraciones
268-4 1972	Cuarta parte: Micrófonos
327 1971	Método de precisión para el calibrado a presión de los micrófonos patrones de condensadores de una pulgada por la técnica de la reciprocidad
402 1972	Método simplificado para el calibrado a presión de los micrófonos de condensador de pulgada por la técnica de la reciprocidad
486 1974	Métodos de precisión para el calibrado en campo libre de los micrófonos patrones de condensador de una pulgada por la técnica de la reciprocidad
U.S.A.	American National Standards Institute 1430 Broadway New York, NY 10018
S1.4-1971	Specification for sound level meters
S1.10-1966	Calibration of microphones
S1.11-1966	Octave, half-octave and one-third octave filter sets
S1.12-1967	Specifications for laboratory standard microphones
U.S.S.R.	The State Committee of Standards 9, Leninsky Prospekt, 117049, Moscow, M-49
Gost 13761-73	Measuring condenser microphones. General requirements
Gost 17168-71 Gost 17169-71	Filters electrical octave and third-octave. General technical requirements
Gost 17187-71	Sound level meters. General technical requirements
International (I.E.C.)	International Organization for Standardization, 1, Rue de Varembé, Geneva, Switzerland
123 (1961)	Recommendations for sound level meters
179 (1973)	Precision sound level meters
179 A (1973)	First supplement to publication 179 (1973) precision sound level meters, additional characteristics for the measurement of impulsive sounds
225 (1966)	Octave, half-octave and third-octave band filters intended for the analysis of sounds and vibrations
327 (1971)	Precision method for the pressure calibration of one-inch standard condenser microphones by the reciprocity technique
402 (1972)	Simplified methods for pressure calibration of one-inch condenser microphones by the reciprocity technique
486 (1974)	Precision method for free-field calibration of one-inch standard condenser microphones by the reciprocity technique
IEC Draft Proposal -	Consolidation and revision of IEC 123 and IEC 179 sound level meters

D. Measurements of Noise Emitted by Machines

Australia	Standards House, 80 Arthur Street, North Sydney
AS.1081-1975	Measurement of airborne noise emitted by rotating electrical machinery
AS.1217-1972	Methods of measurement of airborne sound emitted by machines
Austria	Österreichische Staatsdruckerei 1012 Wien
Bundesgesetz blatt 19. Stück 1974 Nr. 50	Gewerbeordnung 1973
Wiener Landes gesetzblatt 12. Stück 1973 Nr. 16	Gesetz zum Schutz gegen Baulärm
Wiener Landes gesetzblatt 16. Stück 1973 Nr. 20	Emissionsgrenzwertverordnung (für Baumaschinen)
	Österreichisches Normungsinstitut
S 5031 Entwurf	Bestimmung der Schalleistung von Schallquellen — Hallraumverfahren
S 5034 Entwurf	Bestimmung der Schalleistung von Schallquellen; Betriebsmäßige Verfahren für Freifeldmessungen über einem reflektierenden Untergrund
	Österreichischer Arbeitsring für Lärmbekämpfung, Regierungsgebäude, 1012 Wien
ÖAL-Richtlinie Nr. 1	Messung des Geräusches von Maschinen
ÖAL-Richtlinie Nr. 10	Schalltechnische Grundlagen für die Errichtung bzw. Erweiterung von Betriebsanlagen
ÖAL-Richtlinie Nr. 12	Geräuscharme Maschinen, Allgemeines
ÖAL-Richtlinie Nr. 22	Messung der Geräuschabgabe von Baumaschinen
Belgium	Institut Belge de Normalisation, 19 av. de Brabançonne, 1040 Bruxelles
NBN 263- 1951	Conditions acoustiques de travail d'installations de chauffage, ventilation, etc.

Bulgaria	Institut de Normalisation 8, Rue Sveta Sofia, Sofia	NF S 31-022 1973	Détermination de la puissance acoustique émise par les sources de bruit — partie I — méthode de laboratoire en salle réverbérante pour les petites sources à large bande
BDS 6011-66	Measurement of noise emitted by electrical rotating machines		
C.S.S.R.	Office for Standards and Measurements, Praha 1 — Nové Město, Václavské Naměsti 19	NF S 31-023 1973	Détermination de la puissance acoustique émise par les sources de bruit — deuxieme partie — méthode de laboratoire en salle réverbérante pour les petites sources émettant des bruits à fréquences discrètes ou à bandes étroites
ČSN 09 0862	Noise of diesel engines. Method of measurement		
ČSN 12 3062	Fans. prescriptions for measurement of noise	NF S 31-024 1973	Détermination de la puissance acoustique émise par les sources de bruit — troisième partie — méthode d'expertise adaptée à des salles réverbérantes spéciales
ČSN 17 8055	Measurement of noise emitted by computers		
ČSN 35 0000	Measurement of noise emitted by electrical machines	NF S 31-025 1973	Détermination de la puissance acoustique émise par les sources de bruit — quatrième partie — méthodes d'expertise adaptées à des conditions de champ libre sur le plan réfléchissant
ČSN 35 0019	Special testing methods for electrical rotating machines. III. Noise measurement		
ČSN 35 1080 1968	Fundamental tests of power transformers and reactors	NF S 31-026 1973	Détermination de la puissance acoustique émise par les sources de bruit — cinquième partie — méthode de laboratoire en salle anéchoique
ČSN 36 1005	Noise measurement of domestic electrical motor-operated appliances		
ČSN 36 1006 1969	Measurement of noise emitted by large electrical household appliances	NF S 31-030 1975	Code d'essai pour la mesure du bruit aérien émis par les marteaux-piqueurs et brise-béton. (Remplace S 31-030, mars 1974)
Denmark	Dansk Standardiseringsråd, Aurehøjvej 12, 2900 Hellerup	NF S 31-031 1975	Code d'essai pour la mesure du bruit aérien émis par les outils et machines pneumatiques
DS/ISO R.495	Retningslinier for udarbejdelse af forskrifter for måling af støj fra maskiner	S 31-032 1974	Mesure du bruit émis par les engins de terrassement et de levage — principes gènèraux pour l'application des codes d'essais
DS/ISO R.3741	Akustik. Bestemmelse af lydeffekt-niveauer for støjkilder. Præcisionsmetoder for bredbåndskilder i efterklangsrum	S 31-033 1974	Code d'essai pour la mesure du bruit émis par les pelles mécaniques et hydrauliques, conditions de fonctionnement, emplacement des points de mesure
DS/ISO R.3742	Akustik. Bestemmelse af lydeffekt-niveauer for støjkilder. Præcisionsmetoder for rentone- og smalbåndskilder i efterklangsrum	S 31-034 1974	Code d'essai pour la mesure du bruit émis par les chargeuses sur pneumatiques, conditions de fonctionnement, emplacement des points de mesure
	Miljøstyrelsen Kampmannsgade 1 1604 København V	S 31-035 1974	Code d'essai pour la mesure du bruit émis par les bétonnières fixes — conditions de fonctionnement et emplacement des points de mesure
Rapport 2	Industristøj (Industrial noise)		
France	L'Association Française de Normalisation (AFNOR), Tour Europe, 92 Courbevoie	S 31-036 1974	Code d'essai pour la mesure du bruit émis par les bétonnières portées — conditions de fonctionnement et emplacement des points de mesure
NF S 30-006 1966	Régles génèrales pour la rédaction des codes d'essais relatifs à la mesure du bruit émis par les machines	S 31-037 1974	Code d'essai pour la mesure du bruit émis par les groupes électrogènes — conditions de fonctionnement et emplacement des points de mesure
NF S 31-006 1966	Code d'essai pour la mesure du bruit émis par les machines électriques tournantes	S 31-038 1974	Code d'essai pour la mesure du bruit émis par les bouteurs — conditions de fonctionnement et emplacement des points de mesure
S 31-017 1972	Code d'essai pour la mesure du bruit à bord des bateaux et navires		
NF S 31-018 1973	Code d'essai pour la mesure du bruit émis par les bateaux de navigation intérieure	S 31-039 1974	Code d'essai pour la mesure du bruit émis par les chargeuses sur chaînes — conditions de fonctionnement et emplacement des points de mesure
NF S 31-020 1975	Code d'essai pour la mesure du bruit aérien émis par les groupes moto-compresseurs. (Remplace NF S 31-020, Novembre 1970)	S 31-042 1975	Code d'essai pour la mesure du bruit aérien émis par les pilonneuses vibrantes
S 31-021 1970	Règles d'essais acoustiques en plate-forme des ventilateurs à enveloppe		

S 31-043 1975	Code d'essai pour la mesure du bruit aérien émis par les rouleaux vibrants	**Great Britain**	British Standards Institution, 2 Park Street, London W. 1	
S 31-044 1975	Code d'essai pour la mesure des bruits aériens émis par les patins vibrants et les engins à semelles vibrantes	BS. 848: 1966	Part 2 - Fan noise testing	
Germany **(B.R.D.)**	Beuth Vertrieb GmbH. 1000 Berlin 30, Burggrafenstr. 4 — 7 und 5000 Köln, Kamekestr. 2 — 8	BS.4078: 1966	Cartridge-operated fixing tools	
		BS.4196: 1967	Guide to the selection of methods of measuring noise emitted by machinery	
DIN 42540	Geräuschstärke von Transformatoren: Bewerteter Schalldruckpegel (Schallpe- gel)	BS.4718: 1971	Method of test for silencers for air distribution systems	
DIN 45635	Geräuschmessung an Maschinen Bl. 1: Rahmen-Meßvorschrift, Hüllflä- chenverfahren Bl. 10 ff: Besondere Vorschriften für verschiedene Maschinenarten	BS.4813: 1972	Method of measuring noise from machine tools excluding testing in anechoic chambers	
		BS.4999: 1972	General requirements for rotating electrical machines, Part 51 - Noise levels	
VDI 2159	Getriebegeräusche (Messung, Beurtei- lung)	**India**	Indian Standards Institution, Manak Bhavan, 9 Bahadur Shah Zafar Marg, New Delhi 1	
VDI 2568 Bl. 1 — 5 Entwurf	Messung der Geräuschemission von Baumaschinen	IS:4758-1968	Methods of measurement of noise emitted by machines	
VDI 2570 Entwurf	Lärmminderung in Betrieben — Alge- meine Grundlagen	IS:6098-1971	Methods of measurement of the airborne noise emitted by rotating electrical machinery	
	Verlag Stahleisen GmbH. Postf. 8229 4000 Düsseldorf	**Japan**	Japanese Standards Association, 1-24, Akasaka, 4 chome, Minato-ku Tokyo	
SEB 905001- 64	Durchführung von Geräuschmessun- gen	JIS B 1548 (1960)	Sound pressure levels of ball and roller bearings	
SEB 905004- 66	Abnahmegeräuschmessungen und Ab- nahmebericht	JIS B 6004 (1962)	Method of sound level measurement for machine tools	
Germany **(D.D.R.)**	Amt für Standardisierung der D.D.R., Mohrenstrasse 37a, 108 Berlin	**Netherlands**	Nederlands Normalisatie-Instituut, Polakweg 5, Rijswijk (Z-H)	
TGL 39-440	Prüfvorschriften für Fahrzeuggetriebe	NEN 21680	Same as ISO R.1680-1970	
TGL 39-703	Prüfvorschriften für Auspuffgeräusch- dämpfer, Verbrennungsmotoren	**Norway**	Norges Standardiseringsforbund, Håkon 7. gt. 2, Oslo 1	
TGL 39-767	Verbrennungsmotoren, Geräuschmes- sungen, Meßverfahren	NS 4808	Retningslinjer for utarbeidelse av måleregler for støy fra maskiner (inkl. ISO R 495)	
TGL 45-01248	Geräuschmessung. Bestimmung des Schallpegel an Haushaltnähmaschinen			
TGL 50-29034	Geräuschmessungen an rotierenden elektrischen Maschinen, Richtlinien	**Poland**	Polski Komitet Normalizacji i Miar, ul. Elektoralna 2, Warszawa 1	
TGL 153-6011	Wälzlager, Laufgeräusch, Meßverfah- ren	PN-72 E-04257	Electrical rotating machinery. Determination of acoustic parameters of noise	
TGL 153-6012	Wälzlager, (Radial-) Rillenkugellager, Laufgeräusch, zulässige Werte	PN-75 E-06260	Appliances for domestic and similar purposes. Noise level. Examinations and principles of fixing of admissible level	
TGL 21814 6173	Zahnradgetriebe Reihe 10 LA, Uberset- zung 6.3 bis 40. Angaben über den ab- gestrahlten Schalleistungspegel	PN-72 M-43120	Fans. Methods of noise determination	
TGL 21815 6173	Zahnradgetriebe Reihe 10 LA, Ubersch- zung 40 bis 250. Angaben über den abgestrahlten Schalleistungspegel	PN-75 M-47015	Earth moving machinery. Operator's stand. Admissible noise level and methods of tests	
TGL 27641 BL. 8	Prüfung von Transformatoren ab 6,3 kVA. Bestimmung des Geräuschpe- gels	PN M-55725	Machine tools for metals. Test methods and admissible noise levels (Polish Draft Standard for experimental application)	
TGL 200-3110	Elektr. Maschinen. Bestimmung des Geräuschpegels. Begriffe. Prüfverfah- ren	PN-75 M-78030	Drived carriageway cars. Admissible noise level and methods of tests	
TGL 200-4504	Elektrische Hausgeräte, Geräuschmes- sungen, Meß- und Prüfverfahren	PN-71 N-01300	Noise of machines and equipment. Methods for determination of acoustic parameters	
TGL 22423-2 1969	Rotierende elektrische Maschinen. Prüfverfahren: Geräuschmessung			

Roumania	Oficiul de stat pentru Standarde, Str. Edgar Quinet 6, Bucarest 1
STAS 7150-65	Methods of noise measurement in industry
STAS 7301-65	Measurement of noise emitted by electrical rotating machines
South Africa	South African Bureau of Standards Private Bag X 191 Pretoria 0001
SABS 068-1972	The measurement under acoustic laboratory conditions of sound emitted by sound sources (determination of sound power levels under laboratory conditions)
SABS 069-1972	The measurement in the field of sound emitted by sound sources (determination of sound power levels under practical operating conditions)
Sweden	Sveriges Standardiserings-kommision, Box 3295 10366 Stockholm
SEN 330501	Köksfläktar, bestämning av kapacitet och ljudnivå
SMS/ISO R.2151	Mätning av luftburet buller avgivet från motordrivna kompressorer avsedda för användning utomhus
SMS 965	Träbearbetningsmaskiner, mätning av buller, beräkning av ljudeffektnivå
SMS 892	Byggmaskiner, mätning av bulleremission till omgivningen, remissförslag 1973
SMS 2189	Motorkedjesågar, mätning av buller
	Sveriges Menanförbund, Box 5506, 11485 Stockholm
BAS	Ljudnivåtest för svarvar, fräsmaskiner, fräs- och borrverk samt borrmaskiner
U.S.A.	Acoustical Society of America (ASA) American Institute of Physics 335 East 45th Street New York, NY 10017
ASA STD 3 1975	Test-site measurement of noise emitted by engine powered equipment
	Air-Conditioning and Refrigeration Institute 1815 North Fort Myer Drive Arlington, VA 22209
ARI Standard 575 (1973)	Standard for method of measuring machinery sound within equipment rooms
	Air Moving and Conditioning Association 30 West University Drive Arlington Heights, IL 60004
AMCA Standard 300-67	Test code for sound rating
	American Gear Manufacturers Association 1330 Massachusetts Avenue, N.W. Washington, D.C. 20005
AGMA 295.03 (1968)	Specification for measurement of sound on high speed helical and herringbone gear units
AGMA 297.01 (1973)	Sound for enclosed helical, herringbone and spiral level gear drives

AGMA 298.01 (1975)	Sound for gearmotors and in-line reducers and increasers
	American National Standards Institute 1430 Broadway New York, NY 10018
S1.21-1972	American national standard methods for the determination of sound power levels of small sources in reverberation rooms
S3.17-1975	Method for rating the sound power spectra of small stationary noise sources
S5.1-1971	Test code for the measurement of sound from pneumatic equipment
	American Society of Heating, Refrigerating, and Air Conditioning Engineers 345 E. 47th Street New York, NY 10017
ASHRAE 36-72	Methods of testing for sound rating heating, refrigerating, and air-conditioning equipment
ASHRAE 68-75	Method of testing sound power radiated into ducts from air moving devices
	American Textile Machinery Association 1730 M St. N.W. Washington, D.C. 20036
ATMA Test Procedure (1973)	Noise measurement technique for textile machinery
	Compressed Air and Gas Institute 122 East 42nd St. New York, NY 10017
	Test code for the measurement of sound from pneumatic equipment
	National Machine Tool Builders Association 7901 Westpark Drive McLean, VA 22101
	Noise measurement technique
	Institute of Electrical and Electronic Engineers 445 Hoes Lane Piscataway, NJ 08854
IEEE No. 85 1973	Test procedure for airborne sound measurements on rotating electric machinery
	Woodworking Machinery Manufacturers Association 1900 Arch Street Philadelphia, PA 19103
WMMA Test code (1973)	Test code for evaluating the noise emission of woodworking machinery
	Society of Automotive Engineers, Inc. 400 Commonwealth Drive Warrendale, PA 15096
SAE J952b (1969)	SAE standard, sound levels for engine powered equipment
SAE J1046 (1974)	SAE recommended practice, exterior sound level measurement procedure for small engine powered equipment
SAE J1074 (1974)	SAE recommended practice, engine sound level measurement procedure

248

U.S.S.R.	Komitet Standardtov, Leninsky Prospekt 9 b 117049 Moskva M-49
Gost 11929-66	Measurement of noise emitted by electrical rotating machines and transformers
Gost 8.055-73	State system for ensuring the uniformity of measuring. Machines. Measurement methods for the determination of noise characteristics
Gost 15529-70	Ventilators for general purposes. Methods for determination of noise characteristics
Gost 16317-70	Household refrigerators
Gost 19358-74	Automobiles, trains, buses, motorcycles, scooters, motormounted bicycles. External and internal noise. Maximum permissible levels. Methods of measurement
Gost 20444-75	Traffic flows in populated areas. Method of determination of noise characteristic
Gost 20445-75	Building and structures of industrial enterprises. Method of noise measurements at workplaces
International (I.E.C.)	International Organization for Standardization, 1, Rue de Varembé, Geneva, Switzerland
34-9 (1972)	Rotating electrical machines, part 9 noise limits
International (I.S.O.)	International Organization for Standardization, 1, Rue de Varembé, Geneva, Switzerland
R.495-1966	General requirements for the preparation of test codes for measuring the noise emitted by machines
R.1680-1970	Test code for the measurement of the airborne noise emitted by rotating electrical machinery
R.2151-1972	Measurement of airborne noise emitted by compressor/primemover units intended for outdoor use
3741-1975	Determination of sound power level of noise sources precision methods for broad-band sources in reverberation rooms
3742-1975	Determination of sound power level of noise sources — Precision methods for discrete-frequency and narrow-band sources in reverberation rooms
	ISO Draft Proposals
ISO/DIS 3481	Measurement of airborne noise emitted by pneumatic tools and machines - engineering method for determination of sound power levels
ISO/DIS 3740	Determination of sound power level of noise sources — Engineering methods for special reverberation test rooms. Part Ø: Guidelines for the use of basic standards and for the preparation of noise test codes
ISO/DIS 3743	Determination of sound power level of noise sources — Engineering methods for special reverberation test rooms

ISO/DIS 3744	Determination of sound power levels of noise sources — Engineering methods for free field conditions over a reflecting plane
ISO/DIS 3745	Determination of sound power levels of noise sources — Precision methods for anechoic and semi-anechoic rooms
ISO/DIS 3746	Determination of sound power levels of noise sources. Survey methods
	Laboratory tests on noise emissions by appliances and equipment in water supply installations
	Sound measurement procedures for air moving devices connected to either a discharge duct or an inlet duct
	Reverberation room measurement of sound from heating, ventilating and air conditioning equipment
	Noise level measurement at the operator's workplace on agricultural tractors and field machinery
	Noise from earth moving machinery — Determination of sound power level
	The measurement of airborne noise emitted by compressor units including primemovers — Engineering method for determination of sound power level
	Noise from earth moving machinery — Measurement at operator's workplace
	Determination of airborne noise emitted by earth moving machinery to the surroundings — Survey method
	Determination of airborne noise emitted by civil engineering equipment for outdoor use
	Designation of noise emitted by machinery and equipment
	Noise classification of equipment and machinery

Ξ. Measurement of Sound Transmission Loss and Building Acoustics

Argentina	
4063	Measurement of sound insulation in dwellings
4065	Measurement of sound absorption coefficients
Australia	Standards House, 80 Arthur Street, North Sydney
AS.1045-1971	Measurement of absorption coefficients in a reverberation room
DR.75060	Method of measurement of normal incidence source absorption coefficient and specific normal acoustic impedances of acoustic materials by the tube method
DR.74163	Code of practice for building siting and construction against aircraft noise intrusion
DR.72090	Standard method for the rating of sound insulation for dwellings

DOC.979	Standard methods for field and laboratory measurements of airborne and impact sound transmission	**Denmark**	Dansk Standardiseringsråd Aurehøjvej 12 2900 Hellerup
Austria	Österreichisches Normungsinstitut Leopoldsg. 4 1020 Wien	DS/ISO R.140	Felt- og laboratoriemålinger af luftlyds og trinlyds udbredelse
B 8115	Hochbau, Schallschutz und Hörsamkeit	DS/ISO R.354	Måling af absorptionskoefficienter i efterklangsrum
B 8115 Entwurf	Schallschutz und Raumakustik im Hochbau		Statens Trykningskontor
	Österreichischer Arbeitsring für Lärmbekämpfung, Regierungsgebäude, 1012 Wien		Landsbyggeloven, kap. 9, lydisolering (Building code, sound isolation)
			Miljøstyrelsen Kampmannsgade 1 1604 København V
ÖAL-Richtlinie Nr. 8	Geräuscharme Wohn-, Krankenhaus- und Hotelinstallationen		
ÖAL-Richtlinie Nr. 16	Schalltechnische Grundlagen für die Errichtung von Gaststätten und Beherbergungsbetrieben	Publikation nr.9	Støj, bygge- og anlægsvirksomhed (Noise in building construction)
ÖAL-Richtlinie Nr. 17	Lärmminderung durch Schallschluk- kende Ausstattung	**France**	L'Association Francaise de Normalisation (AFNOR), Tour Europe, 92 Courbevoie
Belgium	Institut Belge de Normalisation, 29 av. de Brabançonne, 1040 Bruxelles	NF S 31-002 1956	Mesure, en laboratoire et sur place, de la transmission des sons aériens et des bruits de chocs dans les constructions
NBN576.05- 1963	Mesure en laboratoire de l'indice d'affaiblissement aux sons aériens	NF S 31-003 1951	Mesure du coefficient d'absorption acoustique en salle réverbérante
NBN576.06- 1963	Mesure "in situ" de l'isolement acoustique aux sons aériens	NF S 31-011 1974	Code d'essai pour la détermination en laboratoire de l'efficacité des revêtements de sol en ce qui concerne la réduction des bruits d'impact
NBN576.07- 1964	Mesure en laboratoire de la transmission acoustique des bruits de choc	NF S 31-012 1973	Mesure de la durée de réverbération des auditoriums
NBN576.08- 1965	Mesure "in situ" de la transmission acoustique des bruits de choc	NF S 31-014 1975	Code d'essai pour la mesure du bruit émis par les équipements hydrauliques des bâtiments
NBN576.09- 1968	Mesure du facteur d'absorption acoustique en salle réverbérante	NF S 31-015 1975	Mesure du bruit émis par la robinetterie de puisage (sanitaire et bâtiment)
NBN576.40- 1966	Critéres de l'isolation sonique	S 31-016 1971	Mesure du bruit émis par la robinetterie de bâtiment
Brasil	Associação Brasileira de Normas Técnicas — ABNT Av. Almirante Barroso 54 Rio de Janeiro — RJ	**Germany** **(B.R.D.)**	Beuth Vertrieb GmbH. 1000 Berlin 30, Burggrafenstr. 4 — 7 und 5000 Köln, Kamekestr. 2 — 8
P.M.B.432	Medida local e em Laboratório de Transmissão de Sons Aéreos e dos Ruidos de Impacto (Metodo de Ensaio)	DIN 4109 Bl. 1 — 5	Schallschutz im Hochbau
NB 101	Norma para Tratamento Acústico em Recintos Fechados	DIN18041	Hörsamkeit in kleinen bis mittelgroßen Räumen
C.S.S.R.	Office for Standards and Measurements, 11347 Praha 1, Václavské Námĕsti 19	DIN 52210	Bauakustische Prüfungen. T. 1: Luft- u. Trittschalldämmung, Meßverfahren. T. 2: Prüfstände. T. 3: Prüfungen. T. 4: Einzahl-Angaben
ČSN 36 8840	Measurement of sound insulating properties of building structures	DIN 52212	Bestimmung des Schallabsorptionsgra- des im Hallraum
ČSN 36 8841 1974	Measurement of reverberation time	DIN 52214	Bestimmung der dynamischen Steifig- keit von Dämmschichten für schwim- mende Estriche
ČSN 73 0525 1964	Design in the room acoustics. General principles	DIN 52215	Bestimmung des Schallabsorptionsgra- des und der Impedanz in Rohr
ČSN 73 0526 1968	Design in the room acoustics. Studios and sound recording rooms	DIN 52216	Messung der Nachhallzeit in Zuhörer- räumen
ČSN 73 0527 1973	Room acoustics projects. Rooms for cultural and school purposes. Rooms for public purposes. Administrative rooms	DIN 52217	Flankenübertragung — Begriffe
ČSN 73 0531	Protection against noise transmission in building	DIN 52218	Prüfung des Geräuschverhaltens von Armaturen und Geräten der Wasserin- stallation im Labor
ČSN 83 0535	Sound absorption coefficient measurement in reverberation room	DIN 52219	Messung von Geräuschen der Wasser- installation am Bau

VDI 2719	Schalldämmung von Fenstern
Germany (D.D.R.)	Amt für Standardisierung der D.D.R., Mohrenstrasse 37a, 108 Berlin
TGL 10687 BI. 1 — 8	Bauphysikalische Schutzmaßnahmen, Schallschutz. Siehe S.2. Ubersicht der Grundlagenstandards
TGL 10688 BI. 1 — 12	Messverfahren der Akustik
Great Britain	British Standards Institution, 2 Park Street, London W. 1
BS.2750: 1956	Recommendations for field and laboratory measurement of airborne and impact sound transmission in buildings
BS.CP352: 1958	Mechanical ventilation and air conditioning in buildings (contains a section on sound proofing and anti-vibration devices)
BS.3638: 1963	Method for the measurement of sound absorption coefficients (ISO) in a reverberation room.
BS.CP3: 1972	Part 2: Sound insulation and noise reduction (in buildings)
Hungary	Magyar Szabványügyi Hivatal, Budapest IX, Üllöl út. 25
M.E.-83-65	Technische Vorschriften des Ministeriums für Bauwesen
Italy	Servizio Tecnico Centrale, Ministero dei Lavori Pubblici, Roma
Circolare N. 1769	Criteri di valutazione e collando dei requisiti acustici nelle costruzioni edilizie
Netherlands	Nederlands Normalisatie-Instituut, Polakweg 5, Rijswijk (Z-H)
NEN 1070 1975	Sound insulation measurement in dwellings
NEN 20140	Same as ISO R.140-1960
NEN 20354	Same as ISO R.354
Norway	Norges Standardiseringsforbund, Håkon 7..gt. 2, Oslo 1
NS 3051	Bestemmelse av lydisolering
NS 4804 2.1974	Måling av lydabsorpsjonsfaktorer i klangrom
Poland	Polski Komitet Normalizacji i Miar, ul. Elektoralna 2, 00-139 - Warszawa
PN-70 B-02151	Building acoustics. Soundproof protection for rooms in buildings
PN-61 B-02153	Building acoustics. Terminology
PN-68 B-02154	Building acoustics. Tests on acoustic properties in building partitions
Portugal	Inspecção Geral dos Produtos Agricolas e Industriais (Repartição de Normalização) Avenida de Berna — 1 Lisboa — 1
P-669 1968	Acustica, Ensaio de transmissão dos ruidos aéreos e de percussão (airborne and impact noise transmission)
P-670 1968	Acústica, Determinação em câmara reverberante do coeficiente de absorção e da área sonora equivalente (Determination of sound absorption coefficients)
Roumania	Oficiul de stat pentru Standarde, Str. Edgar Quinet 6, Bucarest 1
STAS 6156-68	Building acoustics. Protection against noise and vibration in buildings. Regulation for design and performance
STAS 6161-60	Methods of measurement of noise in buildings
STAS 8048-67 1967	Measurement of dynamic stiffness of vibration absorbing materials in building acoustics
Sweden	Sveriges Standardiseringskommision, Box 3295, 10366 Stockholm
SIS 025251	Bestämning av ljudisolering i byggnader
SIS 025252	Bestämning av ljudisolering i byggnader, fältmätning
SIS 025253	Metod för värdering av ljudisolering mellan rum i byggnader
SIS 817306	Ljudisolerande dörrar 25 dB, 30 dB och 35 dB
	Liber Förlag, Fack, 103 20 Stockholm
SBN 75 Kap 34	Ljudklimat
	Svensk Byggtjänst, Box 1403, 111 84 Stockholm
KBS 10-1968	Normer för kontorsbyggnader
Switzerland	Schweiz. Ingenieur- und Architekten-Verein
SIA Empflehlung 181-1970	Empfehlung für Schallschutz im Wohnungsbau
U.S.A.	Acoustical and Board Products Association 205 West Touhy Avenue Park Ridge, IL 60068
AMA-1-II 1967	Method of test. Ceiling sound transmission test by two-room method
AM Spec. No. 11 (1972)	Acoustical absorbers
	Air Diffusion Council 435 North Michigan Chicago, IL 60611
AD-63 (1963)	Measurement of room-to-room sound transmission through plenum air systems
FD-72 (1972)	Flexible air duct test code
	American National Standards Institute 1430 Broadway New York, NY 10018
S1.7-1970	Sound absorption of acoustical materials in reverberation rooms
	American Society for Testing and Materials 1916 Race Street Philadelphia, PA 19103

ASTM C384-58 (Reapproved 1972)	Standard method of test for impedance and absorption of acoustical materials by the tube method
ASTM C423-66 (Reapproved 1972)	Standard method of test for sound absorption of acoustical materials in reverberation rooms (ANSI S1.7-1970)
ASTM C634-73	Standard definitions of terms relating to acoustical tests of building constructions and materials
ASTM E90-75	Standard recommended practice for laboratory measurement of airborne sound transmission loss of building partitions
ASTM E336-71	Standard recommended practice for measurement of airborne sound insulation in buildings
ASTM E413-73	Standard classification for determination of sound transmission class
ASTM E477-73	Standard method of testing duct liner materials and prefabricated silencers for acoustical and airflow performance
ASTM E492-73T	Tenative method of laboratory measurement of impact sound transmission through floor ceiling assemblies using the tapping machine (1971)
ASTM E497-73T	Tenative recommended practice for installation of fixed partitions of light frame type for the purpose of conserving their sound insulation efficiency
	Dept. of Housing and Urban Development Washington, D.C.
	A guide to airborne, impact and structure borne noise control in multifamily dwellings
	International Conference of Building Officials 5360 South Workman Mill Road Whittier, CA 90601
UBC 35-1	Laboratory determination of airborne sound transmission class (STC)
UBC 35-2	Impact sound insulation
UBC 35-3	Airborne sound insulation field test
U.S.S.R.	Komitet Standartov, Leninsky Prospekt 9 b, 117049 Moskva M-49
Gost 15116	Sound insulation. Method of measurement. Sound insulation factor
Gost 16297-70	Building wares and materials. The methods of acoustical tests
Yugoslavia	Official Gazette
13 Aug. 1970	Regulation on technical precautions and conditions for sound protection in buildings
International (I.S.O.)	International Organization for Standardization, 1, Rue de Varembé, Geneva, Switzerland
R.140-1960	Field and laboratory measurements of airborne and impact sound transmission

R.354-1963	Measurement of absorption coefficients in a reverberation room
R.717-1968	Rating of sound insulation for dwellings
	Draft Proposal
ISO/DIS 3382	Measurement of reverberation time in auditories

F. Measurement of Vehicle and Traffic Noise

Argentina

4071	Measurement of vehicle noise
Australia	Standards House, 80 Arthur Street, North Sydney
DR.74073	Method for measurement of noise on board vessels
DR.74074	Specifications for the measurement of noise emitted by vessels on waterways, ports, and harbours
DR.75075	Standard method of measurement for the determination of motor vehicle noise emission
	Australian Department of Transport
Australian Design Rule No. 28	"Motor Vehicle Noise"
Austria	Österreichisches Normungsinstitut Leopoldsg. 4 1020 Wien
S 5022	Lärmemissionsmessungen bei Schiffen auf Binnengewässern
	Österreichischen Arbeitsring für Lärmbekämpfung, Regierungsgebäude, 1012 Wien
ÖAL-Richtlinien Nr. 2	Messung des Geräusches von Kraftfahrzeugen
ÖAL-Richtlinie Nr. 2 Blatt 2	Einfache Methode zur Überwachung im Verkehr
ÖAL-Richtlinie Nr. 2 Entwurf	Maßnahmen zum Schutz vor Strassenverkehrslärm
Belgium	Institut Belge de Normalisation, 29 av. de Brabançonne, 1040 Bruxelles
NBN576.30-1962	Méthode de mesure du niveau des bruits émis par les véhicules
Brasil	Associação Brasileira de Normas Técnicas Av. Almirante Barroso 54 Rio de Janeiro — RJ
P.M.B 528	Determinação dos Níveis de Som Emitidos pelos veículos automotores
Resolução 448/71.	Diário Oficial Federal Nr. 6 de 10.01.1972 Medição de Ruido Produzido por veículo

C.S.S.R.	Office for Standards and Measurements, 11347 Praha 1, Václavské Náměsti 19
ČSN 28 1304 1975	Noise measurement and evaluation of town rail vehicles
ČSN 30 0512	Measurement of noise emitted by road motor vehicles
ČSN 30 0513	Measurement of internal noise emitted by road motor vehicles
Denmark	Miljøstyrelsen Kampmannsgade 1 1604 København V
Publikation 24	Støj, trafikmidler (Traffic noise)
Publikation 26	Støj, veje og jernbaner (Noise, roads and railways)
	Statens Biltilsyn
	Bestemmelse om støjgrænser af 19.2.69
	Statens trykningskontor
Nr. 258	Bekendtgørelse om forskrifter mod støj i skibe af 17.6.75
France	L'Association Française de Normalisation (AFNOR), Tour Europe, 92 Courbevoie
NF S 31-007 1965	Mesure du bruit produit par les véhicules automobiles
NF S 31-017 1972	Code d'essai pour la mesure du bruit à bord des bateaux et navires
NF S 31-019 1973	Code d'essai pour la mesure du bruit émis par les véhicules circulant sur rails
NF S 31-028 1974	Code d'essai pour la mesure du bruit à l'intérieur des véhicules circulant sur rails
NF S 31-040 1975	Code d'essai pour la mesure du bruit à l'intérieur des véhicules à moteur
NF S 31-041 1975	Mesure du bruit à la place de travail de l'opérateur sur les tracteurs et les machines agricoles
Germany (B.R.D.)	Beuth Vertrieb GmbH, 1000 Berlin 30, Burggrafenstr. 4 — 7 und 5000 Köln, Kamekestr. 2 — 8
DIN 45636	Außengeräuschmessungen an Kraftfahrzeugen
DIN 45637	Außengeräuschmessungen an Schienenfahrzeugen
DIN 45638	Innengeräuschmessungen in Schienenfahrzeugen
DIN 45639	Innengeräuschmessungen in Kraftfahrzeugen
DIN 45640	Außengeräuschmessungen an Wasserfahrzeugen auf Binnengewässern
DIN 45642	Messung von Verkehrsgeräuschen
DIN 80061	Geräuschmessungen auf Wasserfahrzeugen
VDI 2562	Schallmessungen an Schienenbahnen
VDI 2563	Bestimmen der Geräuschanteile von Straßenfahrzeugen mit Verbrennungskraftmaschine

	Verkehrsblatt
	Richtlinien für die Geräuschmessung an Kraftfahrzeugen
Germany (D.D.R.)	Amt für Standardisierung der D.D.R., Mohrenstrasse 37a, 108 Berlin
TGL 39-852 Bl. 10	Aussengeräusche v. Kfz Meßverfahren, Grenzwerte
Bl. 11	Innengeräusche von Kraftfahrzeugen und Anhängefahrzeugen. Meßverfahren, Grenzwerte
Bl. 12	Aussengeräusche v. Anhängefahrzeugen, Meßverfahren, Grenzwerte
Great Britain	Britisk Standards Institution, 2 Park Street, London, W. 1
Statutory Instruments No. 321 1969	The Motor Vehicles (construction & use) Regulations 1969
BS.3539: 1962	Sound level meters for the measurement of noise emitted by motor vehicles
BS.3425: 1966	Method for the measurement of noise emitted by motor vehicles
Dept. of Env.	Calculation of road traffic noise 1975 with amendment slip No. 1 AMD. 22 1968
India	Indian Standards Institution, Manak Bhavan, 9 Bahadur Shah, Zafar Marg, New Delhi 1
IS:3028-1965	Method of measurement of noise emitted by motor vehicles
Japan	Japanese Standards Association, 1-24, Akasaka 4 chome, Minato-ku, Tokyo
JIS D 1038 (1964)	Noise test method for motorcycles
JIS D 1041 (1964)	Acoustic testing of horns for motorcycles
JIS D 1024 (1967)	Measurements of noise emitted by automobiles
Netherlands	Nederlands Normalisatie-Instituut, Polakweg 5, Rijswijk (Z-H)
NEN 20362	Same as ISO R.362
NEN 22249	Same as ISO R.2249-1973
New Zealand	
1726: 1962	Measurement of noise emitted by motor vehicles. No. 0
Norway	Norges Standardiseringsforbund, Håkon 7. gt. 2, Oslo 1
NS 4806	Måling av støy fra motorkjøretøyer (Inkl. ISO R.362)
	Statens Vegvesen
1972	Støyforskrifter for maskiner og biler som leveres til Statens Vegvesen
1974	Veitrafikkstøy, foreløpige retn. linjer for veietatens holdning i aktuelle saker

Kjøretøyfor-skriftene 31 1969	Rettledende toleransegrenser for veitrafikkstøy (NIBR 0.1122)
	Sjøfartsdirektoratet, Thv. Meyers gt. 7, Oslo
1973	Forskrifter om vern mot støy ombord i skip
Poland	Polski Komitet Normalizacji i Miar, ul. Elektoralna 2, 00-139 - Warszawa
PN-71 S-04051	Automobile vehicles. Test methods and admissible outside noise level
PN-71 S-04052	Automobiles. Test methods and admissible inside noise level
PN-74 S-47013	Lorries, buses and trolleybuses. Drivers cab. Requirements
PN-75 S-76006	Audible warning devices for privileged motor vehicles. Requirements and tests
Portugal	
P-708 1968	Acústica, Processo de medição do ruido emitido por veiculos automóveis (Method to measure noise emitted by motor vehicles)
Roumania	Oficiul de stat pentru Standarde, Str. Edgar Quinet 6, Bucarest 1
STAS E6661-62	Permitted limits of noise emitted by railway vehicles
STAS 6661-70	Acoustics in transportation. Method of noise measurements in railway vehicles
South Africa	South African Bureau of Standards, Private bag X191 Pretoria 0001
SABS 097-1975	Code of practice for the measurement and limitation of noise emitted by motor vehicles
Sweden	Sveriges standardiserings-kommission, Box 3295, 10366 Stockholm
SIS 025131	Mätning av motorfordonsbuller
SMS 2862	Lantbruk, lantbrukstraktorer och självgående lantbruksmaskiner. Mätning av buller på förarplats
	Liber Förlag, Fack, 103 20 Stockholm
	Statens Naturvårdsverk: Riktvärden för buller från motorsports- och bilprovningsanläggningar. Remissutgåva 1974
Switzerland	Eidgenössische Drucksachen und Materialzentrale, Bern 3
—	Lärmbekämpfung in der Schweiz.
	Eidgenössisches Polizei-Departement
30 Okt. 1968	Geräusch an Motorfahrzeugen
30 Okt. 1968	Weisungen über die Geräuschmessungen an Motorfahrzeugen
	1 Bundesrat Bern
27 Sept. 1969 Anhang 4 und 9	Verordnung über Bau und Ausrüstung der Strassenfahrzeuge

U.S.A.	American National Standards Institute 1430 Broadway New York, NY 10018
S6.2-1973	Exterior sound level for snowmobiles
S6.3-1973	Sound level for passenger cars and light trucks
	Society of Automotive Engineers, Inc. 400 Commonwealth Drive Warrendale, PA 15096
SAE J34 (1973)	SAE recommended practice, exterior sound level measurement procedure for pleasure motorboats
SAE J47 (1975)	SAE recommended practice, maximum sound level potential for motorcycles
SAE J57 (1973)	SAE recommended practice, sound level of highway truck tires
SAE J88a (1975)	SAE recommended practice, exterior sound level measurement procedure for powered mobile construction equipment
SAE J184 (1972)	SAE recommended practice, qualifying a sound data acquisition system (ANSI S6.1-1973)
SAE J192a (1973)	SAE recommended practice, exterior sound level for snowmobiles
SAE J331a (1975)	SAE recommended practice, sound levels for motorcycles
SAE J336a (1973)	SAE standard, sound level for truck cab interior
SAE J366b (1973)	SAE standard, exterior sound level for heavy trucks and buses
SAE J377 (1969)	SAE standard, performance of vehicle traffic horns
SAE J672a	Exterior loudness evaluation of heavy trucks and buses
SAE J919a (1971)	SAE recommended practice, sound level measurements at the operator station for agricultural and construction equipment
SAE J986a (1972)	SAE standard, sound level for passenger cars and light trucks
SAE J1060 (1973)	SAE recommended practice, subjective rating scale for evaluation of noise and ride comfort characteristics related to motor vehicle tires
SAE J1077 (1975)	SAE recommended practice, measurement of exterior sound level of trucks with auxiliary equipment
International (I.S.O.)	International Organization for Standardization, 1, Rue de Varembé, Geneva, Switzerland
R.362-1964	Measurement of noise emitted by vehicles
R.512-1974	Road vehicles - sound signalling devices on motor vehicles, acoustic standards and technical specifications
R.2922-1975	Measurements of noise emitted by vessels on inland water-ways and harbours
R.2923-1975	Measurement of noise on board vessels
R.3095-1975	Measurement of noise emitted by railbound vehicles

ISO Draft Proposals	
	ISO Draft Proposals
ISO/DIS 3381	Measurement of noise inside railbound vehicles
	Methods of measurement of noise inside motor vehicles
	Method of control of noise emitted by stationary motor vehicles
	Survey method for the measurement of noise emitted by stationary vehicles
	Measurement of noise emitted by road vehicles
	OECD, Paris
OECD Standard Code	Standard code for the official testing of agricultural tractors (Paris 1970)

G. Special Acoustic Equipment

Australia	Standards House, 80 Arthur Street, North Sydney
AS.Z43	Instrumentation for audiometry - Part I-1971 Pure tone audiometers Part II-1970 Reference zero for the calibration of pure tone audiometers Part III-1969 Reference coupler for the calibration of earphones used in audiometry
AS.1089-1971	Reference coupler for the measurement of the electro-acoustic characteristics of hearing aid earphones
AS.1270-1975	Hearing protection devices
AS.1591	Instrumentation for audiometry Part 4-1974 Mechanical coupler for the calibration of bone vibrators used in hearing aids and audiometers Part 5-1974 Wide band artificial ear
DR.74156	Instrumentation for audiometry — Speech audiometers
C.S.S.R.	Office for Standards and Measurements, 11347 Praha 1, Václavské Náměsti 19
ČSN 36 4805 1968	Tone audiometers
ČSN 36 8256 1966	Artificial ears
Denmark	Dansk Standardiseringsråd Aurehøjvej 12 2900 Hellerup
DS/IEC 118	Måling af tunghøreapparaters elektroakustiske egenskaber
DS/ISO R.389	Akustik. Standard nulpunkts-reference ved kalibrering af toneaudiometre
DS/IEC 126	IEC referencekobler til målinger på tunghøreapparatur, der bruger telefon koblet til øret ved hjælp af ørestykker
Finland	Suomen Standardisoimisliitto PL 205, 00121 Helsinki 12
SFS 2876	Same as IEC 118 (1959)

SFS 2879	Same as IEC 177 (1965)
SFS 2892	Same as IEC 303 (1970)
SFS 2893	Same as IEC 318 (1970)
France	L'Association Française de Normalisation (AFNOR), Tour Europe, 92 Courbevoie
NF C 97-110 1965	Magnétophones semi-professionnels ou à l'usage du grand public: Caractéristiques et méthodes de mesure (Enr.) (24 pages)
NF C 97-130 1969	Disques moulés et appareils de lecture: Caractéristiques et méthodes de mesure (Enr.) (32 pages)
NF C 97-140 1971	Méthodes de mesure des bandes magnétiques couchées, et non perforées, pour l'enregistrement et la lecture magnétique du son (Enr.) (20 pages)
NF C 97-210 1967	Adaptateurs de modulation de fréquence: Caractéristiques et méthodes de mesure (Enr.) (15 pages)
NF C 97-310 1968	Amplificateurs: Caractéristiques et méthodes de mesure (Enr.) (28 pages)
NF C 97-310 add 1 1974	Additif à la norme NF C 97-310 — décembre 1966 (Enr.) (2 pages)
NF C 97-320 1972	Méthodes de mesures des caractéristiques des microphones: Prescriptions générales (Enr.) (34 pages)
	Méthodes de mesures des caractéristiques des haut-parleurs:
NF C 97-330 1973	— Prescripions générales (Enr.) (24 pages)
NF S 31-001 1956	Audiomètre
NF S 31-004 1959	Oreille artificielle
Germany (B.R.D.)	Beuth Vertrieb BmbH. 1000 Berlin 30, Burggrafenstr. 4 — 7 und 5000 Köln, Kamekestr. 2 — 8
DIN 45620	Audiometer zur Hörschwellenbestimmung
DIN 45623	Audiometer für Reihenuntersuchungen
Great Britain	British Standards Institution, 2 Park Street, London W. 1
BS.3171: 1968	Methods of test of air conduction hearing aids
BS.4009: 1975	An artificial mastoid for the calibration of bone vibrators used in hearing aids and audiometers
BS.4668: 1971	An acoustic coupler (IEC reference type) for the calibration of earphones used in audiometry
BS.4669: 1971	An artificial ear of the wide band type for the calibration of earphones used in audiometry
BS.2497:	Reference zero for the calibration of pure-tone audiometers. Part 1, 2 & 3
BS.2042: 1953	An artificial ear for the calibration of earphones of the external type
BS.2980: 1958	Pure-tone audiometers

BS.4847: 1972	Method of measurement of speed fluctuation in sound recording and reproducing equipment
BS.3860: 1965	Method for measuring and expressing the performance of audio frequency amplifiers for domestic, public address and similar applications
BS.2498: 1954	Recommendations for ascertaining and expressing the performance of loudspeakers by objective measurements
India	Indian Standards Institution, Manak Bhavan, 9 Bahadur Shah, Zafar Marg, New Delhi 1
IS:4406-1967	General requirements for hearing aids
Netherlands	Nederlands Normalisatie-Instituut, Polakweg 5, Rijswijk (Z-H)
NEN 20389	Same as ISO R.389

New Zealand

1674: 1962	General service hearing aids. Gr B
1718: 1963	Bone conduction hearing aids. Gr B
1719: 1963	Head-level hearing aids. Gr B
1881: 1964	Pure tone diagnostic audiometers. Gr B. Amendment No. 1, 1969
2233: 1968	Pure-tone screening audiometers. Gr C
Poland	Polski Komitet Normalizacji i Miar, ul. Elektoralna 2, 00-139 - Warszawa
PN-73 Z-70050	Medical equipment. Clear tone classification audiometers. General requirements and tests
Spain	Instituto Nacional de Racionalizacion y Normalizacion Serrano Nr. 150, Madrid 6
118 1959	Métodos recomendados para la medida de las caracteristicas electroacústicas de los aparatos de corrección uditiva. (En revisión)
	Modificación núm. 1 (1973)
177 1965	Audímetros de sonidos puros para diagnósticos generales
178 1965	Audimetro tamizador de tonos puros
268-5 1972	Quinta parte: Altavoces
318 1970	Un oído artificial de la C.E.I. de banda ancha, para el tarado de los audifonos utilizados en audiometria
403 1972	Generadores de señales de frecuencias acústicas
500 1974	Hidrófono patrón CEI
U.S.A.	American National Standards Institute 1430 Broadway New York, NY 10018
S1.5-1963 (R.1971)	American national standard recommended practices for loudspeaker measurements

S3.3-1960 (R.1971)	American national standard methods for measurement of electroacoustical characteristics of hearing aids
S3.6-1969	American national standard specifications for audiometers
S3.7-1973	Method for coupler calibration of earphones
S3.8-1967 (R.1971)	American national standard method of expressing hearing aid performance
S3.13-1972	American national standard artificial head-bone for the calibration of audiometer bone vibrators
S3.19-1974	Measurement of real-ear protection of hearing protectors and physical attenuation of earmuffs
	Institute of Electrical and Electronic Engineers 445 Hoes Lane Piscataway, NJ 08854
IEEE STD 219-1975	Recommended practices on audio and electroacoustics: Loudspeaker measurements
U.S.S.R.	Komitet Standartov, Leninsky Prospekt 9 b, Moskva M-49
Gost 10893-69	Electronic hearing aids
Gost 15762-70	Ear defenders. Hygienic requirements
International (I.E.C.)	International Organization for Standardization, 1, Rue de Varembé, Geneva, Switzerland
118 (1959)	Recommended methods for measurements of the electro-acoustical characteristics of hearing aids
118 amendment 1 (1973)	Recommended methods for measurements of the electro-acoustical characteristics of hearing aids
126 (1973)	IEC reference coupler for the measurement of hearing aids using earphones coupled to the ear by means of ear inserts
177 (1965)	Pure tone audiometers for general diagnostic purposes
178 (1965)	Pure tone screening audiometers
200 (1966)	Methods of measurement for loudspeakers
303 (1970)	IEC provisional reference coupler for the calibration of earphones used in audiometry
318 (1970)	An IEC artificial ear, of the wide band type, for the calibration of earphones used in audiometry
389 (1975)	Acoustics standard reference zero for the calibration of pure-tone audiometers
	IEC Draft Proposal
Supplement to IEC 118:	Recommended methods for measurement of electro-acoustical characteristics of hearing aids with automatic gain control (AGC) circuits

256

International (I.S.O.)	International Organization for Standardization, 1, Rue de Varembé, Geneva, Switzerland
	ISO Draft Proposal
	Measurement of sound attenuation of hearing protectors

H. Measurement of Aircraft Noise

C.S.S.R.	Office for Standards and Measurements, 11347 Praha 1, Václavské Náměsti 19
ČSN 31 0305	Measurement of noise emitted by airplanes
Denmark	Miljøstyrelsen Kampmannsgade 1 1604 København V
Publikation 25	Flystøj (Noise in air traffic)
France	L'Association Française de Normalisation (AFNOR), Tour Europe, 92 Courbevoie
S 31-008 1973	Méthode de représentation du bruit des aéronefs au voisinage d'un aérodrome
NF S 31-029 1973	Description et mesurage des propriétés physiques du bang sonique
Germany (B.R.D.)	Beuth Vertrieb GmbH. 1000 Berlin 30, Burggrafenstr. 4 — 7 und 5000 Köln, Kamekestr. 2 — 8
DIN 45643	Fluglärmüberwachung in der Umgebung von Flugplätzen ...
Great Britain	Board of Trade
CAP. 335 Board of Trade	Noise measurement for aircraft design purposes including noise certification purposes
Netherlands	Nederlands Normalisatie-Instituut, Polakweg 5, Rijswijk (Z-H)
NEN 20507	Same as ISO R.507-1970
NEN 21761	Same as ISO R.1761-1970
Norway	Norges Standardiseringsforbund, Håkon 7. gt. 2, Oslo 1
NS 4809	Metode for beskrivelse av flystøy i områder rundt en lufthavn (inkl. ISO R.507)
NS 4811	Overvåkning af flystøy i områder rundt en lufthavn (inkl. ISO R.1761)
South Africa	South African Bureau of Standards, Private bag X191 Pretoria 0001
SABS 0115 1974	The code of practice for the measurement of noise and determination of disturbance from aeroplanes for certification purposes
SABS 0116 1974	The code of practice for the procedure for calculating basic noise parameters from ICAO aeroplane noise certification data

SABS 0117 1974	The code of practice for the determination and limitation of disturbance around an aerodrome due to noise from aeroplanes
U.S.A.	American National Standards Institute, 1430 Broadway, New York, NY 10018
S6.4-1973	Definitions and procedures for computing the effective perceived noise level for flyover aircraft noise
	Society of Automotive Engineers Inc. 400 Commonwealth Drive Warrendale, PA 15096
SAE ARP 796 (1969)	SAE aerospace recommended practice, measurement of aircraft exterior noise in the field
SAE ARP 865A (1969)	SAE aerospace recommended practice, definitions and procedures for computing the perceived noise level of aircraft noise
SAE ARP 866A (1975)	SAE aerospace recommended practice, standard values of absorption as a function of temperature and humidity for use in evaluating aircraft flyover noise
SAE ARP 1071 (1973)	SAE aerospace recommended practice, definitions and procedures for computing the effective perceived noise level for flyover aircraft noise
SAE ARP 1080 (1969)	SAE aerospace recommended practice, frequency weighting network for approximation of perceived noise level for aircraft noise
SAE AIR 852 (1965)	SAE aerospace information report, methods of comparing aircraft takeoff and approach noise
SAE AIR 876 (1965)	SAE aerospace information report, jet noise prediction
SAE AIR 902 (1966)	SAE aerospace information report, determination of minimum distance from ground observer to aircraft for acoustic tests
SAE AIR 923 (1966)	SAE aerospace information report, method for calculating the attenuation of aircraft ground to ground noise propagation during take-off and landing
SAE AIR 1216 (1972)	SAE aerospace information report, comparisons of ground runup and flyover noise levels
	Federal Aviation Administration, Washington D.C. 20591
	Noise standards Aircraft type certification
International (I.E.C.)	International Organization for Standardization, 1, Rue de Varembé, Geneva, Switzerland
	IEC Draft Proposals
	Electro-acoustical performance requirements for aircraft noise certification measurements
	Frequency weighting for the measurement of aircraft noise (D-weighting)

257

International (I.S.O.)	International Organization for Standardization, 1, Rue de Varembé, Geneva, Switzerland
R.507-1970	Procedure for describing aircraft noise around an airport
R.1761-1970	Monitoring aircraft noise around an airport
	ISO Draft Proposals
ISO/DIS 3891	Procedure for describing aircraft noise heard on the ground (revision of ISO R.507-1966 and ISO R.1761-1970)
	Measurement of noise inside aircraft

APPENDIX A

Stationary Random Signals

As demonstrated in Chapter 2, a *stationary* sinusoidal signal can be completely described by three quantities, the amplitude, the frequency and the phase. It was further shown that a complex, but still periodic signal, composed of many such sinusoids, could be exactly represented by a Fourier Series. The instantaneous amplitude could therefore always be predicted from the signal's describing equation. A process which can be thus described is known as *deterministic;* i.e. its instantaneous amplitude can always be precisely determined from its equation. Deterministic signals are made up entirely of sinusoidal components at discrete frequencies, which in periodic signals, are always multiples of some fundamental frequency, but in quasi-periodic signals, e.g. from several independently rotating shafts, are not harmonically related.

A great number of practical noise sources give rise to signals which can be considered stationary, but are not periodic. Examples are jet noise, aerodynamic noise, traffic noise, crowd noise, most music, and many types of industrial noise. The amplitude of these signals does not vary in a periodic, and therefore predictable, manner. In order to describe them adequately it is ne-

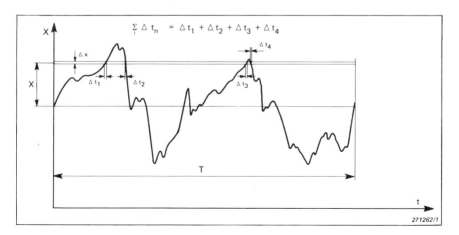

Fig.A1   Time record of a random process

259

cessary to introduce the concept of *amplitude density* instead of *amplitude*. Instead of being able to predict an instantaneous amplitude, we can now only assign a probability that the random signal will fall within a certain amplitude range.

The amplitude scale must be divided up into small intervals, Δx, then the proportion of the total time which the signal spends between the values of x and x + Δx can be defined in relation to the total time over which the signal is being studied. (see Fig.A1). If P(x, x + Δx) represents the probability that the signal amplitude lies in the interval (x, x + Δx)

then
$$P(x, x + \Delta x) = \lim_{T \to \infty} \frac{\sum \Delta t_n}{T}$$

where each Δt_n represents one of the time intervals in the sample T where the signal lies between the amplitude values x and x + Δx.

The probability density p(x) at the amplitude level x is this probability, divided by the interval width (Δx), thus giving a density

Then
$$p(x) = \lim_{\Delta x \to 0} \frac{P(x, x + \Delta x)}{\Delta x}$$

By varying the value of x from -∞ to +∞, p(x) can be plotted as a function of x. The probability density curve describing the instantaneous amplitude of an

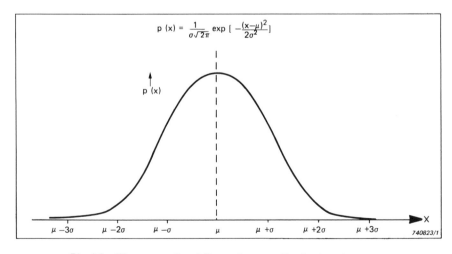

$$p(x) = \frac{1}{\sigma\sqrt{2\pi}} \exp\left[-\frac{(x-\mu)^2}{2\sigma^2}\right]$$

Fig.A2 The normalised Gaussian amplitude density curve

260

acoustic pressure can vary considerably from problem to problem. However, the best known amplitude density curve is that from a normal (Gaussian) process, which is used as the model for many of the random processes encounted in practice. The curve is shown in Fig.A2 and the amplitude density distribution is given by

$$p(x) = \frac{1}{\sigma\sqrt{2\pi}} \, exp\left(- \frac{(x-\mu)^2}{2\sigma^2} \right)$$

where σ = standard deviation
       μ = mean value

This curve may be considered as an e^{-x^2} curve centred on the mean value μ and scaled as follows.

1. Along the x axis it is scaled in terms of σ, the standard deviation from the mean μ. For a zero mean, σ is the RMS value of the signal, and σ^2 the variance

i.e. $$\sigma = \sqrt{\frac{1}{T} \int_0^T x^2 dt} = A_{rms}$$

2. Along the p(x) axis it is scaled so that the integral under the curve for all x is 1, i.e. the probability that x must lie between $\pm\infty$

Statistical Level Analysis

In the above section it was shown how the RMS value (or level) of a non-deterministic fluctuating signal could be determined by applying statistical techniques to the *instantaneous* amplitude values of the signal. The important overall characteristics of a random signal can therefore be described adequately in terms of its average properties. Statistical methods can be applied, not only to the *instantaneous value* of the signal itself, but also to its *RMS value* i.e. its *level* which, because of the fluctuating nature of the signal and the finite observation duration, also varies statistically.

It is not sufficient to describe the sound level history shown in Fig.A3, (which was recorded in a busy Copenhagen street), by any measurement taken at any single instant in time, and some form of statistical description is clearly required. Practical Statistical Noise Level Analyzers such as the Type 4426 resolve the dynamic measurement range into equal class intervals of width Δx (in this case 0,25 dB). The instrument samples the incoming sound level at regular intervals, records up to 2^{16} (65536) of these samples in a digital memory, and calculates the proportion of time the sound level spends

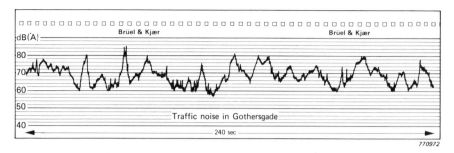

Fig.A3 Typical statistically varying sound level

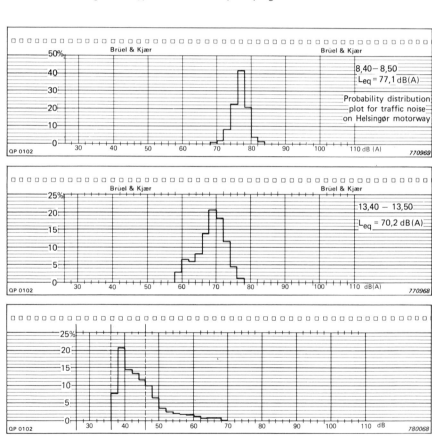

Fig.A4 Typical amplitude density plots
a) Gaussian - Motorway noise
b) Skew - Congested Traffic Noise
c) Highly Skew - Office Noise

262

in each of the amplitude intervals. This is the level distribution histogram and can be read out directly from the digital display on the instrument's front panel, or automatically to a level recorder or alphanumeric printer. The shapes of these histograms varies widely from one type of noise to another, as shown in Fig.A4. Fig.A4a is taken from a motorway noise measurement and shows a typical Gaussian shape. Fig.A4b shows the skew distribution typical of congested city centre traffic. Fig.A4c shows the highly skew distribution spread over a wide amplitude range measured in an office. The standard deviation, σ, and the mean value, μ can be most easily obtained from this type of presentation.

There are however other ways of presenting the same information to more easily bring out other factors. One of these is the *cumulative probability* plot. This is a summation over many Δx intervals. If we move from right to left along the sound pressure level axis of any of the probability distribution histograms in Fig.A4, adding the probability as we do so, then we obtain the probability that the value at which we have arrived is exceeded. This appears as a stepped function which would become a continuous, smooth curve as the class intervals are reduced to zero. A typical cumulative probability plot is reproduced in Fig.A5, and should be compared with the amplitude density plot of Fig.A4b for the same data. From this graph important values such as L_{90}, L_{10}, etc. can be read directly. In the case of the 4426, these calculations are done automatically, internally within the instrument.

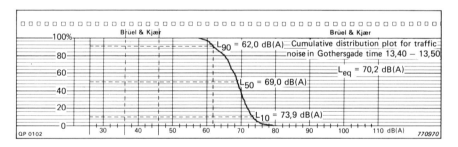

Fig.A5 Typical Traffic Noise cumulative probability plot

APPENDIX B

Decibel and Ratio Conversions

The following table has been prepared in order to facilitate the conversion from *dB* to *sound pressure ratios* and vice versa. However, with a slight modification it may also be used for dB to sound intensity (power) conversion and vice versa.

dB	,0	,1	,2	,3	,4	,5	,6	,7	,8	,9
0	1,000	1,012	1,023	1,035	1,047	1,059	1,072	1,084	1,096	1,109
1	1,122	1,135	1,148	1,161	1,175	1,189	1,202	1,216	1,230	1,245
2	1,259	1,274	1,288	1,303	1,318	1,334	1,349	1,365	1,380	1,396
3	1,413	1,429	1,445	1,462	1,479	1,496	1,514	1,531	1,549	1,567
4	1,585	1,603	1,622	1,641	1,660	1,679	1,698	1,718	1,738	1,758
5	1,778	1,799	1,820	1,841	1,862	1,884	1,905	1,928	1,950	1,972
6	1,995	2,018	2,042	2,065	2,089	2,113	2,138	2,163	2,188	2,213
7	2,239	2,265	2,291	2,317	2,344	2,371	2,399	2,427	2,455	2,483
8	2,512	2,541	2,570	2,600	2,630	2,661	2,692	2,723	2,754	2,786
9	2,818	2,851	2,884	2,917	2,951	2,985	3,020	3,055	3,090	3,126
10	3,162	3,199	3,236	3,273	3,311	3,350	3,388	3,428	3,467	3,508
11	3,548	3.589	3,631	3,673	3,715	3,758	3,802	3,846	3,890	4,416
12	3,981	4,027	4,074	4,121	4,169	4,217	4,266	4,315	4,365	3,936
13	4,467	4,519	4,571	4,624	4,677	4,732	4,786	4,842	4,898	4,955
14	5,012	5,070	5,129	5,188	5,248	5,309	5,370	5,433	5,495	5,559
15	5,623	5,689	5,754	5,821	5,888	5,957	6,026	6,095	6,166	6,237
16	6,310	6,383	6,457	6,531	6,607	6,683	6,761	6,839	6,918	6,998
17	7,079	7,161	7,244	7,328	7.413	7,499	7,586	7,674	7,762	7,852
18	7,943	8,035	8,128	8,222	8,318	8,414	8,511	8,610	8,710	8,810
19	8,913	9,016	9,120	9,226	9,333	9,441	9,550	9,661	9,772	9,886

As 0 dB corresponds to a sound *pressure* ratio of 1, and 20 dB to a sound *pressure* ratio of 10, practically all ratio to dB conversions (and vice versa) are possible by means of the table.

Sound Pressure Calculations:

1) *dB-to-ratio conversion:*
   Subtract a whole number of $n \times 20$ from the dB value to be converted to give a positive remainder between 0 and 20. Look up the ratio in the table corresponding to the remainder. The value sought is then $10^n \times$ value from the table $\times$ reference value.
   Numerical Example:
   If the sound pressure level is 74 dB re. 20μPa. what is then the actual sound pressure (in μPa)?
   Solution
   74 dB = (3 × 20) + 14 dB.
   14 dB corresponds to a pressure ratio of 5,012 (according to table). Thus when 20 log (p/p_o) = 74 dB, then:

   $$p = 10^3 \times 5,012 \; p_o = 10^3 \times 5,012 \times 20 \approx 10^{-5} \, \mu Pa.$$

2) *Ratio-to-dB conversion:*
   Divide the pressure ratio to be converted by 10^n so that a number, A, is obtained which lies between 1 and 10 (i.e. ratio = A × 10^n). Look up the number in the table which is as close as possible to A. Add the dB-value (from the table) corresponding to this number to $n \times 20$. The result is the desired sound pressure level in dB.

264

Numerical Example:
If the sound pressure is found to be 0,356 Pa. what is then the sound pressure level in dB re. 20μPa.?
Solution

$$\frac{p}{p_o} = \frac{0,356}{20 \times 10^{-6}} = 17800 = 1,78 \times 10^4$$

From the table it is found that a pressure ratio of 1,78 corresponds to approximately 5 dB, thus:

Sound Pressure Level = 5 + (4 × 20) = 85 dB re. 20μPa.

Sound Intensity (Power) Calculations.

1) *dB-to-ratio conversion:*
Multiply the dB-value to be converted by 2 and proceed as under "Sound Pressure Calculations" above.
Note: The reference level is in this case normally $(10^{-12}$ W/m$^2)$ which corresponds to the intensity of a free progressive sound wave in atmospheric air with a sound pressure of 20μPa.
Numerical Example:
If the sound intensity level is 83 dB re. 10^{-12} W/m^2 what is then the actual sound intensity level in W/m^2?
Solution
83 dB × 2 = 166 = (8 × 20) + 6.
From the table it is found that 6 dB corresponds to a ratio of 1,955.
Thus, the sound intensity level is:

P = 1,955 × 10^8 × 10^{-12} = 1,955 × 10^{-4}W/m^2

2) *Ratio-to-dB Conversion:*
Proceed as under "Sound Pressure Calculations" above and divide the result by 2.
Numerical Example:
If the sound intensity is found to be 5 × 10^{-3} W/m^2 what is then the sound intensity level in dB re. 10^{-12} W/m^2?
Solution
From the table it is found that a ratio of 5 corresponds to approximately 14 dB, thus:

Sound Intensity Level = $\dfrac{14 + (9 \times 20)}{2}$ = 97 dB re. 10^{-12} W/m^2.

APPENDIX C

Loudness Determination According to Zwicker and Stevens

The subjective loudness or loudness level is estimated from objectively measured sound pressure level data, which must be available in the form of a sound spectrum, normally in 1/3 octave or 1/1 octave bands. If the measured spectrum is available in terms of 1/3 octave data, use can be made of an estimation method suggested by *E. Zwicker.* This is based on a set of graphs, 2 examples of which are shown in Figs.C1 and C2. The cases of free-field and diffuse sound are covered by two sets of graphs. Each set consists of several special graphs, which cover the large dynamic range found in noise measurement in overlapping 30 dB ranges. The procedure contains three steps:

Step 1 Select the appropriate graph and plot the measured 1/3 octave data onto it. Decide whether the sound field being explored is of the *free-field type* (frontal sound), or of the *diffuse field type,* and then choose the corresponding *chart which includes the highest third-octave band level measured.* For 1/3 octave bands above 280 Hz (band centre frequency 315 Hz) the band levels can be directly plotted on the chart. However, because the critical bands in hearing have bandwidths which are wider than 1/3 octave below 280 Hz, the third octave band levels in this frequency range are combined according to the power law illustrated in Fig.2.22 of the main text, and expressed below:

Step 2 Connect the band level lines (see Fig.C5) and average the area enclosed by the "stepped" figure.
The connections between the band levels are made as illustrated in Fig.C5a. If the level in the next higher band is higher, a vertical line is drawn between the two levels, while if the level in the next higher band is lower the two band levels are joined by a downward sloping curve interpolated between the dashed curves on the graph.

The averaging is done by converting the area inside the stepped figure into a rectangle with the same base, i.e. the width of the graph (Fig.C5b).

Step 3 Read the resulting total loudness value (in sones (GF) or sones GD)), or the resulting total loudness level value (in phons (GF) or phons GD)), from the scales shown to the right of the figures C1 and C2. The value is equal to the height of the rectangle.

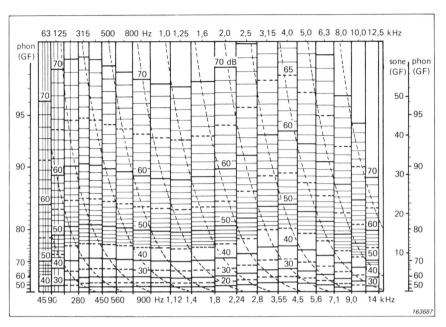

Fig.C1. Frontal sound (40—70 dB)

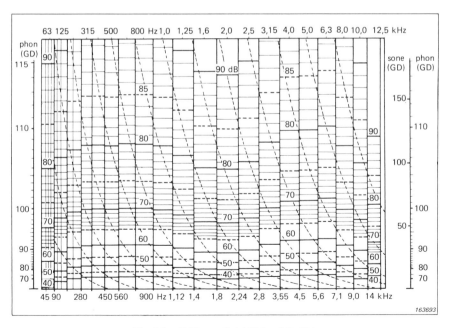

Fig.C2 Diffuse field (60—90 dB)

267

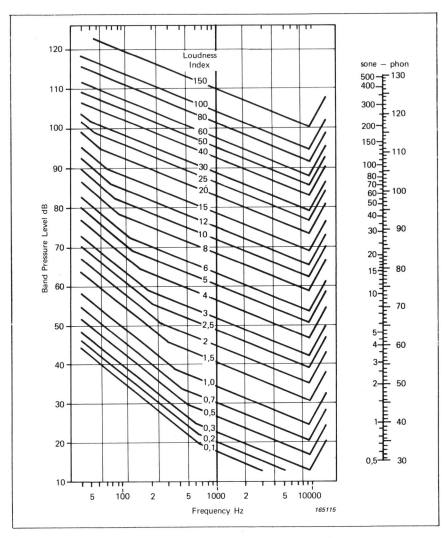

Fig.C3 Contours of equal loudness index

From octave data the loudness (or loudness level) can be estimated by means of a method originally suggested by *S.S.Stevens* (1/1-octave data may, of course, also be constructed from more detailed analyses). Each octave band sound pressure level is converted into a *loudness index* by the curves shown in Fig.C3. The various loudness indices found for each are summed by the formula:

$$S_t = S_m + 0.3(S - S_m)$$

where S_m is the greatest of the loudness indices
S is the sum of the loudness indices of all the bands
S_t is the total loudness (in sones (OD), Octave Diffuse)

By applying the nomographic scales to the right in Fig.C3 the total loudness value can be converted into a total loudness level value (in phons (OD)).

It should be noted that the method due to Zwicker can be used even when the sound spectrum is very irregular and the sound contains pronounced pure tones. The method due to Stevens, on the other hand, can only be used when the sound spectrum is relatively smooth, contains no pure tone, and the sound field is diffuse.

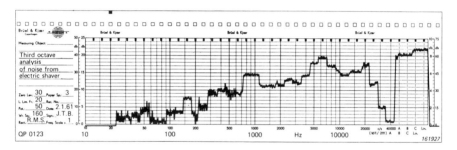

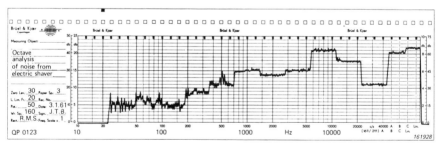

Fig.C4. Analyses of the noise from an electric shaver:
a) 1/3 octave analysis b) 1/1 octave analysis

To demonstrate the use of the two methods consider the sound spectra shown in Fig. C4. The two spectra were obtained from measurements on an electric shaver; the sound field was very nearly diffuse. Fig.C6a shows how the 1/3 octave data were transferred onto the appropriate Zwicker graph, while Fig.C5b illustrates how the stepped curve in a) is transformed into an equivalent rectangle. From the height of the rectangle the total loudness

269

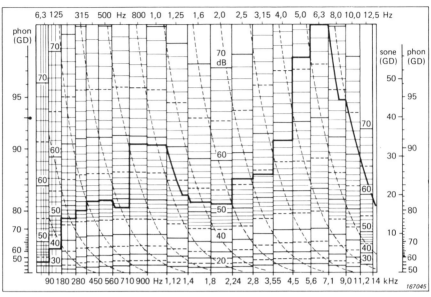

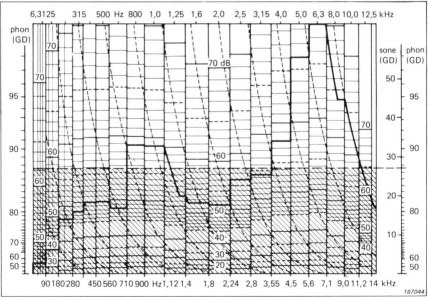

Fig.C5   Calculation of loudness level according to Zwicker's method
a)The 1/3 octave data from Fig.C4 have here been transferred
to the appropriate Zwicker diagram
b) Averaging of the stepped curve, showing how the equivalent rectangle is obtained. The loudness and loudness level
are indicated on the right-hand scale

270

value is found to be approximately 28 sones (GD). The corresponding loudness level value is 87.5 phons (GD).

Band center frequency Hz	31,5	63	125	250	500	1000	2000	4000	8000
Band pressure level (dB)	40	42	40	47	54	60	58	60	72
Loudness index	0	0,16	0,37	1,44	2,84	4,8	5,2	7,0	17,5

780151

$$S_t = S_m + F\ (\Sigma S - S_m) = 17,5 + 0,3 \times 21,8 = 24 \text{ sones}$$

24 sones → 86 phons

Fig.C6   Measurements of electric shaver noise

Fig.C5 shows the conversion of the 1/1 octave band pressure levels to loudness indices, together with the calculation of the overall loudness according to Stevens method, using the equal loudness index contours of Fig.C3.

APPENDIX D

Prediction of Noise Levels in an Enclosure from Sound Power Data

As explained in section 5.1.1, sound power data is primarily used for setting upper limits on machinery output levels, and for comparison purposes when developing quieter equipment or noise control measures. However, it may also be used to predict the sound pressure levels in an enclosure at a distance from the source. This can provide a useful estimate of the subsequent sound levels in, for example, factory premises where noisy machinery is to be installed.

Clearly, the sound pressure level at a particular point in a room depends upon its distance from the sound source and upon the acoustical environmental conditions (i.e. near field, free sound field, reverberant field, semi-reverberant field). Also the directively index (D.I.) of the source plays a role. The directivity index is often stated in practice in the form of a directivity factor, Q, which, in contrast to the directivity index, is a linear quantity.

The mathematical relationship between the sound power level (L_w) emitted from the source and the mean sound pressure level L_p in a semi-reverberant enclosure is:

$$L_w = L_p + 10\ log_{10}\left(\frac{Q}{4\pi r^2} + \frac{4}{R}\right)$$

271

where L_w, L_p and r have the same notational meaning as stated in Chapter 5, section 5.1.2. Q is, as mentioned above, the directivity factor, and R is a constant determined by the sound absorption of the room surfaces:

$$R = \frac{S\bar{\alpha}}{1 - \bar{\alpha}}$$

Here: S = total surface area of the room in m^2
$\bar{\alpha}$ = average energy absorption coefficient of the surface of the room.

The physical meaning of the above expression for the mean sound pressure level, L_p, may best be appreciated with the aid of Fig.D.1. Here the quantity

$$10\,log_{10}\left(\frac{Q}{4\pi r^2} + \frac{4}{R}\right)$$

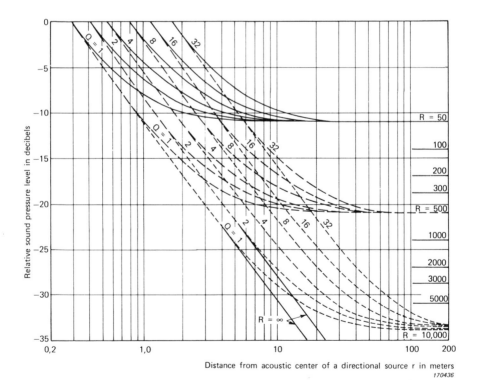

Distance from acoustic center of a directional source r in meters

170436

Fig.D.1. Chart for determination of the sound pressure level in a large room as a function of the distance from the sound source. The room constant, R, and the directivity factor, Q, are plotted as parameters

is plotted against the distance, r, from the sound source in meters, with various values of the room constant, R, in square meters, and directivity factor, Q, greater than unity as parameters. It can be seen that for a specific room constant, and directivity factor, the sound pressure level at a distance r is given by the sum of the ordinate in the figure and the sound power level. With regard to the directivity factor it should be noted that when a machine is installed in the middle of a room, and on a hard surface $Q \approx 2$. If it is installed at the floor close to a wall, i.e. at an "edge" $Q \approx 4$, and if it is installed in a corner $Q \approx 8$. Although these figures are somewhat rough estimates ignoring the detailed radiation characteristics of the machine, they may serve as useful guides for practical estimation purposes at low frequencies.

It should also be noted both from the formulae and from the figure, that the case where $R = \infty$ (complete sound absorption) and $Q = 1$ corresponds to the free suspension of a non-directional sound source in open air (acoustic free-field conditions).

To further illustrate the use of the curves, Fig.D.1, consider an arbitrary case where $R = 500$ and $Q = 2$. From the curve it can be seen that the sound pressure level at a distance of 1 meter from the source is practically the same as it would be if the room was not there (the difference is less than 1 dB). The sound pressure would, however, be the same in all positions in the room at a distance greater than 5 meters from the source. Therefore a machine operator standing very close to a machine will very little benefit if the room is made more absorbant, but a worker at a distance will experience a reduction of 3 dB sound pressure level for each doubling of the room constant R. It should also be noted that the parts of the curves determined by the reverberant sound field are nearly independent of Q.

It is obvious, however, that the direct sound field extends to a greater distance, the greater the value of Q.

In order to make use of the curves, Fig.D.1, in actual practical cases, it is necessary to determine the room constant, R, for the room in question. To do so the volume of the room V in m^3, its total surface area, A in m^2, and its reverberation time, T, in seconds, must be known. Then

$$R = \frac{V}{\dfrac{T}{0.16} - \dfrac{V}{A}}$$

INDEX

276